A NEW THEORY OF HUMAN EVOLUTION

A NEW THEORY OF
HUMAN EVOLUTION

BY

SIR ARTHUR KEITH

PHILOSOPHICAL LIBRARY

NEW YORK

PUBLISHED IN THE UNITED STATES OF AMERICA, 1949,
BY THE PHILOSOPHICAL LIBRARY, INC., OF
15 EAST 40TH STREET, NEW YORK, N.Y.

Printed in England

PREFACE

ALMOST seventy-six years ago—on February 24, 1871, to be exact—Darwin published *The Descent of Man*, and so laid the foundation of our modern knowledge of man's origin. I grew up with the book and when a medical student became, as did so many of my contemporaries, an ardent Darwinist. *The Descent of Man* came of age in 1892, but three years before that I had begun to apply myself to the dissection of anthropoid apes and of monkeys—the forms of life which were deemed most akin to man in structure. I became as much interested in the structural relation of one ape to another as in their combined relationship to the structure of man. For wellnigh a score of years I pursued my inquiries into the anatomy of man and ape, but after 1908 I became interested in the much more important problem: in what circumstances and by what means were the body and the brain of an ape transformed into those of a human being? When and where did this transformation take place? To permit such an evolutionary change to happen I conceived that two conditions were essential: first, that the Primates which were to undergo the change must have formed a social group; second, that the group must have been separated or isolated from all neighbouring groups. I was by no means the first to perceive that isolation was an essential condition of group evolution, but I think I was the first to detect the means by which such isolation was secured. My predecessors attributed isolation to physical barriers—to mountain ranges, to wide seas, and to impassable deserts—whereas I found the "machinery of isolation" to be resident in the mentality of ape and of man. When that idea came to me, I found I was in a position to solve many problems in human evolution which had formerly puzzled me.

From 1908 until the time at which I write (1947) not a year has passed without bringing "grist to my mill." Somewhere someone has discovered a fact, or conceived an idea, which cast a new light on the means and manner by which man had made his

ascent.   One year it was the discovery of fossil remains of man or
of ape; another brought us more exact methods of dating the
antiquity of such fossils.   Our knowledge of the embryology of
man and ape steadily advanced; our information concerning the
mentality and habits of apes and of men has gone on increasing;
our understanding of the manner in which the germinal inheritance of one generation is handed on to the next has grown ever
more precise; the mode in which functional and structural
changes were brought about became more apparent; and
tidings of how primitive peoples live came steadily in from the
most distant lands.   In all of these ways new light has been, and
is being, thrown on the problem of human origins.   These forty
years I have been standing, as it were, at the receipt of custom and,
while pursuing my own inquiries, have gathered into my portfolios each fact or idea as it came along in the hope of gaining
materials from which I might fashion a more precise theory of
man's evolution.   This book represents the harvest of a lifetime.   I have bound my harvest into sheaves, for each essay
represents a sheaf.   And my sheaves, when built together, form
a rick or theory; not a completed one I admit, but yet nearer
completion than any that have gone before.

The appearance of *A New Theory of Human Evolution* was
heralded in the volume of essays I published in 1946 under the
title *Essays on Human Evolution*.   In the preface to that volume
I wrote :—

" There are three main themes on which I believe I can
throw light.   The first theme relates to the manner in which
the final stages of man's evolution or ascent was accomplished.
Most anthropologists conceive a sort of Jacob's ladder up
which mankind has ascended, rung upon rung, to reach his
present estate; whereas I am convinced that the evidence is
now sufficient to permit us to draw a reliable and circumstantial picture of the conditions in which mankind lived
while its major evolutionary changes were taking place.
My second theme relates to the current conception of Race
and Nation.   Most of my colleagues regard a nation as a
political unit, with which anthropologists have no concern;
whereas I regard a nation as an ' evolutionary unit,' with
which anthropologists ought to be greatly concerned.   The

only live races in Europe to-day are its nations.   My third
theme relates to war—'the greatest evil of the modern
world.'

"The natural order in which my three themes should have
been handled was to give first an exposition of my theory of
human evolution; then to trace the origin of nations, of
races, and of the varieties and sub-species of mankind; and
lastly to deal with the origin of man's morality and of war."

My preface then goes on to explain how I was tempted to
reverse the "natural order" of my exposition and to deal first
with the rise of man's morality, of his immorality, and to trace
the scourge of war to its evolutionary roots.   In this present
volume I take up my other main themes—my theory of man's
evolution, the demarcation of mankind into its major divisions or
varieties, the role played by "race" in evolution and the rise of
nations.   My previous volume was a superstructure; the present
volume is an exposition of the fundamentals on which that
superstructure is based.

Readers and critics, having looked at the first essay, in which
my theory is outlined, having glanced at the synopses which
preface each essay, and having read the summary given in the last
essay may be moved to say : Why, this is not a new theory; it is
simply Darwin's theory extended, modified, and brought up to
date ! With such a verdict I will not quarrel; the foundation on
which I have built is that laid by Darwin.   But the theory of
human evolution expounded in my text differs in so many things,
both great and small, from that outlined in *The Descent of Man*,
that I think it is entitled to be called "new."   At least it is a new
rendering of the Darwinian theory.

In a work of this kind an author becomes indebted to hundreds
of men, both living and dead.   I have tried to be just to them in
all my borrowings.   I take this opportunity of acknowledging
my great indebtedness to Mrs. Rupert Willis for the help she has
given me in clarifying my text, and to Miss Gwen Williams for
re-typing my original script.

ARTHUR KEITH.

Downe, Kent,
February 8, 1947.

CONTENTS

ESSAY I

A SUMMARY OF THE NEW OR GROUP THEORY

Synopsis.—*Circumstances which led the author to formulate the
"Group" Theory of Human Evolution. Hormones as part of the
machinery of evolution. A search for the factors which prevent the
swamping of new characters when they first appear. Such factors are
found in the separate grouping of primitive peoples. A mosaic grouping
was in existence among the higher Primates before the emergence of
man's simian ancestry. Evolutionary units defined. The growth of
such units from local groups to tribes, and from tribes to nations. A
great number of small competing units favour rapid evolutionary changes.
The original grouping was determined by territory, not by kinship.
How evolutionary units are kept apart. The importance of a sense of
community. The group theory assumes that in all stages of human
evolution co-operation has been combined with competition. The
behaviour of evolutionary units has always been based on a twofold
code of morality. Such a code favours the rise of the " bad " as well as
of the " good " components of human nature. Human nature is a
product of evolution and is also concerned in the process of evolution.
Extensive migratory movements belong to a late phase of human
history.*

LET me begin this essay by recounting the circumstances which
led me to formulate a new scheme of human evolution to which
I have given the provisional name of " Group " Theory.* In
1908, when I had entered my forty-third year, I was placed in
charge of the vast treasury of things housed in the Museum of the
Royal College of Surgeons of England. Up to that time I had

* In the first draft of this book I used the term " Mosaic " to designate my
theory because it involved a closely-set mosaic of competing groups or tribes.
Later I realized that it was not the closely-set arrangement of groups that was
the essential point of my theory, but the existence of separate competing units
or groups. Hence the name " Group " Theory. Readers will find in my text
traces of the name I used in the first draft.

I

occupied myself with an anatomical exploration of the bodies of man and ape with a view to determining the structural relationship of the one to the other. Soon after taking office at the College of Surgeons there was a shift in the main object of my inquiries; my chief interest became centred, not in the structural resemblances and differences between man and ape, but in the problem of how the many species of ape, and, in particular, the various races of mankind, had come by the forms in which we now find them. In short, I found myself in pursuit of what, in crude terms, may be described as the " machinery of human evolution."

At the time of which I write a fundamental addition was being made to our knowledge of the machinery of evolution by the discovery of substances to which Starling had given the name " hormones." [1] These substances, formed in the organs of the living body and circulating with the blood, served not only to harmonize the several functions of the body but, as Starling inferred, to co-ordinate the development and growth of the organs and regions of the body, and so determine their form and features. To obtain a knowledge of the part played by hormones in the shaping of the human head and body, I applied myself to a close study of those disorders of growth which, we had reason to believe, were due to derangements of the hormone system— the Surgeons' museum being particularly rich in examples of such disorders.

I made a close study of the structural changes effected by an abnormal activity of the hormones emanating from the pituitary gland, as exemplified in the bodies of men and women who had become the subjects of that disorder of growth then known as acromegaly.[2] I noted with interest that in the skulls of such subjects all the features which were overgrown were just those which found such a robust development in the fossil skulls of an extinct race—the Neanderthal race of Europe. It was therefore possible to explain many of the cranial features of Neanderthal man as being due to a vigorous action on the part of his pituitary system. From the study of the dead I passed to that of the living. I came across families which manifested by their large frames and exaggerated features of face a dominance of their pituitaries; I noted, too, that such features often passed from parent to child.

When I proceeded to speculate on how a new race could be

fashioned out of such families I came up against what, at first sight, seemed to be an insurmountable difficulty. These families married into other families, thus scattering abroad their genetic inheritance—their genes; outside marriages brought fresh genes among them. A new race could be fashioned only if such families lived in a small isolated community, inside which all marriages must be contracted. I, therefore, set out in search of such small isolated communities in the modern world, and found that they were still in existence in those parts of the earth which are inhabited by primitive peoples. The evidence gleaned while on this inquiry into the grouping of primitive peoples convinced me that during the whole period of human evolution mankind had been divided into a vast number of isolated local communities, each inhabiting a delimited area or territory. I made the results of this inquiry the subject of the address I gave to the Royal Anthropological Institute, as its President, at the close of 1915.[3] My main thesis was that right down to the dawn of civilization the habitable earth formed a mosaic of separated territories and of peoples, and that such a grouping favoured rapid evolutionary change.

Seeing that the apes which show a structural affinity to man are divided into local groups or communities, we may presume that the mosaic pattern was already in existence when the simian ancestry of man began to spread abroad on the earth. The area of distribution was extended by older, successful local groups giving off broods which formed new groups or communities. The size of a local group depended on the natural fertility of its territory; in primitive peoples which still retain the original mosaic form a local group varies from fifty to 150 individuals— men, women, and children. Such local, inbreeding, competitive groups I shall speak of as "evolutionary units"; they represent the original teams which were involved in the inter-group struggle for survival. I am assuming that the earliest forms of humanity were already organized on a mosaic pattern when the human brain reached that stage of development which made speech possible. Far from speech tending to break down the barriers between local groups, it had an opposite effect, for we know that speech changes quickly when primitive peoples become separated.

Throughout the later stages of human evolution the tendency

has always been towards the production of larger and more powerful evolutionary units. In the continent of Australia, for example, where the native population has always been dependent on the natural produce of its territories, there remain only a few regions where local groups persist as separate evolutionary units; [4] in the greater part of the continent local groups have become federated into large, isolated, inbreeding, evolutionary units, or tribes. Tribes represent a second step in the production of evolutionary units. In Africa, south of the Sahara, all stages in the growth of units are still to be found, from the local groups of Bushmen to large tribal federations, groups under chiefs or kings. The evidence from the New World corroborates that which has been cited from Africa; in pre-Spanish times every stage in the development of evolutionary units was represented; in the extreme south local groups still persisted among the Fuegians; in North America, among the Iroquois, for example, large tribal federations had come into being; in Mexico, and particularly in Peru, tribal grouping had almost reached a third stage, the national.

The conversion of tribal evolutionary units into the still more powerful national units belongs to a late stage of human evolution; indeed, national concentrations became possible only after agriculture and allied arts had made some degree of progress. When the written records of Europe begin, we find that continent divided into a multitude of tribal territories, many of which were of large size, and long before the end of the first millennium B.C. the process of tribal fusion and federation had made considerable headway. I shall not stay now to discuss the feudal stage which intervened between the tribal and national stages in many parts of Europe, because the question which is uppermost in my mind is this: When does a tribal unit become a national unit? It is when tribesmen forget their former loyalties and become conscious of being sharers in, and individual workers for, the common destiny of their new or national unit. Thus the group theory assumes that during the earlier stages of human evolution Nature's competing teams were represented by small, local evolutionary units; later the local units became fused into larger or tribal units; by the fusion and disintegration of tribal units national units came into existence.

In a later essay I shall discuss the effects which an increase in the size of a unit brings about in the rate of evolutionary change; meantime I may say that my main conclusion is that evolutionary change proceeds most quickly when the competing units are small in size and of great number. Such evidence as is afforded by the fossil remains of men who lived during the Pleistocene Age—the latest of geological periods, the duration of which is estimated at 500,000–600,000 years—suggests rapid structural changes. At the beginning of that period we find the poor-brained fossil men of Java and of China, while towards the end of that period we can instance the rich-brained Cro-Magnon type of Europe.

Many anthropologists hold the opinion that the original grouping of mankind was by kinship, and that it was only when such groups settled on the land that the demarcation became territorial. My inquiries of 1915 left me in no doubt that a territorial group was primary; every one of the units I have specified—local communities, tribes, and nations—inhabited and claimed the sole ownership of a demarcated tract of country; all were bound to their homeland by a strong affection; and life was willingly sacrificed to maintain its integrity. I therefore came to regard the territorial sense—a conscious ownership of the homeland, one charged with a deep emotion—as a highly important factor in human evolution. Every such territory serves as an evolutionary cradle. In assigning priority to kinship, authorities have been misled by the exceptional case of the Children of Israel. They emerged from the desert divided into twelve tribes grouped according to kinship; only after their arrival in Palestine did they become territorial. Among the great people of modern times the only ones known to me who succeed in maintaining their identity without the aid of a territorial bond are the Jews. (See Essays XXXVII–XXXVIII.)

A sense of territory helps to keep primitive communities apart; and when we dig into human nature we find a more potent machinery to secure the isolation of such communities. My gropings of 1915 led me to believe that the chief factors in securing isolation were (a) clannishness, a mental state which impels us to favour our kind and to be indifferent or averse to all outside our kind; and (b) the state of mind which Giddings [5] had named the "consciousness of kind." It is the latter factor that I would now emphasize, only I would speak, not of consciousness of kind, but of consciousness of community. Among primitive peoples the range of sympathy is confined to their own community. Local communities, our primary social units, being small, every face in them was known to members, strangers being immediately detected and their presence resented. This consciousness of kind, this community sense, is a character not only of human social groups but of all animal societies whatsoever, be they ant or be they ape. On the other hand, a knowledge of blood relationship has been attained by man only, and could not have been reached until the human brain began to manifest its high faculties.

The group theory assumes that the social organization and mentality still displayed by primitive peoples were those which regulated the conduct of evolving groups of humanity in past geological ages. If this assumption is permitted, then we can give a reasonable explanation of how human races arose; if it is rejected, then we can neither explain the origin of humanity as it now is, nor can we understand the strange duality of man's mentality.

The process which secures the evolution of an isolated group of humanity is a combination of two principles which at first sight seem incompatible—namely, co-operation with competition. So far as concerns the internal affairs of a local group, the warm emotional spirit of amity, sympathy, loyalty, and of mutual help prevails; but so far as concerns external affairs—its attitude towards surrounding groups—an opposite spirit is dominant: one of antagonism, of suspicion, distrust, contempt, or of open enmity. The spirit of co-operation helps to strengthen the social bonds of a group; the spirit of antagonism not only secures the isolation of the group but compels it to maintain its powers of defence and, if the group is to extend its dominion, its powers of offence.

In brief, I hold that from the very beginning of human evolution the conduct of every local group was regulated by two codes of morality, distinguished by Herbert Spencer as the "code of amity" and the "code of enmity." [6] There were thus exposed to "natural selection" two opposing aspects of man's mental nature. The code of amity favoured the growth and ripening of all those qualities of human nature which find universal approval—friendliness, goodwill, love, altruism, idealism, faith, hope, charity, humility, and self-sacrifice—all the Christian virtues. Under the code of enmity arose those qualities which are condemned by all civilized minds—emulation, envy, the competitive spirit, deceit, intrigue, hate, anger, ferocity, and enmity. How the neural basis of such qualities, both good and bad, came into existence during the progressive development of the human brain, we do not know, but it is clear that the chances of survival of a struggling, evolving group would be strengthened by both sets of qualities. These two sets of opposite qualities must be balanced to secure continuous, progressive evolutionary changes; an over-development of the elements which subserve the code of amity would make its group vulnerable to its enemies; an overgrowth of those which support the code of enmity would lead ultimately to the destruction of the group.

It will thus be seen that I look on the duality of human nature as an essential part of the machinery of human evolution. It is the corner-stone of my mosaic edifice. Human nature is both a product and a process. It has been built up as a product of man's evolution, but it has been developed so as to serve in the process of evolutionary change.

Besides the qualities in human nature which directly subserve one or other of man's two codes of morality, there are others which are of equal service to either code, and which work for the welfare of the evolutionary group. In the forefront I would place that quality of will known as courage; man can be courageous in ill-doing as whole-heartedly as in well-doing. There is the inborn love of self, and yet a readiness to sacrifice self in causes both good and bad. There is that form of mental hunger known as curiosity; urged by this appetite, man discovers with equal zest things which kill and things which cure. There are the virtues of prudence and of temperance, which may be made the playthings of either code. Man may use his gifts of reason and of imagination to further good or bad ends. Loyalty rules among thieves as well as among honest men. If a group is to prosper, there must be within it a desire for children and a love of them. A love of knowledge is also advantageous. All these mental qualities have survival values. A love of beauty may also minister to the survival of a group.

The major obstacle to the acceptance of the group theory of human evolution is the belief, held by most of my contemporaries,

B

that from the very beginning mankind has been always on the move, jostling against and mixing with one another, and that there has been no long quiescent period when local groups were stationary—such being an essential postulate of my theory. The belief that man has always been a migratory animal is based upon the happenings of a comparatively recent period of human history. Dawning history reveals vast movements of peoples in Europe, in Asia, in Africa, in the New World, and in the islands of the Pacific. It is inferred that these movements of historical times were but a continuation of the movements of the earliest prehistoric period. I regard this view as a mistaken one, for two reasons. My first reason, a minor one, is based on the conditions under which our Pleistocene ancestors had to live. They were dependent on the natural produce of their territories; to gain a bare livelihood was a daily preoccupation. Lack of supplies made long-range migratory movements impossible; incursions into neighbouring territories could have been of the nature of only local forays. It was only after domestication of animals and of plants had made some advance that there were sufficient stocks of food to make long-range and extensive migratory movements possible.

My chief reason for disbelieving in early migratory movements is this. We have to account for the fact that each major racial type of mankind is confined to a single area of the globe; the Negro type to Africa, the Mongol type to Eastern Asia, the Caucasian type to Western Asia and Europe, the Australoid type to Australia and neighbouring islands. If the group theory is accepted, then we can explain such a distribution; a long period in which local groups were comparatively stationary would bring about such a distribution. If there had been, as has been maintained by distinguished authorities,[7] free migration and mixture in the human world from primordial times, then such distribution of types cannot be explained.

In this preliminary essay I have enumerated the chief points which make up my conception of the mode of man's evolution. To this conception I have ventured, with some degree of temerity, to give the name " Group " Theory. In the essays which make up the remainder of this book, evidence in support of my thesis will be brought forward and discussed.

REFERENCES

[1] Bayliss and Starling, *Proc. Roy. Soc.*, 1904, vol. 73, p. 310. See also Professor Starling's lecture on "The Chemical Correlations of the Functions of the Body," *Lancet*, 1905, vol. 2, p. 339.

[2] Keith, Sir A., "An Enquiry into the Nature of Skeletal Changes in Acromegaly," *Lancet*, 1911, vol. 1, p. 722. See also my Herter Lectures on "The Evolution of Human Races in the Light of the Hormone Theory," *Johns Hopkins Hosp. Bull.*, 1922, vol. 33, pp. 155, 195.

[3] Keith, Sir A., "Certain Factors concerned in the Evolution of Human Races," *Journ. Roy. Anthrop. Inst.*, 1916, vol. 46, p. 10.

[4] Wheeler, G. C., *The Tribe and Intertribal Relations in Australia*, 1910.

[5] Giddings, Franklin H., *Principles of Sociology*, 1898.

[6] Spencer, Herbert, *Principles of Ethics*, 1892, vol. 1, pp. 316, 471.

[7] See Dixon, Roland B., *The Racial History of Man*, 1923; Haddon, A. C., and Huxley, Julian S., *We Europeans*, 1935.

HOW FAR THE GROUP THEORY DIFFERS FROM OTHER THEORIES OF MAN'S ORIGIN

Synopsis.—*The group theory assumes, in common with other theories of man's origin, that the human stem sprang from a simian root. Former authors who have assumed that primitive humanity was divided into numerous small groups or communities. Gumplowitz and Sumner as pioneers. Territorialism and patriotism have not been recognized previously as factors in human evolution. The importance of " group consciousness" recognized by Darwin. Competition and selection are accepted as factors. The combination of co-operation with competition has also been recognized previously. How isolation of groups is secured. Group perpetuation. Inbreeding as a factor. The role of genes in evolution. Multiple small units are assumed to favour rapid evolutionary changes. Fertility has been the subject of most rigorous selection. Primitive groups normally remained fixed to their territories, yet under certain conditions movements took place. Group and individual selection went on hand in hand. Civilization brought about the formation of large groups. The effects of increase of group on evolutionary change. The group theory supplies a background for human evolution. The conception of human nature as a product of evolution is not new, but the contention that it plays an important role in evolution has not been made before.*

WHEREIN does the group theory, outlined in the preceding essay, differ from other explanations of man's evolutionary origin? This essay is an answer to that question; in it I propose to discuss the points in which I am in agreement with other students of human evolution as well as those wherein we differ. Such a discussion should help my readers to obtain a clearer idea of the conception I have in mind when I speak of the group theory. In one important point I am in agreement with all my predecessors, with those of the Darwin–Huxley period and their successors—namely, that the simian root or stock which gave origin to the monkeys of the Old World, and to anthropoid or man-like apes, was also that which gave birth to humanity.

I regard the division of evolving humanity into a multitude of small, separate, competitive communities or societies as the chief feature of my theory. The following passage shows that Darwin was familiar with the idea: [1] " Therefore, looking far enough in the stream of time, and judging from the social habits of man as he now exists, the most probable view is that he aboriginally lived in small communities." Walter Bagehot (1826–77), who was the first to apply Darwinism to the problem of modern politics, describes man's early condition thus: " In the beginning of things . . . each was a parish race, narrow in thought and bounded in range." [2] Aristotle, speaking of the first appearance of governments, says: " The world was then divided into small communities." [3] The same idea was entertained by Archdeacon Paley,[4] and by Henry Home of Kames.[5] Writing of a comparatively late phase of human evolution, that of Palæolithic man, the late Prof. Karl Pearson inferred that the social unit " could hardly have been larger than that of a family." [6] Thus there is nothing new in postulating that early mankind was divided into an exceedingly great number of small communities; what is new is that this mosaic of humanity endured throughout the entire period of man's major evolution and provided the most favourable circumstances for bringing about rapid changes in brain and in body.

Mention must be made here of two men who have preceded me and have realized very clearly that early mankind was separated into a very great number of small competitive communities or social units. One was Prof. Louis Gumplowitz of Graz (1838–1909), who spoke of " innumerable petty units "; [7] the other, Prof. W. G. Sumner of Yale (1844–1910). " The conception of primitive society that we ought to form," wrote the latter, " is that of small groups scattered over a territory. . . . The size of the group is determined by the conditions for the struggle for existence." [8] Neither of these authors, however, perceived how favourable was the co-existence of a multitude of separate, inbreeding, competitive social units for bringing about rapid, progressive evolutionary changes.

Sumner, in the passage just quoted, adds a feature to which I attach great importance as a factor in human evolution—namely, that of "territory." Each local group, or combination of local groups, lived within a demarcated area; a group claimed to own such a territory as its homeland; to this homeland, as to its fellows, a group was bound by that particular form of affection (or prejudice) known as patriotism. The role of patriotism in bringing about evolutionary change will form the subject-matter of a separate essay. My present object is merely to emphasize the place given to it in the group theory of human evolution; so far as I know, the evolutionary significance of territorialism and of patriotism has not been recognized by previous writers on human evolution.

We now turn to examine the mentality of the small groups into which early mankind was divided. We may infer, from what we know of social animals, that the members of each human group were conscious of membership of their own particular community, and were equally aware that their group was different from all other groups. We may designate this mental trait as " group consciousness." It was not until Darwin came to write *The Descent of Man* (1871) that he perceived that social animals are actively conscious, not of their race or of their species, but only of the community or group to which they belong. " Sympathy," he noted, " is directed solely towards members of the same community, and therefore towards known, and more or less loved members, but not to all the individuals of the same species." [9] In another passage Darwin amplifies his meaning thus : " Primeval man regarded actions as good or bad, solely as they obviously affected the welfare of the tribe, not of the species." [10]

Herbert Spencer, Darwin's great contemporary, went still farther in defining the mentality of the groups into which primitive men were divided. Group consciousness induced a discrimination in the behaviour of primeval mankind; their conduct towards members of their own group was based on one code—the code of *amity*; while that to members of other groups was based on another code—that of *enmity*.[11] As a result of group consciousness, which serves to bind the members of a community together and to separate the community from all others, " there arises," to use the words of Professor Sumner, "a differentiation between ourselves—the ' we ' group or ' in ' group—and everybody else—the 'out' group." [12] Thus in a wide field of evolving groups of early mankind there were two mental factors at work: one was "group consciousness"; the other, a dual code of behaviour. Both produce evolutionary results, and are therefore included as elements in the group theory.

Into the group theory come those evolutionary factors which received their first impress from Darwin—competition, selection, survival. Darwin knew that in the mosaic of primitive humanity competition acted chiefly by setting one social group against all neighbouring groups; selection or survival depended on "team-work." Here are Darwin's own words: "And natural selection, arising from the competition of tribe with tribe, in some such large area . . . would, under favourable conditions, have sufficed to raise man to his high position." [13] The competition which Darwin had in mind was that of team against team; this was also the conception held by Russel Wallace. [14]

Two further extracts from Darwin will serve to give my readers a more exact idea of the evolutionary role of competition in a world of primitive humanity broken up into separate units. "When of two adjoining tribes one becomes less numerous and less powerful than the other, the contest is soon settled by war, slaughter, cannibalism, slavery and absorption." [15] Here Darwin emphasizes the cruel side of competitive evolution, but the next extract—and many more might be cited—leads us to realize that he was quite aware, so far as concerns human evolution, that co-operation was combined with competition: "When two tribes of primeval men, living in the same country, came into competition, the tribe including the greater number of courageous, sympathetic and of faithful members would succeed better and conquer the others." [16] Thus competition favoured the tribes which were rich in co-operative qualities. It may be regretted that Darwin did not lay greater emphasis on the part played by co-operation in his scheme of evolution. Kropotkin [17] went to the opposite extreme by exaggerating the part played by "mutual aid" and minimizing competition as a factor in evolution. In the group theory competition and co-operation are regarded as twin factors which work together to bring about evolutionary change. Quite independently Dr. W. C. Allee came to the same conclusion. [18]

In the group theory isolation of competing groups is regarded as a condition which must be present if effective, progressive evolutionary changes are to be brought about. Moritz Wagner [19] held that isolation was a cardinal factor in evolution, an opinion which was never fully accepted by Darwin. The most Darwin would admit was that " although isolation is of great importance in the production of new species, on the whole I am inclined to believe that largeness of area is still more important." [20]   After Darwin's time G. J. Romanes [21] sought to restore isolation as a factor in evolution to the place given to it by Wagner. There is thus nothing new in giving isolation a leading place in my theory of human evolution; what is new is the mode by which isolation of competing groups is maintained. The isolating machinery is assumed to be embedded in man's mentality. In every region of the modern world, where tribes still exist as independent entities, we find two opposite dispositions at work—one being *group affection*, which holds together the members of a community, and the other, *group aversion*, which keeps competing, evolving societies apart. These opposite dispositions are not confined to human societies; they are to be seen at work in the communities into which all social animals are divided. We may assume, therefore, that in the very earliest stages of man's evolution, even in his simian stages, " human nature " was already converted into an instrument for securing group isolation.

The group theory assumes that each of the many thousands of groups or communities into which early mankind was divided was the carrier and custodian of a particular assemblage of germinal seeds or genes; no two groups had exactly the same assemblage. If a group is to work out the evolutionary destiny inherent in its genes, it is necessary, not only that it should be isolated, thus preventing intercrossing, but that its integrity and its perpetuation should be maintained for a long succession of generations. Here again we find human nature called in to serve evolutionary ends. There are few desires more deeply ingrained in a man's nature than that which seeks for an endurance of his family, his kin, and his country. Thus, in the group theory, each unit of primitive humanity is regarded as a closed society, one in which mating is confined within the limits of the community; all were inbreeding societies.

Thus my theory gives inbreeding a high place among the factors which bring about evolutionary changes. If it should happen that among the genes circulating within the limits of a group there are those of a recessive or evil nature, then, if the inbreeding group be small, these recessive genes will soon be brought together in the course of conjugation. They will thus produce their evil results by bringing about defects in the development of the body, or irregularities in the growth of its parts, or deficiencies in one or more of its functions. Inbreeding, in the presence of defective genes, would thus lead to a speedy extermination of a group. But if it should be that a group's stock of genes were entirely healthy, prone to give rise to variations of a favourable, progressive nature, then inbreeding would tend to enhance their virtues and speed up the rate of evolutionary change. Thus it is assumed that a vast mosaic of competing, isolated units or groups provides the most favourable conditions for bringing about a rapid evolutionary advance.

The later stages of man's evolution seem to have been effected in a surprisingly short period of time. At the beginning of the last geological period—the Pleistocene, with an estimated duration of little more than half a million years—the human brain was relatively small and simple, as shown by discoveries made in Java, China, and England, whereas at the end of the period Cro-Magnon man presents us with the human brain at its zenith.

The theory I am postulating assumes that the character which underwent the most rigorous degree of selection during the small-group period was that of fertility. The tribe with the most and the best parents was the tribe which endured; if the fertility of a tribe failed, its end was soon in sight.

My theory assumes that the competing communities of primitive man were tied to their territories and were in a geographical sense stationary. This is also the opinion of Sir A. M. Carr-Saunders.[23] There is very little evidence of tribal migration or of invasion of neighbouring territories in aboriginal Australia. Conditions during the small-group phase of early man must have been less static than with the Australian aborigines, otherwise successful and progressive types would have been penned up within their territories for ever. The conditions which induce a tribe to spread beyond the limits of its territory are complex. An increase in numbers and in power are conducive to extension, but there must be also a profound change in the emotional mentality of the tribe which bursts its borders. Thus it is assumed that a disposition to remain fixed and an opposite disposition to move have each of them a place in bringing about evolutionary change.

Although it is assumed that, during the most progressive stages of human evolution, the group or team was the unit on which selective agencies wrought their effects, yet it also recognizes that there was a constant selection of the individuals which made up a group or team. Individual and group selection went on hand in hand.

The group theory assumes that the segregation of mankind into a multitude of small units came to an end with the dawn of civilization. With the coming of agriculture evolutionary units began to grow, culminating in the multi-millioned nations of modern times. What effect has the increase in size of unit had on evolutionary change? To answer this question requires knowledge and faculties beyond those at my disposal, but in a broad way I see that in large populations, crowded in cities, the result has been to render evolutionary changes diffuse, inchoate, and indeterminate, tending to produce a homogeneity of type rather than a number of sharply differentiated local types, as was the case when the evolutionary units were small. Besides, civilization is subjecting modern nations to hundreds of selective agencies of which early man knew nothing. The civilized mind condemns the naked manifestation of all factors which played a part in early evolution.[24]

My predecessors, in outlining their conceptions of man's evolution by means of diagrams, have omitted all reference to the actual background amid which evolutionary changes took place.[25] My theory supplies this background; it assumes that from the earliest to the latest stage of human evolution mankind existed as separated societies, all of them competing to a greater or less degree for their place in the living world. And as the conditions amid which the later stages of human evolution were effected still exist in tribal areas of the earth, we have opportunities of observing how far the assumptions made by the theory postulated here may be regarded as right or wrong. Anthropoid apes still exist as local groups. I am of opinion that a more extended study of anthropoid groups will provide information which will justify us in assuming that particulate grouping was also true of the simian stages of human evolution.

The group theory makes two large assumptions in respect to human nature; first, that it has been built up and matured as man progressed from a simian stage to the full-blown stage met with in modern man; second, that human nature is so constituted as to serve as a chief factor in controlling human evolution. Human nature, as we have seen, keeps the members of a group together; it serves also to keep groups apart; it urges groups to maintain their integrity and continuation; it imbues groups with their competitive spirit. The assumption that man's nature is a product of evolution is not new. We find Bagehot making this statement as early as 1869: "In those ages (of the primitive world) was formed the comparatively gentle, guidable thing which we call human nature." [26] Prof. Wm. McDougall also took an evolutionary view of human nature: "There can, I think, be no doubt, that the principal condition of the evolution of man's moral nature was group selection among primitive societies, constantly at war with one another." [27] Lastly a confirmatory statement by Wm. James:—

"The theory of evolution is mainly responsible for this. Man, we have now reason to believe, has been evolved from infra-human ancestors, in whom pure reason scarcely existed, if at all, and whose mind, so far as it can have any function, would appear to have been an organ for adapting their movements to the impressions received from the environment, so as to escape the better from destruction. . . . Our sensations are here to attract us, or to deter us, our memories to warn or encourage us, our feelings to impel, and our thoughts to restrain our behaviour, so that on the whole we may prosper and our days be long in the land." [28]

Thus it will be seen that most of the factors which go to make up the group theory have already been cited by students of human evolution. It is in the way in which these separate factors have been combined so as to co-operate in bringing about evolutionary changes that my theory differs from other theories of human evolution.

REFERENCES

[1] *The Descent of Man*, ch. XX, p. 901, Murray's reprint of 2nd ed., 1913.
[2] Bagehot, W., *Physics and Politics*, 1896, p. 70.
[3] Aristotle's *Politics*, bk. III, ch. XV, p. 99 in Everyman ed.

[4] Paley, Wm., *Moral and Political Philosophy*, 1788, bk. VI, ch. I.

[5] Home, Henry (Lord Kames), *Sketches of the History of Man*, 1813, vol. 2, p. 18.

[6] Pearson, Karl, *Ann. of Eugenics*, 1930, vol. 4, p. 1.

[7] Gumplowitz, Louis, *Sociologie et Politique*, Paris, 1898, p. 143.

[8] Sumner, W. G., *Folkways*, 1906, p. 12.

[9] *The Descent of Man*, Murray, 1913, p. 163.

[10] *Ibid.*, p. 182.

[11] Spencer, H., *Principles of Ethics*, 1892, vol. 1, pp. 316, 322.

[12] Sumner, W. G., *Folkways*, p. 12.

[13] *The Descent of Man*, Murray, 1913, p. 97.

[14] Wallace, A. R., *Anthrop. Rev.*, 1864, vol. 2, p. 158.

[15] *The Descent of Man*, Murray, 1913, p. 282.

[16] *Ibid.*, p. 199.

[17] Kropotkin, P., *Mutual Aid: A Factor in Evolution*, 1902.

[18] Allee, W. C., *Social Life of Animals*, 1939, p. 35; *Science*, 1943, vol. 97, p. 517.

[19] Wagner, Moritz, *Die Darwinische Theorie und des Migration-Gesetz des Organismen*, 1868.

[20] *Origin of Species*, 6th ed., 1885, p. 82.

[21] Romanes, G. J., *Darwin and after Darwin*, 1897.

[22] *Origin of Species*, p. 80.

[23] Carr-Saunders, Sir A. M., *The Population Problem: A Study in Human Evolution*, 1922, p. 238.

[24] Keith, Sir A., *Essays in Human Evolution*, 1946, p. 118.

[25] Keith, Sir A., *The Construction of Man's Family Tree*, 1934.

[26] Bagehot, W., *Physics and Politics*, p. 218.

[27] McDougall, Wm., *The Group Mind*, 1920, p. 264.

[28] James, Wm., *Talks to Teachers*, 1902, p. 24.

EVIDENCE OF THE PARTICULATE GROUPING OF HUMANITY DURING THE PRIMAL * PERIOD OF ITS EVOLUTION

Synopsis.—The need for the recognition of two periods in human evolution, primal and post-primal. Evidence of a former tribal organization in Scotland, England, Wales, Ireland, France, Germany, and Spain. Evidence of a tribal grouping among the early Romans. City-States represent tribal entities. Tribalism in Ancient Greece, in the Balkans, in Hungary, and in Russia. Tribalism in Ancient Egypt and Mesopotamia. Tribalism in Asia Minor and in Arabia. The small nations of Biblical Palestine. The mosaic of peoples in the Caucasus, in Persia, in the western Himalayas, in Tibet, and Indo-China. The tribes of Mongolia and Manchuria; the villages of China; the tribes and castes of India. Evidence from Australasia, from the islands of Timor and Celebes, from New Guinea, New Hebrides, and from Australia. The tribal grouping of the Indian population of the New World. Africa as a continent of tribes in all stages of evolution. The evidence of archæology. Evidence of social grouping among the Primates. From the evidence cited, the author holds that the division of early, evolving humanity into a multitude of small social groups may be assumed as true.

IN this essay I propose to make a hurried circuit of the globe, noting as I pass from country to country the evidence for assuming that their populations are now, or were in former times,

* Students of human evolution are handicapped by the lack of a term to indicate the period of man's evolution before the dawn of civilization and the period which succeeded the dawn. Here I use the term " primal " to cover the very long first period and " post-primal " to indicate the second—the age of civilization. If we assume that 7000 B.C. marks the first glimmerings of civilization, then the post-primal period would have a duration of about 9000 years, whereas we must attribute a duration of a million years or more to the primal period.

divided into separate groups or tribes. I shall begin my survey
with the Highlands of Scotland, which is but meet for one who,
by birth, is half a Highlander. At the end of the sixteenth century
Highlanders were still grouped in clans; there were then forty-
two of them, twenty-two in vigorous health, twenty of them
broken.[1] Each clan had its chief, its territory, its allegiances, and
its enmities. Savage measures applied after the Jacobite rebellion
of 1745 brought the clan system of the Highlands to an end.
The clans of the eighteenth century may be regarded as the debris
of an earlier tribal organization, for in the first century of our era
Highlanders had been confederated into sixteen tribes, while the
Lowlanders—the population south of the Forth—were arranged
in five tribes.

At the corresponding period, the first century of the Roman
occupation, the population of England had become confederated
into fifteen large units or tribes. Wales, in the Roman period,
could claim only three tribes, but there is evidence that these were
compounded out of nearly fifty local groups, corresponding to
the Scottish clans and Irish septs.[3] As for Ireland, the number of
her tribes during the earlier centuries of our era is most uncertain,
but Keating [4] was probably near the truth when he put the
number of tribes or septs at 110. Prichard,[5] a very reliable
authority, gives the number of Irish tribes as sixteen. The clan
system in Ireland was stamped out by warlike measures adopted
by Elizabeth, James I, and Cromwell, but the clan spirit remained,
and remains, untamed. Gibbon counted thirty independent
tribes or nations of the first century in Britain; if he had had the
means of estimating the number of British tribal units a thousand
years earlier, he would, in all likelihood, have had to multiply his
estimate by ten.

We now turn to France as she was in the year 58 B.C., when
Julius Cæsar led his army against her tribal communities. The
number of her tribal States is estimated variously, and no wonder,
seeing that conquest and coercion were always altering estimates.
Gibbon gives the number of her independent States as one
hundred. Prichard [6] gives the number as seventy, while Hubert [7]
is content with sixty, but states that these had been compounded
out of some five hundred local clans or septs (*Pagi*). Hume [8]
quotes Appian to the effect that there were four hundred nations
in Gaul—nations here meaning separate local communities. In

any case, we cannot doubt that the Celtic inhabitants of Gaul were divided into hundreds of separate units, which, in the last century before our era, were being consolidated into larger tribal units. In ancient Germany, as in Gaul, the process of tribal amalgamation was also at work; when the Romans appeared on the Rhine, German tribes numbered about forty.[9] In Spain of the same period there were at least thirty-five demarcated tribes.

I have failed to find any estimate of the number of separate peoples and tribes which occupied Italy in the year 753 B.C.—the date traditionally assigned to the foundation of Rome. A little later there were then springing up city-States in the Grecian south, and Etrurian confederations of cities were being formed in Etruria.[10] The founders of Rome were three confederated pastoral tribes.[11] South of them, in Latium, they were neighboured by some thirty townships, each representing a self-governing community; in the mountainous country to the east there were numerous hill tribes. The founders of Rome, as they grew in numbers and expanded in territory, created new tribes, so that these ultimately numbered thirty-five, but such were artificial, State-devised tribes, quite different in nature from the independent, self-governing tribes and peoples which had grown up in Italy in the course of past evolutionary events. By the beginning of the second century B.C. all the tribes and peoples of Italy had been stripped of their independence, their evolutionary destinies passing under the control of Rome.

Ancient Greece had an area of about 25,000 miles square—being rather smaller than Scotland. When the seven tribes, four Ionian and three Dorian, descended on that land towards the end of the second millennium B.C., they found its inhabitants divided into territorial tribal units; they also found a number of old-established city-States. Coming as conquering, dominant peoples, one may infer that the invaders accepted the tribal divisions which were already in existence, merely imposing on the ancient tribes their persons, their will, and their tongues. The earliest records give four tribes to the State of Attica; these, I infer, represent the tribal units taken over and dominated by the conquerors. Later, in Athens as in Rome, tribes were reconstituted and artificial tribes created. The twelve tribes of Elis may also represent a pre-Grecian division.[12] Paterson has estimated that there were 150 independent sovereign States in Ancient Greece.[13]

When these States were being established in Ancient Greece, the inhabitants of that part of Europe which lies between the Adriatic and the Black Sea retained their tribal organization. It was so in Thessalia, Macedonia, and Thrace. In Thrace, according to Herodotus, there were fifty tribes grouped into twelve nations. Even in modern times the inhabitants of Montenegro are grouped into more than forty tribes.[14] The Magyars, when they invaded Hungary, were divided into 108 septs or clans.[15] In Russia of the thirteenth century there were sixty-four independent States. Gibbon mentions that in early Russia there were 4,600 village communities, each being an independent entity. In the lands lying to the north of the Black Sea, extending from the Crimea to the mouth of the Danube, there were 129 separate dialects or tongues—evidence of a multitude of peoples grouped in that area.[16]

Egypt carries her history into the past more reliably, and more completely, than any other country. Before the union of the Crowns (3200 B.C.) the population of Upper Egypt was grouped in tribal communities along the banks of the Nile. "Each of these tribes was recognized as possessor of its district, which was denoted by the name of some sacred animal." [17] The number of pre-dynastic tribes, or Nomes, has been variously estimated; one authority gives twenty, another forty.[18] During periods of dissolution which overtook Egypt from time to time during the course of her long history one or more of the local communities reasserted their independence. The Berberines, who occupied the banks of the Nile south of Egypt, were also grouped in tribes. Thotmes of the eighteenth dynasty claimed to have conquered 113 of them. Major G. W. Murray states that fifty Bedouin tribes frequent the outskirts of modern Egypt.[19]

The city-States which began to be established in the valleys of Tigris and Euphrates towards the end of the fifth millennium B.C. represented separate, independent tribal entities. Round the area of lands occupied by the city-States the native peoples retained their original grouping—that of small tribes. For example, when an early king of Agade carried war across the Persian Gulf, he met with, and conquered, thirty-two petty kings; Tiglath-pileser (1115–1102) of Assyria prided himself on the conquest of forty-two peoples.

Asia Minor is now, and always has been, a mosaic of peoples. The Hittites and Mitanni arose to power through a series of tribal confederations.[20]   The modern Kurds are divided into more than three hundred tribes, speaking ten dialects.[21]   The Vilayet of Mosul has been described as "a mosaic of races," each village having its own dialect.   South of the area we have glanced at, from Syria in the north-west to Oman in the south-east, lies the vast mosaic of Arab peoples in all stages of tribal evolution.   Dr. E. Epstein[22] has made a survey of the Arabs inhabiting the southern part of Palestine, known as the Negeb, which is little more than half the size of Yorkshire, and found them divided into five tribes and seventy-five sub-tribes.   Palestine itself was occupied by seven independent nations at the time of invasion by the Children of Israel.   In his conquest of Palestine, Joshua claims to have encountered and overcome " Kings thirty and one " (Joshua xii, 24).

Proceeding now farther towards the east, we may note as we go the " Babel of tongues and peoples " to be found in the valleys of the Caucasus and the Iliyats of Persia, formerly divided into seventy-three tribes,[23] and so reach the valleys and uplands at the western end of the Himalayas.   Here we find the most extensive paradise of robust, independent tribes in all the world.[24]   Between the Indus and Afghanistan are five millions of people grouped in warlike tribes; in Afghanistan itself, and also in Baluchistan, the former tribal organization is still traceable; on the Pamir, and in the western valleys of the Himalayas, separate peoples and tongues are to be counted by the score.   If we make our way to the Far East, crossing Tibet to reach the mountainous lands which lie to the south of China, we meet with a bewildering assortment of peoples and tongues; some have merely the status of a local group; many are separate village communities; others are tribes; while some have reached a status which may be called national.   "From the north-western Himalayas to the south-eastern extremity of Farther India," wrote that most able anthropologist A. H. Keane,[25] " I have collected nearly a thousand names of clans, septs and fragmentary groups and am well aware that the list neither is, nor ever can be, complete, the groups being in a constant state of fluctuation."

c

In the days of Jenghis Khan the Mongols were divided into 226 clans out of which forty confederacies had been formed. The Manchus at the time of their conquest of China were divided into sixty tribes. The early history of tribalism in China is unknown, but the strong spirit of localism manifested by her half-million village communities may be taken as evidence that the Chinese still retain a particularist mentality. In contrast to China, India still retains abundant evidence of a tribal distribution of her original population. The castes of India are self-governed, closed societies, tribal in their organization. Indeed, it is often difficult to say whether a particular community is to be called a caste or a tribe. There are 2,378 tribes and castes in India,[26] and 225 languages are spoken.

A few instances will serve to show the multi-partite distribution of the peoples of Australasia. In the small island of Timor, Dr. H. O. Forbes found, when he visited it in 1884,[27] that forty languages were spoken. In the eastern half of the island, under Portuguese rule, there were forty-seven independent States, each under its Rajah. Evidently the number of States and tongues has undergone a reduction, for in a Report issued in 1944 [28] Dr. Mendes Correa gives the number of separate tongues as eight, and the number of dialects as fifteen, while he makes no mention of separate States. In the small compass of the northern peninsula of the island of Celebes a conglomeration of separate tribes is kept apart by having twelve different tongues. No census has yet been made of the social units of the great island of New Guinea; they must run into hundreds; some are tribes, others are separate village communities. " In the New Hebrides and in New Caledonia," as J. Macmillan Brown reported in 1916,[29] " each village has its own dialect "—evidence that these communities keep apart. We are also ignorant of the number of tribes into which the aborigines of Australia were divided before the white settlement began. If we accept 300,000 as the number of aborigines in virgin Australia, which is the customary estimate, and assign 150 to the average tribe, the original number of tribes would have been about 2,000; probably an underestimate.

A few examples from the New World will suffice to illustrate the tribal constitution of its pre-Columbian population. In the census of the United States for 1910, Prof. R. B. Dixon prepared a detailed Report on the Indian population, which at that time numbered 305,000. The tribes represented by this population numbered 280; of these, seventy-seven had a membership of five hundred or more; forty-two were reduced to a following of ten or less. What is now the State of California gave a home to 101 tribes; Alaska had sixty-six, besides forty "local groups" of Eskimo. Some of the Indian tribes were very large—the Cherokees, for example, numbering over 30,000—but the average was about 2,000. As with Rome and Greece, so with Ancient Mexico and Peru; in all four cases there is clear evidence of an early tribal constitution. Regarding South America, I shall content myself with citing the list of tribes inhabiting the basin of the Amazon, prepared by Sir Clements Markham in 1910.[30] After purging his list of synonyms, the final number he reached, for this area, was 485. In the extreme south, in Tierra del Fuego, the native Yahgans still live in separate local groups, as do the Eskimo in the extreme north. Thus, in the native population of the New World every stage in the evolution of human groups was represented, from local communities to organized States.

Africa is a continent of tribes, but it would take me too far afield to attempt a systematic survey of them.[31] In 1930 the population of Tanganyika Territory, numbering five millions, was divided into 117 tribes.[32] In Northern Rhodesia eighty-one tribes have been enumerated. Dr. W. Hambly[33] gives a list of 117 tribes in the Congo basin and another of sixty-three for tribes in Uganda and Nyasaland. According to Keane there were 108 Sudanese tribes; the Berber tribes of the High Atlas number twenty (Prichard). The Dutch on their first arrival in South Africa came in contact with the Hottentots and Bushmen. "The original Hottentots," Prichard has noted,[34] "were a numerous people, divided into many tribes . . . with flocks and herds." The numbers in a tribe varied from several hundreds to a couple of thousand.[35] Bushmen, on the other hand, were distributed in local groups, thus retaining what I suppose to be the original organization of mankind. Some of the peoples living in the more remote parts of Uganda appear also to have retained a separate local grouping.[36] Even when confederated into kingdoms, as in modern Uganda, or in the kingdoms which arose in the region of Lake Chad in the fifteenth century, the African peoples retain a tribal organization. Thus in modern Africa we find every stage in tribal evolution from the local group to a federal tribal kingdom.

We have now completed a hurried circuit of the globe, and the evidence we have met with supports the contention that all living peoples are now, or were originally, divided into small separate units or groups. The conditions of life in the primal period, when mankind depended on the natural produce of the soil for a subsistence, made the existence of large local groups an impossibility. The evidence we have gathered, then, is in conformity with the postulates of the group theory.

There is one source of evidence bearing on the particulate distribution of the early races of mankind which is only now becoming available—namely, that provided by the excavation of ancient sites of habitation. Archæologists are finding that the distribution of stone tools and other remains of human culture in such sites are definitely localized.[37] This should be so if early mankind was separated into local groups. So far all the discoveries of fossil remains of early men favour a differentiation into local types.[38]

The new theory requires proof that mankind was divided into social groups, not only during the earliest stages of human evolution, but in its pre-human or simian stage. Darwin inferred it had been so when he wrote: "Judging from the analogy of the majority of the Quadrumana, it is probable that the early ape-like progenitors of man were likewise social."[39] The leading authority on this matter, Dr. C. R. Carpenter,[40] has declared that "all types of Primates which have been adequately studied in the field have been found to show the phenomenon of territorialism." Territorialism implies division into groups, each group occupying its own area of forest or jungle. Professor Hooton has recently summarized the evidence bearing on the group organization of the higher Primates.[41]

Such, then, is a summary of the evidence on which I rely when I assume that mankind, during the primal period of its evolution, was divided into an exceedingly great number of isolated social communities.

REFERENCES

[1] Johnston, T. B., and Robertson, J. A., A Historical Geography of the Clans of Scotland, 1899; Browne, Jas., A History of the Highlands and of the Clans of Scotland, vol. 4, 1852.

[2] Skene, Wm. F., *Celtic Scotland*, 1876.

[3] Brooke, F. A., *The Science of Social Development*, 1936.

[4] O'Dwyer, Sir Michael, *The O'Dwyers of Kilnamanagh*, 1933.

[5] Prichard, J. C., *Physical History of Mankind*, 1841, vol. iii, p. 138.

[6] *Ibid.*, p. 67.

[7] Hubert, Henri, *The Greatness and Decline of the Celts*, 1934, p. 3.

[8] Hume, David, *Essays and Treatises*, 1772, vol. i, p. 457.

[9] Gibbon, E., *Decline and Fall*, Everyman ed., vol. i, p. 228.

[10] Whatmough, J., *The Foundations of Roman Italy*, 1937.

[11] Alton and Golicher, Spencer's *Descriptive Sociology: The Romans*, 1934.

[12] Smith's *Dictionary of Greek and Roman Antiquities*, 3rd ed., 1891.

[13] Paterson, W. R., Introduction to *The Peoples of all Nations* (Harmsworth), vol. i, 1922.

[14] Durham, M. E., *The Burden of the Balkans*, 1905; *Jour. Roy. Anthrop. Inst.*, 1909, vol. 39, p. 85.

[15] Latham, R. G., *The Ethnology of Europe*, 1852, p. 243.

[16] Niederle, L., *La Race Slav*, 1911, p. 24.

[17] Myres, Sir John, *The Dawn of History*, p. 58.

[18] Newberry, P. E., *Nature*, 1923, vol. 112, p. 940; Murray, G. W., *Sons of Ishmael*, 1935.

[19] Murray, G. W., see under reference 18.

[20] Garstang, J., *The Hittite Empire*, 1929. Harmsworth's *Universal History*, ch. 23.

[21] Sykes, Mark, *Jour. Roy. Anthrop. Inst.*, 1908, vol. 38, p. 451.

[22] Epstein, E., *Palest. Explor. Quart.*, 1939, vol. 71, p. 59.

[23] Prichard, J. C., *Physical History of Mankind*, 3rd ed., vol. iv, p. 57.

[24] Keane, A. H., *Man: Past and Present*, new ed., 1920, p. 543.

[25] *Ibid.*, p. 185.

[26] O'Malley, D. S. S., *Indian Caste Customs*, 1932.

[27] Forbes, H. O., *Jour. Roy. Anthrop. Inst.*, 1884, vol. 13, p. 402.

[28] Correa, A. A. Mendes, *Timor Portugês*, 1944.

[29] Brown, J. Macmillan, *Man*, 1916, p. 113.

[30] Keane, A. H., *Man: Past and Present*, new ed., 1920, p. 347.

[31] Keith, Sir A., *Jour. Roy. Anthrop. Inst.*, 1916, vol. 46, p. 10.

[32] *Handbook*, issued by the Govt. of Tanganyika Territory, 1930.

[33] Hambly, W. D., *Source-Book for African Anthropology*, Field Museum, 1937.

[34] Prichard, J. C., *Physical History of Mankind*, vol. i, p. 180.

[35] Theal, G. McCall, *History and Ethnography of Africa South of the Zambesi*, 1907.

[36] Wayland, E. J., *Jour. Roy. Anthrop. Inst.*, 1931, vol. 61, p. 187; Roscoe, Rev. J., *ibid.*, 1909, vol. 39, p. 181.

[37] Childe, V. Gordon, *The Dawn of European Civilization*, 2nd ed., 1938; Daniel, G. E., *An Essay on Anthropological Method*, 1943.

[38] McCown and Keith, *The Stone Age of Mount Carmel*, vol. 2, 1939.

[39] Darwin, C., *The Descent of Man*, Murray, 1913, p. 166.

[40] Carpenter, C. R., *Trans. N.Y. Acad. Sc.*, 1942, ser. 11, vol. 4, p. 254.

[41] Hooton, Professor E. A., *Man's Poor Relations*, 1942, p. 156.

OWNERSHIP OF TERRITORY AS A FACTOR IN HUMAN EVOLUTION

Synopsis.—Attitude of anthropologists to tribe and territory in 1921. Later it was recognized that territorialism occurs not only among primitive peoples, but pervades the animal world, and was therefore in existence long before man appeared. Evidence from Dr. Heape. Man, the frontier-maker. Trespass and territory. The bonds which bind a group to its territory. Ancestral spirits as a bond. Although tribes are normally soil-bound, an urge to emigrate may arise. In the primal world of mankind we must assume that groups were both static and dynamic. The soil-bond is acquired, but its acquisition depends on an inborn aptitude. There is also a universalist disposition. The part played by territory in the machinery of human evolution. Darwin's observations among the Fuegians. Anthropoid apes have a sense of territory. Archæological evidence of localism. Nomadic peoples have circumscribed bounds. A sense of territory is much older than a knowledge of kinship.

MY inquiries of 1916 [1] left me convinced that early mankind had been separated into small social units or groups; another surmise also proved true—namely, that each group, so far as information was available or could be obtained, lived on a delimited area of territory of which it counted itself the eternal owner. Why did I make this surmise? It was because I had conceived that if a group were to work out its evolutionary destiny, to develop its germinal potentialities, it must not only be kept from other groups, but must remain anchored to its homeland for a continuity of generations. Ownership of territory would provide both these conditions.

How far my fellows were from sharing in my beliefs may be illustrated by an extract from an address given in 1921 by one of the leading anthropologists of my time—Sir Baldwin Spencer: [2]

" The extraordinary number of tribes (of Australia), each with its own dialect and occupying its own country, is one of the most difficult things to explain in Australian ethnology." The conditions which my colleague found so difficult to explain were just those which I had been in search of in 1916; they are essential parts of the machinery of group evolution.

At the time this is written (February, 1945) naturalists throughout the world recognize that group ownership of homeland—territorialism—is not a human prerogative, but pervades the whole of the animal kingdom. Early interest in this subject was certainly stimulated by Howard's observations on bird territories.[3] Our present knowledge of this subject, as far as animals in general are concerned, has been summarized by Dr. Julian Huxley,[4] and by Professor Allee,[5] so there is no need for me to touch on it, save to give one instance which illustrates the close similarity there is in the arrangement of bird and human territories: " Chaffinches in the southern U.S.S.R. can be distinguished solely on the basis of variation in song; they are divided into well-defined populations, each confined to a given area." [6] I am tempted to correlate variations of song in bird groups with variations of dialect in human groups.

My friend Dr. Walter Heape (1855–1929), who made many important additions to our knowledge of the sexual processes in animals, became interested in his later years in their migrations, hoping to trace a connection between the migratory impulse and the state of the sexual system. His inquiries led him to study the opposite of the migratory impulse—the tendency of animals to cling to their homelands. After his death in 1929 at the age of seventy-four, the data he had collected were edited and published by Dr. Marshall.[7] Two extracts from this work will put readers in touch with Dr. Heape's main conclusions : " What I aim at emphasizing is the fact that within the area over which a species is distributed, separate bodies or, as I shall call them, colonies of that species, occupy definite parts of that area, and rarely, if ever, leave that territory " (p. 30). The above extract relates to animals in general; the next bears on the law of territory as it affects man : " In fact, it may be held that the recognition of territorial rights, one of the most significant attributes of civilization, was not evolved by man, but has ever been an inherent factor in the life history of all animals " (p. 74).

I may usefully supplement these quotations, with which I am in complete agreement, with observations made by various authors bearing on the delimitation of tribal territories. Canon Pythian-Adams, describing the Arab tribes of the region of Mount Sinai, reports : " Even to-day the limits of tribal territory are laid down with remarkable clearness." [8] Spencer and Gillen, in their account of The Northern Tribes of Central Australia (1904), record " that from time immemorial the boundaries of the tribes have been where they are now fixed." After noting the diversity of the dialects spoken by the native tribes of Tasmania, Mr. Norman Walker adds : " Groups kept to their own territory; trespass meant war." [9] The following quotation from Malinowski refers to the village communities of the Trobriands : " The roaming grounds of every group are subject to exclusive, although collective, rights of this group." [10] The identification of a tribe with its territory is shown by the Arab custom of using the same name for territory as for tribe; the ancient Greeks had a similar custom.[11]

Man is the only animal that surrounds his territory by a de-limited frontier; a frontier is, to him, a matter of life and death; he regards it with a sentiment which is almost religious in its intensity. " To infringe boundaries of a neighbouring tribe," writes Keane, " is to break the most sacred law of the jungle and inevitably leads to war." [12] Every tribal boy has to learn from his elders the limits within which he may roam and hunt, but there is something inborn in a boy's nature which makes him eager for such learning. At what point of his evolution man turned a frontier-maker we can only guess; certainly his faculties of conscious observation and of reasoning must have made a considerable advancement towards their present degree of pro-ficiency. Anthropoid apes, although they confine their wander-ings within a locality, have no sense of frontiers. The street dogs of Constantinople are said to have had a sense of territory and to have resented trespass; wolf-packs are also credited with a similar partiality.[13] Baboons resent intrusions on the places where they sleep and breed,[14] but this is rather a manifestation of a sense of " home " than of territory. The robin resents the rival who trespasses on his " home " territory.[15]

The penalty inflicted on an uninvited or unaccredited stranger who crossed a tribal frontier of aboriginal Australia was death;

all authorities are agreed on that. It was also the law in primitive tribal communities in other parts of the earth. One can understand why a tribe should resent and repel invasion of its territory by another tribe; if it did not, then independent tribal life came to an end. That a tribe should seek to protect its game and the natural produce of its land is also understandable; if it did not, it would starve. But why this resentment against a single intruder? Here, I think, we are dealing, not with a trespass of territory, but with a trespass on the tribe or community. We shall see, when we come to deal with the manifestations of " group consciousness," that animal communities of all kinds resent the advent of " gate-crashing " strangers. It is to this ancient category of instinctive animal reaction that I would assign the practice of the Australian aborigine towards strangers. A group that was destitute of this reaction would be liable to germinal contamination.

What are the bonds which bind a primitive group to its territory? Every group, being surrounded by other groups, each jealous of its territory, may be said to be hemmed in, and thus confined to its territory. This is a negative bond, but there are also those of a positive nature. There are mental bonds; a deep affection binds a group to its soil. Radcliffe-Brown, who visited and studied the tribes of Western Australia,[16] has this to say about the attachment of a native to his locality : " Just as the country belonged to him, he belonged to it . . . wanted to die in it." So with the Bushman of South Africa ; " he is strongly attached to his territory." [17] Malinowski described these bonds in purely objective terms. " The Australian tribe," he wrote, " is bound to its territory by tradition, totemic cult, and initiation ceremonies." [18] Now, these terms are true as far as they go, but they leave out the main element of the bond—the ready, passionate response made by the Australian lad to his elders when they expound to him the sacredness of their soil. Love of one's native soil is the basal part of patriotism, and will be dealt with when that subject is considered. Affection for locality of birth is instinctive in all social animals.

Tribes are bound to their territory by a peculiarly human bond. Spencer and Gillen [19] note that Australian tribes never invade the territory of a neighbour, and explain their behaviour thus : " No such idea ever enters the head of the Central

Australian, because he believes that every territory is the home of the spirit ancestry of its original owners and is therefore useless to any one else." The belief that gods and ancestral spirits are endemic in their soil is held by tribal peoples in many parts of the world—in Melanesia, in North Burma, in India, and in West Africa—such peoples being thereby bound to their territories. There is a well-known Biblical record of this belief: " The nations which thou [the king of Assyria] has planted in the cities of Samaria know not the manner of the God of the land." [20] The Marquis of Halifax (1633–95) touched the same theme when he declared there was a " divinity in the soil of England."

So far I have been giving my reasons for believing that in the primal world human groups were rooted to the soil. If that had been the case—as it appears to have been in aboriginal Australia— then an enterprising group, multiplying in numbers and in power, would have had no advantage over its static neighbour. It was otherwise among the tribes of Gaul and ancient Germany; tribes were normally bound to the soil, but from time to time a different and dynamic mood arose in them, which compelled them to pull up their roots and, by conquest, win a new abode. For progressive evolutionary change both moods are needed: the steadfast mood which anchors a group to its territory, and the impetuous mood which urges change. I assume that both of these moods had their place in the primal world of mankind. The exodus of a people had a likeness to the mass migration of animals, a subject in which Dr. Heape was greatly interested and of which he wrote: [21] " There is surely some nervous excitement attending the proceeding, both during the preparation for exodus and during the progress of the journey. In some cases it would seem that a condition of hysteria is reached."

In support of the soil-bond I might cite Walter Scott's patriotic lines :—

> Breathes there the man, with soul so dead,
> Who never to himself hath said,
> This is my own, my native land !

But were I to bring Scott forward as a witness, I know that there are hundreds who would answer that, not only was their " soul dead," but, so far as concerned their native land, it had never been alive.[22] Patriotism, they declare, is an acquired passion. I agree with them. If I had been born in Ireland, I would have been a patriotic Irishman; if in France, a patriotic Frenchman. But I could have been neither unless I had been born with that in me which answers the call of the soil.

Yet I know that such is not the whole truth of this matter. Many of those who decry patriotism are moved by the high ideal that seeks the union of all peoples in a universal whole. There is, I admit, imbedded in human nature, a vague longing to lift the spirit of fellowship above the narrower limits of tribe, nation, and race, and this feeling seeks to replace the patriotic spirit. Human nature, as we shall try to prove in a future essay, is dual, and in patriotism versus universalism we have a contradiction which man's dual mentality makes possible. I ought to add that the spirit of patriotism—love of the soil—may die of starvation in the hearts of those born in great cities.

I have been placing before my readers the grounds for believing that the primal world, inhabited by evolving mankind, was a chequerboard of territories on which the great game of evolution was played. We have now to inquire more minutely into the part played by territory in that game. Let us begin with a modern instance. In 1933 gold was discovered in the native territory of Kenya, and natives were evicted in order that the gold might be mined. A writer in *Nature* [23] rightly protested against the eviction, and on the following grounds : (*a*) The land owned by a tribe is necessary for its subsistence; (*b*) it is equally necessary for the solidarity of the tribe; (*c*) dissolved from its territory a tribe's organization, its automatic form of government, falls to pieces ; and (*d*) the territory is the home of the living spirits of the ancestors of the evicted natives. Here, then, in a modern instance, we have brought home to us the part played by territory in securing the independent and continued existence of a tribal group; without territory a separate community could not work out its evolutionary destiny. Here, too, we have an illustration of the way in which civilization clears native inmates from their chequerboard territories to make room for larger units.

It has always seemed to me a curious thing that Darwin, who was the first to observe the limitation of groups of primitive humanity to definite tracts of land, should never have attributed an evolutionary significance to his observations. His studies were made in December, 1832, when the *Beagle* landed in their native habitats three young Fuegians who had wintered in

England to learn the ways of civilized man.[24] " The different tribes," wrote Darwin, then in his twenty-fourth year, " have no government or chief, yet each is surrounded by other hostile tribes, speaking different dialects, and separated from each other only by a deserted border or neutral territory. . . . I do not know anything which shows more clearly the hostile state of the different tribes than these wide borders or neutral tracts." These observations relate, not to organized tribes, but to local groups of humanity, living under the most primitive conditions, and reflects what I assume to have been the universal state in man's primal world.

In the preceding essay I gave a quotation (p. 26) from Dr. Carpenter [25] to the effect that territorialism existed in all kinds of Primates which had been examined for this condition. We may presume, I think, that all the genera which emerged from the primate stem were subjected to group evolution, and that territorialism was in existence long before the differentiation of mankind. " The chimpanzees," records Dr. Heape (p. 67), " are, in fact, home-loving like all apes, and do not forsake the place in which they were born unless under special stress of circumstances." Dr. Carpenter also noted the fact " that gibbons are intolerant of trespass by other gibbons "—evidence that this anthropoid has a sense of territory. Professor Hooton of Harvard is one of the few writers who have discussed the possibility of a relationship between territorial grouping and evolution. After a review of the group distribution of Primates, he adds the following passage :—

" It would appear that this primate tendency to maintain territoriality must be closely bound up with the differentiation of races, and varieties, and even species, by selection and inbreeding. . . . Further, it would seem necessary to postulate some such innate or acquired habit . . . to account for the early differentiation of the physical varieties of races of mankind." [26]

I quote this passage as evidence of the large measure of agreement there is between Professor Hooton and myself as to the part played by territory in the process of evolution.

When dealing with the division of primitive mankind into small groups, in the preceding essay, I alluded to the light that archæologists are throwing on this problem (p. 26). Here I would add other instances where excavation of ancient sites provides evidence of localism and, presumably, of territory. For example, Mr. T. T. Paterson when examining stone industries (Clactonian, Ievallois) which have an antiquity of perhaps 100,000 years found evidence of " local industrialism." [27] Leslie Armstrong, in his investigation of tools of caveman of the Upper Palæolithic period, observed that " industries display local differences." [28] Hubert records that in Loraine tribal fortification of the early Iron Age can still be detected; [29] and several other instances might be cited.

At the beginning of this essay I noted the fact that my contemporaries were reluctant to accept the idea that primitive societies were small and stationary.[30] They were impressed by the migratory tendencies which have pervaded so many peoples during historical times, and they assume that this had also been the case with early men. I have indicated my reply to this objection in an earlier essay (p. 8). They were also impressed by the belief that nomadic peoples knew no bounds. As regards this matter Dr. Heape came to the same conclusion in 1929 as I did in 1916. " The great majority of nomadic peoples and nomadic animals," he affirmed, " roam only over a definite territory " (p. 16).

Perhaps the chief obstacle to the acceptance of my doctrine was the belief that then prevailed among anthropologists—namely, that the original groups of mankind were formed on the basis of kin—of blood relationship—and that it was at a later date that territory became a bond. The advocates of the priority of kin had the powerful support of Sir Henry Maine, Durkheim, Andrew Lang, Marett, and of many others.[31] On the other hand, men like Haddon and Rivers, who based their opinions on observations made in the field and among primitive peoples, were convinced that, from the first, human groups were based on territory. From the evidence now available we cannot any longer doubt that the bond of territory is infinitely older than that of kin. The anthropoid mother knows her young child; there is some evidence that she even recognizes her children until they reach a certain age, but man is the only animal that can trace blood relationships and is therefore capable of constructing genealogies. Man must have reached a considerable degree of mental capacity before he became genealogist. I would hazard the guess that man marked out frontiers before he constructed genealogies. And yet the fact remains that there are peoples in the world of to-day who are devoid of territory and yet maintain their solidarity. Such peoples will come up for consideration when the evolution of races is discussed (Essay XXXVII).

REFERENCES

[1] Keith, Sir A., *Jour. Roy. Anthrop. Inst.*, 1916, vol. 46, p. 10.

[2] Spencer, Sir Baldwin, *Presid. Add. Austral. Ass. Adv. Sc.*, 1921.

[3] Howard, Eliot, *Territory in Bird Life*, 1920.

[4] Huxley, Julian, *Evolution: The Modern Synthesis*, 1942, ch. V.

[5] Allee, Prof. W. C., *The Social Life of Animals*, 1939, ch. V.

[6] Huxley, Julian, *Nature*, 1940, vol. 146, p. 43.

[7] Heape, Walter, *Emigration, Migration, and Nomadism*, edited by F. H. A. Marshall, 1931.

[8] Pythian-Adams, Canon, *Palest. Explor. Quart.*, 1930, vol. 62, p. 192.

[9] Walker, N., *Man*, 1931, p. 51.

[10] Malinowski, B., *Nature*, 1925, vol. 116, p. 928.

[11] Thomson, Geo., *Aeschylus and Athens*, 1941.

[12] Keane, A. H., *Man: Past and Present*, new ed., 1920, p. 161.

[13] Reade, Carveth, *The Origin of Man*, 1920, p. 43.

[14] Marais, Eugene N., *My Friends the Baboons*, 1939.

[15] Lack, D., *The Life of the Robin*, 1943.

[16] Radcliffe-Brown, A. R., *Jour. Roy. Anthrop. Inst.*, 1913, vol. 43, p. 143.

[17] Theal, G. McCall, *History and Ethnography of Africa South of the Zambesi*, vol. 1, 1907.

[18] Malinowski, B., *Family Life among the Australian Aborigines*, 1913, p. 153.

[19] Spencer and Gillen, *The Northern Tribes of Central Australia*, 1904, p. 30.

[20] 2 Kings XVII, 25.

[21] Heape, Walter, see reference 7, p. 21.

[22] Fyfe, Hamilton, *The Illusion of National Character*, 1940.

[23] *Nature*, 1933, vol. 131, p. 37.

[24] Darwin, C., *The Voyage of the Beagle*, ch. X, p. 216.

[25] Carpenter, C. R., *Trans. N.Y. Acad. Sc.*, 1942, ser. 11, vol. 4, p. 248.

[26] Hooton, E. A., *Man's Poor Relations*, 1942, p. 331.

[27] Paterson, T. T., *Proc. Prehist. Soc.*, 1937, vol. 3, p. 87.

[28] Armstrong, A. Leslie, *Mem. & Proc. Manchester Lit. Phil.*, 1939, vol. 83, p. 110.

[29] Hubert, Henri, *The Greatness and Decline of the Celts*, 1934.

[30] Hawkes, C. F. C., *Man*, 1942, p. 125; Poynter, C. W. M., *Amer. Anthrop.*, 1915, vol. 17, p. 509; Stone, J. F. S., *Proc. Prehist. Soc.*, 1941, vol. 7, p. 114.

[31] The evidence was summarized by Moret and Davy in *From Tribe to Empire*, trans. by V. Gordon Childe, 1926.

GROUP SPIRIT AS A FACTOR IN HUMAN EVOLUTION

Synopsis.—Group spirit defined.   Sympathy, which is the basis of the group spirit, is confined to communities of a species, and does not extend to the species as a whole.   This is true of human and of animal groups, and is presumably true of the primal groups of humanity. Consciousness of kind : its various applications.   " Like will to like " examined.   Man's social appetite as a driving force.   Primal groups were " closed " societies.   Aversion to strangers: a genetical explanation.   How far the group spirit is inborn, and how far acquired. The dual spirit generates a dual code of morality.   Group formation leads to group selection.   Evolution in the primal world of humanity was mainly a group or team selection.   There was no colour bar in the ancient world.   The group spirit was evolved from the family spirit.

I AM seeking to build up a picture of the life led by mankind during the primal age, the age which saw man attain his manhood.   In the two preceding essays evidence has been given for believing that mankind was then divided into small groups, and that each group occupied its own tract of land.   In this essay we are to inquire into the means which keep members of a group together and, at the same time, keep them apart from surrounding territorial groups.   These means, we shall find, are embedded in man's mental nature.   There is a disposition or spirit in every man which leads him to extend his sympathy, his goodwill, and fellowship to the members of his group; he is also conscious of his membership and feels that his own life is part of that of his group.   To this bundle of mental traits, which gives unity to a group and separation from other groups, I am applying the term " group spirit," which has thus much the same connation as " *esprit de corps*."   Group spirit induces a certain form or pattern of behaviour; this form of behaviour I shall speak of as " clannishness."

Having thus defined the terms I am to use, I now turn to the evidence which permits us to assume that a group spirit prevailed in the small communities of primal man. As usual, Darwin supplies the most telling evidence. " Sympathy," he notes, " is directed solely towards members of the same community, and therefore towards known, and more or less loved members, but not to all individuals of the same species." [1] Primitive groups being small, their members were known to one another by personal contact. Darwin was of the opinion that " the confinement of sympathy to the same tribe " was one of the chief causes of the low morality of savages.[2] In this instance Darwin viewed tribal life from the point of view of a civilized observer. Two further quotations from Darwin will throw additional light on group mentality. " Primeval man regarded actions as good or bad, solely as they obviously affected the welfare of the tribe—not that of the species, nor that of an individual member of the tribe." [3] Writing of living tribal peoples he notes that " the virtues are practised almost exclusively in relation to the men of the same tribe," while the corresponding vices " are not regarded as crimes " if practised on other tribes.[4] Darwin's observations have been confirmed over and over again by travellers who have studied primitive groups of mankind at first hand. On such evidence we have grounds for assuming that the small communities of early man were also swayed by a group spirit.

When that evidence is supported by the knowledge that all social animals whatsoever, be they ants or be they apes, are subjects of the group spirit, we may assume with a high degree of assurance that man's simian ancestors and the earliest forms of man were also its subjects. In the following passage Darwin refers to social animals :—

" For the social instincts lead an animal to take pleasure in the society of its fellows, to feel a certain amount of sympathy with them and to perform certain services for them . . . but these feelings and services are by no means extended to all the individuals of the same species, only to those of the same association." [5]

Darwin was by no means the first to note that mutual sympathy did not extend to all members of a species, but was limited to groups of a species. A wise and observant Scottish judge, Henry

Home of Kames (1696–1782), noted that in animals " affections are limited to a community " and not to the species. " Every species," he continues, " is divided into small tribes . . . which do not associate," and then he proceeds to cite examples he had observed. He also makes the pertinent remark that the size of a group is determined by two circumstances : it must be big enough for its defence and not too big for its provender.[6] Later, he continues : " The social appetite in man comprehends not the whole species but a part only, as among animals. One of moderate extent invigorates every manly virtue . . . nature has wisely limited the social appetite." [7]

Thus we find that every species of social animal is divided into independent groups ; that each group is dominated by a separatist, self-regarding group spirit ; that competition, selection, and survival involve a struggle, not between species, but between groups of the same species. Such, we must assume, was the state of evolutionary conditions on the chequerboard of primal humanity.

The group theory, then, assumes that in all social animals— and man is eminently such—there is an instinctive or inborn urge to the formation of social groups. Group spirit is the mental machinery involved in group formation. As a label for this machinery Prof. Franklin Giddings,[8] towards the end of the nineteenth century, gave the name " consciousness of kind," intending to give a more precise meaning to the term " sympathy " as used by Adam Smith.[9] Giddings's use of this term will best be made clear by quoting one of his illustrations : " The southern gentleman who believed in the cause of the Union, none the less threw his fortune with the Confederacy, if he felt himself to be one of the southern people and a stranger to the people of the North." The southern gentleman was pitting reason against his inborn sympathy, and his " consciousness of kind," or group spirit, won. Professor Giddings cites the social groups or communities which were formed as civilization spread westwards across the United States, groups containing representatives of many European nations. In such cases association made unlike kinds into compact social groups. A group was formed, not because its members were conscious of kind, but because all were inheritors of the group spirit of early man.

It is important to note that Professor Giddings applies his term to a much wider field than is included under the term group spirit. He applies it to the recognition which members of the same species display towards one another, as dog to dog, or cat to cat, or man to man. Now, such recognition is quite different from that which leads a member of a group to recognize fellow members. Social sympathy, even among animals, is confined to fellow members, and one may assume it was also so among the groups of primitive, evolving humanity.

Our main concern in this essay is with the mentality which controlled group organization in man's primal world. There are, however, in modern mankind certain mental exhibitions of a group-forming tendency which will repay consideration here. " Like will to like " is a truism which has come down to us from the ancient Greeks. We see this aphorism illustrated in the cities of the East, where each nation or sect occupies its own quarter. We see it again in the cities of the New World, where immigrants from the Old World seek out groups of their fellow nationals. Like has sought out like, and in such instances we may attribute such preferences to " consciousness of kind " or to group spirit. But in the following instances of like seeking out like we move into another class of phenomena. Darwin records instances of animals of a particular breed, or those possessing certain markings, preferring mates of the same breed or markings.[10] Julian Huxley gives an instance of a similar preference in a human community.[11] Among the Indians of the Panama there is a community of albino or " white " natives; the surrounding coloured Indians have " a feeling against marrying white "; so the whites are left to mate together. " Here in man himself," adds Dr. Huxley, " is a case showing with almost diagrammatic clarity how evolutionary change may originate." Darwin's examples, and Huxley's, are cases of sexual selection apparently based on a recognition or consciousness of kind, but the purpose served has nothing to do with the formation and maintenance of social groups.

There is one circumstance underlying the group spirit which is in need of emphasis. This spirit assumes the existence of man's social appetite and the need of satisfying that appetite by seeking its gratification in the company of his fellows; without that appetite there could be no group formation. This is true of all social animals, and we may therefore assume it to hold for the most primitive of men. It is only when human beings are deprived of all contact with their fellows that they learn what the compelling force of social starvation really is. We may safely assume that our most remote ancestors were thus constituted, and that the member who strayed from his group was urged back to it by social hunger; and so groups were kept intact.

There is another assumption which may be made with a high degree of safety as regards the primal groups of mankind—namely, that each group formed a " closed society," the only entrance into it being by birth, although entrance by adoption cannot be altogether excluded. Farmers know very well that their field herds resent the introduction of strangers and seek to exclude them from their midst, even strangers of exactly the same breed. If, however, the original herd is turned on fresh pastures, previously unknown to it, and before the strangers are added, the strangers will be more readily accepted, which suggests that a sense of territory may also be concerned.[12] Dr. Carpenter, who has made a special study of monkey groups, observed that intruding strangers were forcibly expelled, although he did see one persistent young male ultimately accepted by a group.[13] The native colony of Gibraltar apes, having become depleted in numbers, was reinforced by animals of the same species introduced from Africa. All the introduced apes, save a strong male, were killed by the original colonists.[14] A female gibbon that had been some time in captivity was released by her owner in her native forest in Java near a group of her own species; she was driven off by the group. Seeing how prevalent an antipathy to strangers is among primate groups, it is highly probable that it was also a trait of the earliest human groups.

" No propensity," asserts Lord Kames, " is more general in human nature than aversion to strangers." [15] He then asks a question: " What good end can this perversion promote? " The question can be put in another form: Why are the groups formed by social animals in a state of nature maintained as closed societies? An explanation can be given on genetic grounds. If we regard a group as having been separated from other groups in order to inbreed, and so to work out the evolutionary potentialities of its genes, then we can see why it should resent instinctively the intrusion of outsiders bringing with them strange genes. The rejection of strangers might also be explained on social grounds : if they came in numbers they would disrupt the automatic government of the group. Epinas was in the right when he averred that " hatred of strangers is an index of tribal consciousness." [16] He might well have added that the friendly reception of strangers could be used as an indication of the degree to which the " old Adam " of the group spirit has been eradicated from man's nature by civilization.

We come now to a question of the highest importance. Is the group spirit which we are attributing to primitive communities of mankind, and which pervades the modern world under the name of " race consciousness," an instinct born in a child's nature, or is it acquired as the child grows up? Darwin's answer is equivocal. He emphasized the limitation of sympathy to the members of a group, and added, " Sympathy, although gained as an instinct, is also strengthened by exercise and habit." [17] Now, every social group, whether simian or human, is a school in which the young absorb the traditions, the customs, the habits, the prejudices, and modes of behaviour of the group. A child sees the group spirit at work as it grows up, and accepts a clannish behaviour as part of its heritage. Mr. J. H. Taylor,[18] Dr. Raymond Firth,[19] Julian Huxley,[20] and many more, regard the manifestations of the group spirit or race consciousness as the result of what the young learn in the school of the tribe. Bring a white boy up in a Bantu tribe, and the boy will have the group spirit of a Bantu tribesman. Those authors, in my opinion, have considered only one side of the problem—namely, the direction or complexion taken by the group spirit. They have concentrated their attention on the product and forgotten the producer, which is an inborn disposi-tion. Can it be said that sympathy, which is a disposition to suffer with, and to aid others, and which is the basis of the group spirit, is an acquired quality of human nature? The disposition to sympathize is certainly inborn, but, as Darwin contended, it can be strengthened by example and practice.

It may be asked in reply : why is sympathy and the group spirit limited to a community? Is that not a result of tuition or ex-ample? Let us see what we can learn of this matter by noting the action of this spirit in herds of cattle. When Darwin was on the Beagle, he visited a large ranch in Uruguay, so that he might acquaint himself with the management of large herds of cattle. When feeding, the animals formed groups, each group having a membership varying from forty to a hundred; the membership of each group was constant; the cattle discriminated between their own and other groups. " During a stormy night," adds Darwin, " the cattle all mingle together, but next morning the tropillas (or groups) separate as before; so that each animal must know its fellows out of ten thousand others." [21] Here, then, we see the group spirit at work among social animals, controlled by an innate disposition or instinct and not by a taught or acquired tradition. May we not assume, then, that the group disposition or spirit was also inborn in the most primitive forms of humanity? In them, we must presume, it was moulded and biased by the tradition and the teaching of the groups.

It will thus be seen that the group spirit implies a discrimination between groups. A tribesman's sympathies lie within the compass of his own tribe; beyond his tribe, begin his antipathies; he discriminates in favour of his own tribe and against all others. This means also that the tribesman has two rules of behaviour, one towards those of his group and another to the members of other groups. He has a dual code of morality: a code of " amity " for his fellows; a code of indifference, verging into " enmity," towards members of other groups or tribes. Seeing, then, that all social animals are subject to the group spirit, and that it brings about a dual code of morality, may we not assume that on the chequerboard of the primal world the same spirit animated evolving groups of mankind?

The question now arises: Why was primitive humanity divided into small, separate, contending groups? My answer is that which both Darwin and Wallace gave—namely, that men who were arranged in groups or teams, each dominated by a spirit of unity, would conquer and outlive men who were not thus grouped. In brief, human evolution was, and is, a process of team production and team selection. No doubt, in our primal world there was individual selection within each team or group, but it was the team worker rather than the strong individualist who was favoured. In this way the group spirit played a leading role as a factor in human evolution.

In this essay I have kept flitting between the ancient and modern world of humanity, carrying facts and assumptions from the one to throw light on the other. Continuing my argument along these lines, I would now call attention to the fact that, in the modern world, at the time history begins, each large area was inhabited by its own physical variety of mankind. If we take the area of Mongolian distribution, for example, and beginning on the Arctic shores with our steps turned in a southward direction, we shall meet as we proceed no sharp break in the physical type until we reach the shores of Australia. The type with which we begin is very different from that with which we end, yet the change is so gradual that nowhere can we distinguish one local community from another by physical criteria. Now, I assume that the distribution of mankind in the ancient world was similar. Adjacent local groups were of the same physical type; their differences were cultural; each group had its dialect, its customs, its traditions; each had its own spirit. Nowhere was there a colour bar; only in recent times have communities of black and white been brought into juxtaposition. When such communities are brought to live side by side, the community spirit is apt to assume a new fierceness and receives another name, " race consciousness." To this aspect of the group spirit I shall return when I come to deal with the evolution of races (see Essay XXXV). The turbulent group or tribal spirit is here aggravated by the fact that the contestants have been fitted out by Nature in different physical uniforms.

One other point concerning man's group spirit deserves consideration before this essay is brought to a close. Can any rational explanation be given of how it became a constituent element in human nature? I regard it as an extension of the family spirit, the spirit or disposition which leads the members of a human family, both parents and children, to discriminate between their own and other families. The members of a normal family are prejudiced in favour of one another. Their attitude towards their own family is different from that which they hold to other families. They resent the intrusion of strangers to a place in the family circle. When children graduate from parental control to take their place in the life of their group, the family feeling or spirit expands so as to embrace all the members of a group, as if the group had become their family. As Darwin and many others have maintained, the mental bonds which hold a family together gave rise to those which unite members of a social group or tribe.

REFERENCES

[1] Darwin, C., *The Descent of Man*, Murray, 1913, ch. IV, p. 162.

[2] *Ibid.*, p. 183.

[3] *Ibid.*, p. 182.

[4] *Ibid.*, p. 179.

[5] *Ibid.*, p. 150.

[6] Home, Henry (Lord Kames), *Sketches of the History of Man*, new. ed. 1813, vol. 2, p. 12.

[7] *Ibid.*, p. 21.

[8] Giddings, Franklin H., *The Principles of Sociology*, 1898, p. 17.

[9] Smith, Adam, *The Theory of Moral Sentiments*, sect. 1, ch. I–V.

[10] Darwin, C., *Animals and Plants under Domestication*, vol. 2, ch. XIV.

[11] Huxley, Julian, *Nature*, 1924, vol. 114, p. 464.

[12] Hunter, John, *Essays and Observations*, edited by Sir Richard Owen, 1861, vol. 1, p. 51.

[13] Carpenter, C. R., *Trans. N.Y. Acad. Sc.*, 1942, ser. 11, vol. 4, p. 248.

[14] *The Field*, Feb. 8, 1913, p. 283.

[15] Home, Henry, see under reference 6, pp. 23, 30.

[16] Epinas, Alfred, *Des Sociétés Animales*, 1877, new ed. 1925.

[17] See under ref. 1, p. 934.

[18] Taylor, J. G., *Popular Psychological Fallacies*, 1938, p. 243.

[19] Firth, Raymond, *We, The Tikopia*, 1936, pp. 129, 342.

[20] Haddon, A. C. and Huxley, Julian S., *We Europeans*, 1935, p. 233.

[21] Darwin, C., *A Naturalist's Voyage round the World*, ch. VIII, p. 144.

PATRIOTISM AS A FACTOR IN HUMAN EVOLUTION

Synopsis.—Group spirit and patriotism compared. Patriotism considered under three heads: (a) its relationship to group territory; (b) its relationship to the life of the group, to the fighting spirit, and to loyalty; (c) its relationship to group status. Qualities which have been ascribed to patriotism. Patriotism as a factor in evolution. Patriotism is made up of two elements: the one is mental and is inbred; the other is educative and is acquired. Patriotic feelings may remain latent. Patriotism is an expansion of the individual instinct of self-preservation. The relation of fear to patriotism. Patriotism has a kinship with religion. Group spirit and patriotism are based on partiality—a congenital warping of the judgment. Patriots obey a dual code of morality. It may be said that evolutionary procedure is based on injustice. Chauvinism.

In the preceding essay we examined the mental machinery which breaks social animals into groups or communities, and which serves to maintain each group as a separate unit. Seeing that this mental machinery, the group spirit, is of ancient origin, we have presumed that the groups of early humanity were also under its sway. In this essay we are concerned with another set of mental activities—namely, those which serve to safeguard and protect the group which, when danger threatens from without, or from within, muster forces for the defence of the group. This set of mental activities, which automatically arms the members of a group in its defence, is known as patriotism. Since such defensive mental reactions are to be observed in social animals of all kinds, we may safely presume that patriotism had a place among the primal communities of mankind.

Patriotism is an exaggerated and prejudiced form of affection which is manifested by members of a group or tribe in at least three directions. First, it leads to the development of special bonds of affection between a group and its home territory, and so anchors it to its homeland. The homeland may be bare and barren, but, in the eyes of the native, patriotism turns it into the best and most desirable of all lands. The alchemy of love, working in the fevered brain of Don Quixote, turned a plain country wench into a princess. So the alchemy of patriotism, working in the brain of a tribesman, converts a moorland into a paradise. The more a man loves a thing the more ready is he to defend it, to fight for it, and, if need be, to sacrifice his life to save it. Thus is the territory of a group safeguarded and the integrity of the group preserved. Patriotism provides the group with a mental armour for the defence of its homeland. Seeing that all social animals manifest a predilection for their native habitat, we may presume that the primal groups of humanity had a special attachment to their homelands and were in this sense patriotic. The blackbird which risks her life to save her nest and brood from the maw of a prowling cat gives an exhibition of blind patriotism.

A tribesman's patriotic bias is not confined to the care of his homeland; it extends to his group or tribe and to everything connected with the tribe—to its welfare, to its prosperity, to its safety, and to its good name and fame. The tribal totem, or god, he regards as more powerful than other totems or gods; his tribal speech, customs, manners, and ways of life are superior to all others. In times of peace the patriotic feeling or spirit is more or less at rest. But when the life of the tribe is threatened, these feelings rise to fever heat; they become a violent passion which takes control of the tribesman's will and forces it blindly on to action. Next door, as it were, to the feelings which support the patriotic impulse are those which sustain man's fighting spirit, which supplies the physical force needed in defence of the group. Thus man's patriotism lies at the root of war. As every group or community of social animals is provided with a mental machinery for its defence, we may safely assume that the very earliest groups of humanity were not destitute of it. The male gorilla manifests patriotic feelings when his group is in danger, for he then turns on, and attacks, the assailant, and kills or is killed, so that his group may live.

There is an aspect of patriotism which deserves special consideration. We have already noted that it involves a strong and constant partiality in a man for everything connected with his group. This is especially true of his attitude to the elders or leaders of his group, or, if leadership has passed into the care of chief or king, then to chief or king. The leaders being at the centre of group defence, we should expect patriotic devotion to go out to them in special measure. So it does, only it takes a peculiar form—the form known as fidelity or loyalty. Loyalty is a blind, prejudiced, unswerving, unreasoned attachment to those in command. Yet I do not regard loyalty as a constituent part of patriotism. In this I am in opposition to a very clear thinker, Prof. W. G. Sumner, who defined patriotism as "loyalty to one's group."[1] Loyalty is akin to patriotism and, like the fighting spirit, is a close adjunct to it. Loyalty finds its natural place in the leadership and organization of a group, and will come up for further consideration when these subjects are discussed in a later essay. (See Essay XII.)

There is a third aspect of patriotism to which I attach a high importance. It imbues the members of a group with a sense of pride in their membership; it fosters the conviction in their minds that their group is the paragon of groups. This was the aspect of patriotism which caught Darwin's attention in the person of Jimmy Button, a Fuegian lad who was carried back to his native land on board the *Beagle*. "He was of a patriotic disposition," Darwin notes, "and he liked to praise his own tribe and country, in which he truly said there were plenty of trees, and he abused all the other tribes; he stoutly declared there was no devil in his land."[2] An Australian aborigine has the conviction that his tribe is the hub of the universe. Westermarck[3] found this type of tribal exaltation among all native peoples, so we may venture to ascribe it to the groups of humanity which peopled the world in primal times.

It will have been noted that Jimmy Button's patriotic feelings gave vent, not only to praise of his own tribe, but led him on to decry all neighbouring tribes. Patriotism leads on to emulation, to jealousy, to competition between neighbouring tribes, and is thus a source of contempt and of strife. No tribesman, or band of tribesmen, will remain unmoved if they hear any aspersion cast on their tribe. The good faith of a tribe, its honour, its status or place among other tribes, and the superiority of its god or totem are sacrosanct; such convictions must not be questioned by anyone outside the tribe or even within it. Thus patriotism incites an unending contest for tribal status. "Patriotism," said the late J. M. Robertson, " is pride of power . . . a banal pride." [4] Certainly pride of power moves the heart of the modern patriot. and one may suspect that power or prowess was equally potent in ancient days. Patriotism gives to a tribe a feeling of invincibility, a valuable asset for any human community involved in the struggle for survival.

McDougall describes patriotism as " a master sentiment," [5] and seeing that in the throes of war it can and does overcome the strongest of man's instincts, that of self-preservation, this description must be regarded as valid. Hankins regards it as " the most powerful of social forces." [6] " The supreme value of patriotism," wrote Martin Conway, " is not in provoking hostility, or resisting the rivalry of other countries, but in its unifying, nation-making force." [7] George Orwell says of patriotism that " as a positive force there is nothing to set beside it." [8] Gibbon regarded patriotism as " a public virtue," and as " a source of strength in war." [9] I look on patriotism as an heirloom which has come down to modern man from a very remote past.

We have now to seek for an answer to the important question : In what way does patriotism serve as a factor in producing new types of mankind? Let us proceed on the assumption that primitive humanity was separated into exclusive, self-contained groups; such separation permitted each group to work out its own germinal potentialities. To do that, each group must be master of its own independence; only as an independent unit can a group work out its evolutionary destiny, and it must maintain that independence over countless generations. Patriotism is the safeguard of independence; it is its bulwark. It is the guardian of the territory of the group, for if the homeland is lost the group is scattered. Patriotism seeks to maintain the integrity of a group; it comes to the rescue when an external attack is threatened and when internal disruption is feared. It works so as to secure the welfare and prosperity of a community. Being based on a partiality or congenital squint of the mind, patriotism tends to engender opposition and animosity in neigh-bouring groups, and this fosters the jealous and competitive spirit which exists between neighbouring groups. In all these ways patriotism serves as a factor in human evolution. Adam

Smith, in discussing the operations of patriotism as seen among modern nations, has this to say of it: " Independent and neighbouring nations, having no common superior to decide their disputes, all live in continual dread and suspicion of one another. . . . Each nation foresees, or imagines that it foresees, its own subjugation in the increasing power of its neighbours." [10] I am of the opinion that this description of patriotism among modern nations may be freely transferred to the ancient groups in man's primal world.

Are we to count those prejudiced feelings and modes of action which go to the composition of patriotism as aptitudes which are built into the constitutions of our brains, are ready-made at birth, as it were, or are they merely due to a bent or inclination we acquire as we grow up? My answer is that the predisposition to regard with favour what is our own is an aptitude born in us, but the direction that aptitude takes is a matter of education. Let us take the case of speech; no one will deny that a child is born with an aptitude for speech, but the form of speech is determined by that of its group. I am persuaded that patriotism is of this dual nature. "Patriotism," F. S. Oliver has affirmed, " is mainly instinctive; deliberate reason has nothing to do with it; it affects all classes, rich and poor." [11] " For indeed, who is there alive," asks Swift, " that would not be swayed by his bias and partiality to the place of his birth?" [12] Lord Kames complains that patriotism " gives the vulgar too much partiality, while it is unbecoming in a man of rank." [13] Herein we have set before us the attitude towards patriotism of the educated European of the eighteenth century, an attitude shared by the cosmopolitan-minded of the present time.

If patriotism is inborn, how are we to answer those writers and thinkers who declare they are free from it? Sir Thomas Browne, for example, assures his readers: " I feel not in myself those common antipathies that I can discover in others; those national repugnances do not touch me, nor do I behold with prejudice the French, Italian, Spaniard, or Dutch." [14] Was Sir Thomas, then, born deaf to the calls of patriotism? Or had he by discipline and reason made himself deaf to its calls? The latter explanation seems the more probable. We must also consider another explanation, that of latency. Darwin has recorded the case of birds in volcanic islands which had no fear of man, but acquaintance with man proved that their sense of fear was not absent, but only latent.[15]   In the piping times of enduring peace, and in city populations devoid of all public spirit, conditions are lacking which call out the impulses of patriotism.   In man's primal world, with group contending with group, all the conditions were present to evoke the patriotic spirit.

Patriotism has an ancient lineage; bees give a demonstration of it when they issue to repel invaders from their hive; the gander, when his partner is brooding, turns aggressive; bison bulls form a ring round cows and calves if the herd is attacked. We may regard a group of primal humanity as a brooding community; unless the brood is protected from attack, a group comes to an end.   Patriotic feelings and impulses supply the protective armament.   Patriotism has also a close similarity to the feelings which exist between members of a family.   Partiality, which is the basis of patriotism, reigns within a family; its members resent any imputation made on their conduct or honour, individually or collectively.   Group patriotism may therefore be regarded as an expansion of family partiality.

There is another aspect of patriotism which received the attention of Hume.[16]   " Men," he noted, " are vain of the beauty either of their country, or their county, or even of their parish.   Here the idea of beauty plainly produces a pleasure. This pleasure is related to pride.   The object or cause of this pleasure is, by supposition, related to self, the object of pride. By this double relation of sentiments and ideas, a transition is made from the one to the other."   Hume might well have continued his argument by pointing out that a man may transfer pride in himself to pride in the group of which he is a member, or might enhance his personal pride in the reflected glory of his group.   The argument goes much deeper than Hume carried it, for we shall seek to prove in a future essay that a tribesman extends or transfers every one of his own emotions and instinctive impulses from himself to his tribe or group (see Essay IX).   Take the strongest of a man's instinctive impulses—that which compels him to protect and preserve his own life.   This impulse to preserve himself he transfers to his group or tribe.   Self-preservation is individual patriotism;   when the preservation impulse is transferred, it becomes group patriotism.   The group impulse, in the throes of war, masters the strongest of individual impulses or instincts, that of self-preservation; at this present time (February, 1945) millions of men are proving its mastery by dying that their homelands may be preserved.

Fear has an important relation to patriotic feelings; fear is the sentinel of patriotism. In quiet times when no enemy is in sight and no danger threatens, group feelings are in a state of calm. But when the life of a group is threatened, when danger becomes imminent, then fear appears and stirs the patriotic feelings into activity. If the peril is great, then patriotism becomes a master passion. Mr. C. R. Aldrich [17] sees in fear the basis of patriotism, whereas I regard fear as merely the stimulus or "trigger" of patriotism.

Religion and patriotism touch each other at many points; both are nursed by emotions which lie close together in man's mentality. Religion seeks for immortality in another world, whereas patriotism, by working for the perpetuation of its group, seeks for an immortality in this. Early religion worshipped ancestors; patriotism has under its care the dead, the living, and the unborn. "Patriotism," said Oakesmith,[18] "turns doubt into devotion; it moves men to a passionate self-surrender." Religion has the same power. Prichard [19] relates that the natives of Dahomey of his time worshipped their king as their god; they "recognized his divine right to dispose of their persons and lives according to his unrestrained will." In modern Japan patriotism reached the same divine heights; the Emperor was both god and king. In Joan of Arc religious zeal became frenzied patriotism. The ancient Greeks mixed their religion with their patriotism (H. A. L. Fisher). The Marquis of Halifax (1620–92) recognized the kinship of patriotism to religion when he wrote: "Our Trimmer is far from idolatry . . . in one thing only he cometh near it, his country is in some degree his idol . . . but for the earth of England . . . there is divinity in it." Elsewhere I have sought to prove that patriotism has a more powerful sway over the human heart than has religion (*Essays on Human Evolution*, 1946, p. 68).

The line which separates the subjects dealt with in the preceding essay under the term "group spirit" and those discussed in the present essay under the heading of "patriotism" is thin and somewhat shadowy; yet, in the main, group spirit is made up of these feelings and impulses which are concerned with the formation and maintenance of groups, while those included in patriotism have to do with defence of groups. Both group spirit and patriotism have this in common : both are based on an inborn biasing of the mind, on a partiality so strong that the affairs of the home group are seen in one light, while those of neighbouring groups are viewed in quite another light. The mode of conduct which the home tribesman commends when extended to neighbouring groups, he bitterly resents when applied to himself or to his group. The tribesman's sense of justice automatically obeys two laws—one law for his group and another for other groups. Among all primitive peoples living under tribal conditions in the modern world the tribesman is observed to be a " dual-codist," obeying the " code of amity " in all matters concerning his own group, and obedient to the " code of enmity " in all affairs outside his group or tribe. We may infer that our remote ancestors, working their way to a higher status, were also dual-codists. I shall seek to prove in the next essay that obedience to the dual code is an essential factor in group evolution. Without it there could have been no human evolution. Thus is human evolution based on injustice, and man's mentality has been biased to make him the willing subject of the dual code. Civilization strives, so far with little success, to bring all human conduct within one code—the code of mutual love.

In this essay patriotism has been pictured in its milder mood, in its defensive, non-aggressive form. But just as a man's personal pride may mount into the heights of vanity, so may a group's patriotism become inflamed and passionate, reaching the aggressive state known as chauvinism. This aspect of patriotism will come up for further consideration when nations and nationalism are dealt with in a later essay.

REFERENCES

[1] Sumner, W. G., *Folkways*, Boston, 1906.
[2] Darwin, Charles, *A Naturalist's Voyage round the World*, ch. X, p. 208.
[3] Westermarck, E., *The Origin and Development of Moral Ideas*, 1906, vol. 2, ch. XXX.
[4] Robertson, J. M., *Patriotism and Empire*, 1899.
[5] McDougall, Wm., *The Energies of Men*, 1932, p. 224.
[6] Hankins, F. H., *The Racial Basis of Civilization*, 1926, p. 64.
[7] Conway, Martin, *The Crowd in Peace and War*, 1915, p. 246.
[8] Orwell, G., *The Lion and the Unicorn*, 1941.
[9] Gibbon, E., *Decline and Fall*, ch. I, Everyman ed., p. 6.

[10] Smith, Adam, *The Theory of Moral Sentiments*, pt. 6, sect. 2, ch. 2.

[11] Oliver, F. S., *The Endless Adventure*, 1935.

[12] Swift, Jonathan, *Gulliver's Travels*, pt. 4, ch. 7.

[13] Home, Henry (Lord Kames), *Sketches of the History of Man*, new ed., 1813, vol. 2, p. 128.

[14] Browne, Sir Thomas, *Religio Medici*, Dent's Temple ed., pt. 2, p. 86.

[15] Darwin, C., see under ref. 2, p. 403.

[16] Hume, David, *Essays and Treatises*, 1772, vol. 2, p. 198.

[17] Aldrich, C. R., *The Primitive Mind and Modern Civilization*, 1931.

[18] Oakesmith, J., *Race and Nationality*, 1919.

[19] Prichard, J. C., *The Physical History of Mankind*, 4th ed., vol. 2, p. 92.

HOW CO-OPERATION WAS COMBINED WITH COMPETITION TO SERVE AS A FACTOR IN HUMAN EVOLUTION

Synopsis.—*The* Origin of Species *gave rise to the impression that the methods of evolution were brutal. When Darwin came to write* The Descent of Man, *he emphasized the importance of group selection. Group selection favoured the growth of man's " good " qualities. Co-operation and mutual aid have high survival values. Pioneers of group selection. Man's co-operative impulses have been evolved from an instinctive basis. Man the most consciously co-operative of all animals. Man's " competitive complex." Group or team competition has a strong attraction for man. It is assumed that the human groups in the primal world were competitive to a varying degree. Man is the most competitive as well as the most co-operative of social animals, and in primitive groups these two qualities were combined so as to form a single evolutionary instrument. In this, the author is in agreement with Professor Allee. The combination of co-operation is possible only in groups in which behaviour is regulated by a dual code of conduct. Primitive man was unconscious of his dual morality. A dual standard of justice is essential for group evolution. Early humanity is assumed to have been under the dual code. Group selection implies an " ethical " injustice.*

THE general impression created by the *Origin of Species*, when it was published at the end of 1859, was that evolution was a brutal process involving individuals in a lifelong struggle with one another for survival. Such an impression was in keeping with the picture Thomas Hobbes (1588–1679) had painted of man's early state—namely, as a " war of everyman against everyman." [1] Certainly, when writing the *Origin of Species*, Darwin did emphasize the individual struggle and the ruthless nature of the evolutionary process, as, for example, when he penned the last

E

sentence of chapter VIII, part of which reads: "one general law leading to the advancement of all organic beings—namely, multiply, vary, let the strongest live and weakest die." Even as late as 1888 we find Huxley writing: "As amongst these so among primitive men . . . life was a continual free-fight, and beyond the limited and temporary relations of the family, the Hobbesian war of each against all was the normal state of existence." [2]

When Darwin came to write *The Descent of Man* in 1870, his conception of the process of evolution had undergone a profound, but apparently an unnoted change; group selection now replaced individual selection—at least so far as social animals were concerned, and most animals are social. I have already cited passages from *The Descent of Man* illustrative of this changed attitude (p. 12), and now I shall cite others to exemplify Darwin's conception of group evolution. Here is my first example: [3] "For those *communities* which included the greatest number of the most sympathetic members would flourish best and rear the greatest number of offspring"; the group or team held together by mutual sympathy is stronger than one not so blessed. Another instance: [4] "When two tribes of primeval man, living in the same country, came into competition, if (other circumstances being equal) the one tribe included a great number of courageous, sympathetic, and faithful members, who were always ready to warn each other of danger, to aid and defend each other, this tribe would succeed better and conquer the other"; group selection thus favouring the growth of fidelity and courage. A third passage: [5] "A tribe including many members who, from possessing in a high degree the spirit of patriotism, fidelity, obedience, courage and sympathy, were always ready to aid each other, and to sacrifice themselves for the common good would be victorious over most other tribes." As a postscript to this passage Darwin adds: "And this would be natural selection." Here, then, is a case of group selection which is certainly "natural," but in its methods and results it differs altogether from the instances advanced in the *Origin of Species*.

I shall note very briefly other mental qualities which Darwin regarded as giving strength to a group or tribe, and also those which he believed led to their undoing. "A tribe which was contented and happy flourished better than one which was discontented and unhappy ";[6] " selfish and contentious people will not cohere and without coherence nothing can be effected ";[7] " no tribe could hold together if murder, robbery, treachery were common." [8] Thus Darwin came to see that it was not a man's individual merits that gave him survival in primal times; all depended on how such a man could fit his merits into the social life of his group. Darwin realized very clearly that a group of primitive mankind was a nursery of all social virtues, and that it was by group selection that man had come by all those mental and moral qualities which have raised him so high above all other animals.

I must not permit my readers to forget the object of my present search; it is to discover the mental qualities which we may legitimately attribute to the human groups we have assembled on the chequerboard of the primal world. In the two preceding essays I have given grounds for attributing to them a " group spirit," and a spirit of patriotism; and now, with Darwin's aid, I am giving my reasons for regarding them as co-operative societies, for in societies or tribes where fellowship, goodwill, and a team spirit prevail, then there must be co-operation. The recognition that the group and not the individual was the unit of selection brought a new principle into evolution. Russel Wallace was the first (1864) to perceive that human evolution was a matter of group selection; [9] Bagehot recognized it; [10] so did Herbert Spencer [11] and Sutherland; [12] but the witness I would cite now is Winwood Reade, because his evidence is based on experience among primitive peoples—those of West Africa. " But this sympathy," wrote Reade in 1872, " is extended and intensified by the struggle for existence; that herd which best combines will undoubtedly survive, and that herd in which sympathy is most developed, will most efficiently combine. Here, then, one herd destroys another not only by means of teeth and claws, but also by means of sympathy and love . . . in the first period of the human herd, co-operation was merely instinctive, as in baboons." [13]

Karl Pearson was also aware (1888) of the important role taken by co-operation as a factor in the survival of human communities,[14] but the old conception of evolution being a " tooth-and-claw " business must have remained vigorous, for when Prince Kropotkin published *Mutual Aid: a Factor of Evolution* in

1902, it was received as a revelation. In one sense it was a new doctrine, for it attributed man's rise in the animal scale to his capacity for "mutual aid." Such a surmise will explain man's good qualities but, as we shall see presently, we have also to account for those which are regarded as evil.

A leading authority on animal psychology, Prof. W. C. Allee, affirms that "automatic co-operation is a fundamental principle of biology"; [15] equally fundamental is the fact that the co-operative activities of a community are restricted to that community. Further, co-operation, so far as the higher animals are concerned, can exist only if members of a community are united by the bonds of mutual affection, sympathy, and goodwill, and, as these emotions and feelings never extend beyond the limits of an animal or primitive human society, we may infer that, so far as concerns the primal groups of humanity, co-operative activities were equally restricted. "Social animals," said Darwin, "are largely guided by special instincts in the aid which they give to the members of the same community; but, they are likewise in part impelled by mutual love and sympathy, assisted apparently by some amount of reason." [16]   As he penned that sentence Darwin must have had in mind the enormous expansion of man's feelings, sympathies, desires, and imaginings which took place as the human brain rose in organization and power, and the thousand and one ways in which men could then co-operate and give mutual aid. Man has the capacity to co-operate far beyond that of any other social animal; we may assume that even early man had this capacity to a considerable degree, and that the primal groups, postulated in the group theory, were independent co-operative units.

Having presented my case for regarding the groups of primal humanity as co-operative units, I now turn to give my evidence for regarding them as competitive units. There is ingrained in man's mental nature a bundle of activities to which we may give the name of the "competitive complex." As the base of this complex lies man's desire for place and power—ambition; as an accessory is that form of resolution known as courage. There are the passions of emulation, rivalry, jealousy, and envy, which served as stimuli or "triggers" to bring the competitive complex into action; competition leads to conflict, and conflict may pass into anger, and anger into violence. Now, everyman is heir to all these ancient mental qualities—to a greater or lesser degree. We are apt to think that those feelings and impulses serve the occasions of only the individual man, but we have already noted (p. 51) that all man's individual passions and impulses may pass into collective action on behalf of the group. This is especially true of the competitive complex; man's love of team competition is as strong as that for individual against individual. In 1944 the sale of war saving-certificates was going badly in Britain, but the moment one team of collectors was set against another there was a triumphal increase. When the Government of Russia wished to stimulate a desire for learning among its students, it appealed to the competitive spirit by setting the students of one institute against those of another, in what were called "socialist competitions." The desired effect was attained.[17] Games in which teams compete against teams are the most popular form of sport in the Anglo-Saxon world; they seem to satisfy the "competitive instinct" which is so strongly developed within the Anglo-Saxon breast. We may assume that early man had the spirit of team competition.

In man's primal world the stage was certainly set very favourably for a great game of competition. Each group was a separate entity, with its own interests, which were antagonistic to those of neighbouring groups. It may be thought that in a thinly populated primitive world, groups would be so far apart that their interests could not clash. In primal times groups depended for a subsistence on the natural produce of their territories. In those areas where Nature's harvests were abundant we should expect the groups to multiply in size and in number and so encroach on each other. Even then the degree of competition which would ensue must have depended on the temperament of adjacent groups. Among the aboriginal tribes of Australia the competitive spirit is in abeyance; it is kept just sufficiently active to maintain tribal isolation and integrity. It was otherwise with the tribes of Mongolia and of Germany; between tribes in these two regions of the globe there were rivalries, conflicts, and wars. We may assume that in the ancient world, as in the modern, there were regions where tribes were aggressively competitive and others where life was held on easy terms.

Man is the most competitive of animals; his spirit of competition outstrips that of every other Primate just as far as his brain surpasses theirs. Competition, one would infer, has been an important factor in man's evolutionary ascent. Man is also the most consciously co-operative of all animals; we may confidently assume that his co-operative capacity has been a potent factor in his evolutionary progress. Modern men of business are of the opinion that co-operation and competition are incompatible forms of human activity. Yet every successful football team shows that such a combination is not only possible but highly profitable. For unless a co-operative spirit prevails among the members of a team, unless each man sinks his individuality in his team, there can be no competitive strength; the higher the co-operative spirit, the greater the competitive power. The greater the opposition met with in competition, the greater grows the co-operative spirit within the team. I assume that it was in this way that co-operation was combined with competition in the human groups of the primal world; welded together, as in a team, they gave a human group a strong place in the evolutionary field. In all home activities of a group co-operation replaced individual rivalries, but in all affairs which concerned the outside affairs of the group the "competitive complex" had free play. I regard the combination of co-operation with competition as the most potent of all the agencies which determined the evolutionary destiny of human groups.

That groups of primitive humanity should be imbued with a team spirit, and should have forged out of co-operation and competition a single and effective instrument to serve in their evolutionary advance, seems an almost trite idea, yet in all my reading I have come across only one author who has given it a clear expression—namely, Prof. W. C. Allee.[18] As to the factors which are concerned in the natural production of new forms of organic beings, I find that I have more in common with him than with any other biologist, excepting his idea that evolution should culminate in making mankind into a single co-operative community. Julian Huxley, in his comprehensive work on evolution,[19] seems to have had in mind a combination of competition with co-operation when he wrote: "The development of social life, with consequent inter-group struggle within the species, may produce the most peculiar selective results, as is especially to be seen within our own species"—a statement based on inferences made by Dr. R. A. Fisher, who gives reasons for believing that selection, which is competitive in nature, tends to produce co-operative mental qualities, such as public spirit and patriotism.[20]

Now, in order that the members of a team may apply the "C.-and-C." factor (competition with co-operation), they must have two rules or codes of conduct: they must behave in one way to their fellow members, but in quite another manner to members of the opposing team. It must have been so with groups of primitive humanity: the members of a group had one rule of conduct for their fellows and quite another for members of neighbouring groups. This duality of behaviour is not peculiar to man; it holds for all neighbouring groups of social animals. Duality of conduct is made possible because the mentality of all social animals is dual. It is especially true of human mentality; the man who loves, sympathizes, and is kind at one moment may hate, be callous and cruel at the next; in man's mental armoury every virtue has its corresponding vice. "Rude tribes and civilized societies," said Herbert Spencer,[21] "have had continually to carry on an external defence and an internal co-operation: external antagonism and internal friendship. Hence their members have acquired two different sets of sentiments and ideas, adjusted to their two kinds of activities."

Here, I think, the pioneer of evolutionary thought places the cart before the horse. Man did not acquire his dual mentality as a result of practising two codes of morality, but he practised a dual code because of the twofold organization of his nervous system. A bee behaves in one way to its fellow workers, but in an altogether different way to those who are not of its hive. The bee's behaviour is regulated by instinct, and instinct depends on an innate organization of nerve cells. Man is the descendant of a remote ancestry, the conduct of which was regulated by instinct. On this instinctive basis man's powerful brain has been evolved, but the fundamental dualism has been retained.

The bee, of course, is not aware that it has two rules of conduct, two standards of justice, nor is any social animal. Only man has become conscious of it, and he only when he has entered the realm of high civilization. The daily conduct of most men is based on a dual code; it seems to them so natural to love their friends and to hate their enemies that they believe that they are obeying only one moral code in doing so. If, as I have assumed, man's mentality has been built on an instinctive basis, then this unconscious practising of a dual code is understandable, for instinctive action lies below the level of conscious control. Even in the human brain, when impulses ascend into the field of consciousness—into the eye of the mind—from the old centres of instinct, they bring with them such an emotional force that reason, far from playing the part of judge, jumps down from its throne to become a partisan. Conscience sits unmoved, believing such occurrences to be in the normal order of events.

I am assuming that ancient, evolving humanity was dual minded and had two codes of behaviour. For a moment let us suppose that it was not so and that there was only one code, the code of amity or co-operation. Then the sympathy of the members of a group would no longer be restricted to their own circle, but would well out to embrace members of all neighbouring groups. If a group no longer considered its own things much more precious that those of other groups, in no need of defence, then patriotism would be superfluous; if men and women behaved towards members of other groups as they did towards members of their own group, then all barriers between them would vanish and a general fusion would ensue. And with the disappearance of groups, not only competition and conflict would be eliminated, but co-operation as well, for groups are the nurses of co-operation as well as the agents of competition. If students of evolution are right in regarding each isolated group as an experimental brood, then with the dissolution of the dual code such broods would be brought to an end. What direction would human evolution have taken if man had been uni-codal? I cannot tell, but it would have been very different from that it did take under the rule of the dual code. Evolution would certainly have become disorganized, indeterminate, and inchoate, as indeed it is becoming in the modern world. And, after all, man is a very exceptional result for evolution to have attained under the stress of competition and of elimination.

Seeing that all social animals behave in one way to members of their own community and in an opposite manner to those of other communities, we are safe in assuming that early humanity, grouped as it was in the primal world, had also this double rule of behaviour. At home they applied Huxley's ethical code, which is Spencer's code of amity; abroad their conduct was that of

Huxley's cosmic code, which is Spencer's code of enmity. The subservience to these two codes—co-operation within groups and competition between groups—made evolutionary advance possible; and we may infer that the groups which co-operated best were also the groups which were most successful in the competition for survival. Man is the most co-operative of animals and also the most competitive; it can hardly be a coincidence that the animal that has risen highest in the scale of beings is the one in which these two qualities find their highest development.

To the ethically minded the practice of the dual code is anathema, for it implies two standards of justice—the favourable standard which members of a group apply to themselves, and the harsh standard they seek to impose on those not of their community. Such is my reason for asserting, at the close of the preceding essay, that evolutionary advance was made possible by the practice of injustice.

REFERENCES

[1] Hobbes, Thos., *Leviathan*, 1651, pt. 1, ch. XIII, Everyman ed., p. 66.

[2] Huxley, T. H., "Evolution and Ethics", *Collected Essays*, 1898, vol. 9, p. 204.

[3] Darwin, C., *The Descent of Man*, Murray, 1913, p. 163.

[4] *Ibid.*, p. 199.

[5] *Ibid.*, p. 203.

[6] *Ibid.*, p. 185.

[7] *Ibid.*, p. 200.

[8] *Ibid.*, cp. 179.

[9] Wallace, A. R., *Anthropological Rev.*, 1864, vol. 2, p. 158.

[10] Bagehot, Walter, *Physics and Politics*, 1869, pp. 43–53.

[11] Spencer, Herbert, *Principles of Ethics*, 1892, vol. 1, p. 314.

[12] Sutherland, Alex, *The Origin and Growth of the Moral Instinct.*, 1898, ch. XI.

[13] Reade, Winwood, *The Martyrdom of Man*, Watts's reprint, 1934, p. 357.

[14] Pearson, Karl, *The Grammar of Science*, 1894, Everyman ed., p. 306.

[15] Allee, W. C., *The Social Life of Animals*, 1939, p. 35.

[16] See under ref. 3, p. 167.

[17] Crowther, J. C., *Education and Industry in Soviet Russia*, 1932.

[18] See under ref. 15, ch. VII.

[19] Huxley, Julian, *Evolution: The Modern Synthesis*, 1942, p. 129.

[20] Fisher, R. A., *The Genetical Theory of Natural Selection*, 1930, chap. XI, p. 249.

[21] See under ref. 11, p. 322.

MENTAL BIAS AS A FACTOR IN HUMAN EVOLUTION

Synopsis.—*The development of group mentality in the child. The early recognition of faces. The limitation of sympathy to known faces. The early manifestation of mental qualities concerned in evolutionary competition. The development of mental biases concerned in patriotism. The opinions of Locke and of Reid concerning biases connected with the preservation of the individual and of the species. How the modern student of evolution regards these biases or instincts. Hume's approach to the study of human nature and to man's prejudices. The author agrees with Hume in regarding man's inclination or aptitude to form prejudiced opinion as being inborn. The influence of desires, aversions, interest, etc. Hume's cultural prejudice and his inability to account for man's behaviour being regulated by a dual code. The belief that the " species is wise " has a true foundation. Human mentality has been biased to serve as a powerful factor in determining the direction of human evolution. Altruism and idealism as sources of bias. They seem to serve no evolutionary purpose. The evolution of altruism. It is a form of mental disarmament. Theories also serve to bias the minds of authors; this is particularly true of those who write on anthropology.*

IN the three preceding essays I have discussed the part played by the mentality of early man in shaping the evolutionary destiny of the groups into which mankind was divided in primal times. The evidence on which my discussion was based was drawn from what is known of the mentality of tribal man in the modern world, and to some extent on what we know of the social behaviour of animals akin to man. There is another source of evidence which I have not yet touched on—namely, that provided by the study of the developing mentality of very young children, particularly of those group-forming qualities which I have ascribed to early man. By the time a baby has entered its fourth month of life it has become conscious of faces; [1] it distinguishes the known face from the unknown; the known face pleases while the unknown displeases. Have we not in this the first manifestation of the group spirit—a " consciousness of kind," a discrimination which separates the faces of the family community from those not of that community? The babe returns the smile of the known face with a smile, while it is upset by the smile of the unknown face. Sympathy is limited to the known group. Have we not here the beginning of that characteristic of the group spirit—the limitation of sympathy to the home community? To account for the babe's behaviour we have to assume that it has been born with a mental bias—an inclination as well as an aptitude to love the known but to turn away from the strange or unknown. And the purpose of the bias is to serve in group formation. Here, then, is the subject of the present essay—the biasing of man's mentality to play a part in the process of his evolution.

Before the end of its first year a child's affections became biased in opposite directions; in one direction its preferences are so strong that they may be described as love, while in another direction its aversions are of the nature of hate. Thus early is laid the basis of the love–hate mentality which prevails between independent groups of primitive humanity—the subject to which the preceding essay was devoted. With love and hate come manifestations of anger and jealousy, pride and resentment— the main mental ingredients which go to the make-up of the " competitive complex." Seeing how early in life a child's feelings and passions assume this biased mode of action, we must assume that the bias is determined by a particular structure and organization of its nervous system. We may speak of such inborn or innate mental biases as being " instinctive " if they serve a purpose in life's economy.

As to patriotism, a particular form of mental bias or prejudice,[2] dealt with in Essay VI, we must assign its development and manifestations to a later stage of a child's life than those just mentioned, unless we accept Hume's opinion that a child's concern or pride in itself is a form of patriotism—namely, " self-patriotism." This form of patriotism begins before the end of the first year, but its more usual manifestations appear in later childhood, when a mother becomes to her children the best of women, and father the greatest of men. "The nearer in kind the nearer in affection" (Hobbes). Although well over seventy years have come and gone since I nursed the illusions of childhood, I have still a vivid recollection of my dismay when certain of my boyhood prejudices were challenged. My father farmed in the valley of the Deveron, a small river in Scotland which separates Aberdeenshire from Banffshire. He was, in reality, an ordinary farmer, and his livestock was not unusual, but I held the opinion that he was the most expert of farmers and that his stock was of the highest merit. To my surprise I learned, in a moment of confidence from a friend, the son of a neighbouring farmer, that he held a like high opinion of his father and of his father's stock, an opinion that struck me as being absurd. Neither his prejudice nor mine was shaken by our confabulation! Often since then I have thought of the strength which a primitive group of humanity must have drawn from the prejudice or, which is the same thing, the conviction that it was the best and bravest of all groups and that its homeland was the best of all territories. Group pride is a breeder of confidence; it becomes a source of evil only when it reaches that point of fervour or intoxication which is named jingoism or chauvinism.

Often as I read the works of authors of the seventeenth and eighteenth centuries I have felt, as they expounded the fundamentals of human nature, that they enjoyed one advantage which is denied to us who are disciples of Darwin. They believed in Creation. Let me cite one or two examples to illustrate my meaning. Let us begin with one from John Locke (1632–1704): "Our all-wise Maker, knowing what it is that determines the will, has put into man the uneasiness of hunger and thirst to move and determine their wills; for the preservation of themselves and of their species . . . for the continuation of the species." [3] Locke has only to call in the Creator to account for all the instinctive forces or impulses we find at work in man's nature, whereas I have to demonstrate that there still exists inside man and outside him forces or powers which could have created human nature as we now find it—human nature with all its bends, biases, prepossessions, and instinctive urges. My second example is taken from the *Philosophy* of Thomas Reid (1710–96): "The wise Author of our Being hath implanted in human nature . . . inferior principles of action . . . to preserve the species . . . to produce changes and revolutions in the theatre of life . . . hath not trusted reason with the preservation of the species . . . hath not thought fit to leave this important task to reason alone, otherwise the race would long ago have been extinct." [4]   Here the Scottish philosopher handles in the simple terms of Creation the problem I am now discussing—the inclination of the human mind to certain lines of thought and action, these forces being attributed to " inferior principles of action." The bending or bias has been implanted to serve an evolutionary purpose—namely, the preservation of the species. The " inferior principles of action " ensure that mankind will mate, will engender children, will care for children, and will devote their lives to the rearing of them, will be partial to them, and in due time will sink their own individuality in that of their children. This eighteenth-century conception of human men- tality is acceptable to the twentieth-century students of evolution, save as regards two matters : we regard " the inferior principle of action " as coming to man, not by a special act of implantation, but as an inheritance from forebears whose lives were mainly regulated by instinct ; we prefer to speak, not of the preservation of the species, but of the preservation of the group.

The preference of the term " group " to that of " species " becomes evident when we recall the main object of this dis- cussion. It is the evolution of the separate groups into which primitive humanity was divided, particularly the part played by biased mentality in the preservation and evolution of primal groups. We have already noted the extent to which the social attributes of the human mind have been biased to serve such purposes ; and now we must realize that a group's mentality is even more completely enslaved to serve in the major business of reproduction. Every generation of a group owes its existence to the self-sacrificing labours of a preceding generation, and should, if the group is to continue, hand on the entire trust or capital it has received to a succeeding generation. Our Scottish philosopher adds as a postscript to the passage quoted above that the " inferior principles of action " implanted in man's nature " have been successful hitherto in ensuring the continuation of the race." This is true of humanity as a whole ; there is no lack of births. But how many groups and peoples have come to an untimely end just because they spent on themselves the capital of altruism which should have gone to the rearing of another generation? The strength of the reproductive bias is a guarantee of the survival of a group.

Both Locke and Reid approached the study of human nature under the conviction that they had to deal with a "special creation"—such a conviction serving as a potent bias to their interpretation. There is another author of the eighteenth century whose observations on human nature may help us to interpret the mentality of early man still more accurately than those of his contemporaries—namely, David Hume (1711-76). Hume, who held that "the material world has a principle of order within itself," [5] was more likely to err in the direction taken by those who regard human nature as a product of evolution. "Nature," wrote Hume (meaning, as I suppose, the creative powers inherent in living things), "has given all animals a like prejudice in favour of their own offspring; this passion arises from the original structure and formation of human nature." [6] Here we find Hume affirming his belief that a pronounced bias or instinct is determined by the organization of man's nervous system. "Reason," he declares, "discovers objects as they really stand in nature," while our feelings have "a productive faculty, and gilding and staining all natural objects with the colours borrowed from internal sentiment, raises in a manner a new creation." Primitive man, as the powers of his brain expanded, and as the rigidity of instinct was replaced by a liberality of choice, looked out, not on the world as it really was, but on one made attractive by the glamour created by his inner feelings and by the liveliness of his imagination. Such a bias gave him an incentive to live. According to Hume, "Nature has succeeded in deceiving us into the opinion that human life is important." [8] Men find surcease from the troubles of life in sleep, which is akin to death, yet so strongly are they biased in favour of life that escape from it by suicide is regarded as an act of insanity. Nevertheless, when men realize that their country or their group is in danger, their instinct for self-preservation is superseded by a still stronger basis—one which compels them to offer their lives in order that their homeland and their group may survive. These instances serve to illustrate the extent to which human nature has been biased to serve evolutionary purposes.

Human mentality may be biased by many circumstances and

conditions. Desires and aversions, unreasoned likes and dislikes, turn our minds this way and that. Especially potent is that form of mental activity known as " interest "; whenever questions concerning our own welfare or that of our community arise, our emotions are aroused and our interest is intensified. A common interest served as a bond to keep the members of primitive groups together and helped to secure unity of action. Hope turns our minds in one direction, while fear, the stronger agent, turns them in another direction. Fear gives unity of action to a group. Our minds are tuned to accept what flatters our self-vanity and to reject what tends to lower our personal status. We are biased or swayed by our national pride. Pride of family and of class bear in upon us. We are ready to believe all that is good of our friends and all that is evil of our enemies. Our minds are enslaved to our prejudices to a far greater extent than is usually recognized.

Hume had a mind of the highest order, penetrated and controlled by an unflinching intellectual integrity; yet he had a ruling prejudice. He valued those elements in human nature which fitted a man to take a place in the polite society of his time. " We are naturally partial to ourselves and to our friends," he admitted; and then adds, " We are capable of learning a more equitable conduct." [9] When dealing with those mental qualities which make up man's code of amity, which I have discussed in the preceding essay, his pen moved swimmingly; love, friendship, goodwill, taste, tact, easy manners, benevolence, and humanity had his approval because they were agreeable as well as useful. It was when he proceeded to explain the presence in human nature of those qualities which make up man's code of enmity that his style became cramped; the exhibition of passion, of contention, of vanity, of brutish manners, of ambition, avarice, jealousy, envy, and hatred was fatal to all social and polite intercourse, and therefore vicious and bad. Yet Hume admitted that " we cannot diminish or extinguish our vicious passions without diminishing or extinguishing such as are virtuous; and rendering the mind totally indifferent and inactive." [10] He regarded love and hatred as being " due to a constitution of nature of which we can give no further explication." [11] Man's code of enmity was an enigma to uni-codal Hume, but that which was an enigma to him finds an easy solution at the hands of the student of human evolution. Human nature was elaborated and matured in that prolonged primal age of mankind when every human group contended with neighbouring groups. As shown in the preceding essay, man's dual nature was an essential factor in his evolution.

In this essay I have sought to concentrate the attention of my readers on the great extent to which the mentality of primitive man was modified and biased to serve in the welfare of his group, which means, ultimately, in the welfare and evolutionary destiny of his race or species. We may assume, I think, that a steady process of selection went on among the groups of primitive humanity, and that the groups with minds most suitably biased to give a united team or group spirit would be the groups rewarded by the prize of survival. If my argument is sound, then may there not be truth in what has come to be known as " wisdom of the species "? In this connection statements made by Edmund Burke (1729–97) are often quoted. For example: " Whenever the people have a feeling, they are commonly in the right." [12] Or again: " Prejudice with its reason has a motive to give action to that reason and an affection which will give it permanence. Prejudice is of ready application in an emergency. . . . Through just prejudice a man's duty becomes a party of his nature." [13] Here we find an able statesman justifying prejudice in a modern society, while I am dwelling on its evolutionary utility among ancient societies of evolving man. Aristotle seems to have believed in the collective wisdom of lower animals. In his *Ethics* this passage appears: " Even in the lower animals there is some natural good principle above themselves which aims at the good peculiar to them." [14] Darwin believed that the safety of a tribe lay in the guidance of tribal opinion. For example: " Actions are good or bad as they affect the welfare of the tribe. . . . Judgment of the tribe is best in the long run for all its members." [15] The part played by all those mental activities, which are of an instinctive or biased nature, in the preservation of the individual or the species, and in securing the perfection of the species, was very completely recognized by E. von Hartmann (1842–1906). [16] James Dunbar, a professor in the University of Aberdeen, penned this epigrammatic statement in 1781: " Instinct carries out the policy of nature." [17] If we construe " the policy of nature " as being the way of evolution, then we may say that the human brain has been evolved to serve as a factor in carrying out that way.

There remains for our consideration one of the most powerful inclinations or biases of the human mind—that which receives a multitude of names—altruism, idealism, humanitarianism, benevolence, and many others. Altruism gives rise to a feeling of serenity. It is destitute of self-interest, is non-competitive, and apparently serves no evolutionary purpose; its field of action is entirely within the code of amity; it aims at a higher and better life. Altruism is the mother of all forms of missionary enterprise. Benevolence, wrote Hume, " is a disposition, a bias, a generous concern for our own kind "—our own kind meaning here the whole family of mankind. Altruism is accompanied by that degree of emotional fervour known as enthusiasm. " Enthusiasm," said Hume, " arises from pride, hope, presumption, a warm imagination, together with ignorance." [18] Under a heightened degree of zeal, altruism may assume the ugly forms of bigotry or of fanaticism. " Ideals," William James noted, " give inner joy, but are luxuries if they stay at that." [19] In the opinion of Herbert Spencer ideals may intoxicate the judgment; " they may strain nature out of its inherited form." [20]

Having asserted that all instinctive tendencies of the human mind work for the preservation of the individual or of his community, how are we to account for one which serves no such purpose? I agree with Wilfrid Trotter [21] that altruism is both inborn and instinctive. The explanation of the origin of altruism which I would offer is very similar to that given by Darwin.[22] Altruism is a vast expansion of family sympathy. Family sympathy has a diffusive and exuberant quality; it becomes wider and wider in its influence, until it includes all members of a primal group; it again expands when groups are fused into tribes and again when tribes are combined to form nations. The peoples that have survived to form the large nations of modern times are those which were gifted with a full endowment of generous sympathy, a quality nearly akin to altruism.

Such, however, is only part of the explanation I have to offer for man's altruistic qualities. In reality, altruism is an evolutionary disarmament. All the emotions which wait upon the practices concerned with man's evolution are painful. Competition, contest, emulation, rivalry, hatred, anger, cruelty,

F

injustice—in short, all of those feelings included in the
" evolutionary complex "—give rise to uneasiness and anxiety.
Altruism signifies a complete abandonment of the evolutionary
outlook; the altruistic man or woman is willing to sacrifice
self for foe as readily as for friend; altruism, in reality, is a
longing for peace. Hence the warm, large-hearted feeling which
accompanies it.

I am particularly interested in a form of mental bias which has
its place, not in the evolution of man, but in the evolution of
science, especially the branch of it which most nearly touches me
—namely, anthropology. Time was, and not so long ago, when
the ruling bias of my predecessors was the theory of creation as
expounded by Moses. Observations which did not fit into that
theory were rejected or modified. And now we are dominated
by the conviction that evolution is true, and I am bound to
confess that so far as the workings of Nature are known, our
observations, so far as they concern man, fit very comfortably into
that theory. Alas! many of these observations cannot be fitted
into our conception of what civilization is, and especially what it
ought to be. Hence many of my colleagues, votaries to the
altruistic ideal of a universal brotherhood, refuse to handle the
uglier aspects of the evolutionary process as manifested in the
world of to-day. The actions of the living nations lie outside
their purview, yet to me the behaviour of nations now alive is
very similar to that which I have ascribed to primal groups of
humanity, swallowed up in the past of so long ago. " The
profoundest of all infidelities," write Herbert Spencer, " is the
fear that the truth will be bad." [23]

REFERENCES

[1] McDougall, Wm., *The Energies of Men*, 1932, p. 76; Duff, Charles, *This Human Nature*, Watts's reprint, 1937, p. 41.

[2] I have preferred to use the term " mental bias " rather than prejudice for the following reason. In 1931 I published a small book with the title : *The Place of Prejudice in Modern Civilization*, and found that many of my critics construed " prejudice " not as a biased action of the mind, but as the belief or opinion formed as the result of that activity. For example, my friend Dr. Ashley Montagu, in referring to my booklet (*Sc. Monthly*, 1942, vol. 54, p. 342), asserts that all prejudices are learned, being a cultural inheritance. The forms taken by the biased action of the mind are learned from those among whom we grow up but the mental bias is innate. Our aptitude to learn to speak is one thing, the language we learn to speak is quite another.

[3] Locke, John, *An Essay concerning Human Understanding*, Campbell Fraser's ed., 1894, bk. 2, ch. XXI.

[4] Reid, Thos., *Essays on the Active Powers of Man*, 1788, Essay 3, pt. 2, ch. III.

[5] Huxley, T. H., *Collected Essays*, 1897, vol. 6 on Hume, p. 177.

[6] Hume, David, *Essays and Treatises*, 1772, vol. 1, p. 169.

[7] See under reference 5, p. 238.

[8] See under reference 6, p. 184.

[9] *Ibid.*, vol. 2, p. 252.

[10] *Ibid.*, vol. 1, p. 180.

[11] *Ibid.*, vol. 2, p. 208.

[12] Burke, Edmund, by John Morley, 1902, p. 64.

[13] *Ibid.*, p. 251.

[14] Aristotle's *Ethics*, Everyman ed., p. 237.

[15] Darwin, Charles, *The Descent of Man*, Murray, 1913, pp. 182, 186.

[16] Hartmann, E. von, *The Philosophy of the Unconscious*, 1869.

[17] Dunbar, James, *Essays on the History of Mankind*, 1781.

[18] Hume, David, *Essays and Treatises*, 1772, vol. 1, p. 70.

[19] James, Wm., *Talks to Teachers on Psychology*, 1902, p. 294.

[20] Spencer, Herbert, *Principles of Ethics*, 1892, vol. 1, p. 561.

[21] Trotter, W., *The Instincts of the Herd in Peace and War*, 2nd ed., 1919, p. 123.

[22] See under reference 15, p. 188.

[23] Spencer, Herbert, *Essays, Scientific, Political, and Speculative*, 1891, vol. 1, . 61.

RESENTMENT AND REVENGE AS FACTORS IN HUMAN EVOLUTION

Synopsis.—*The author's reasons for attributing the feeling of resentment and the practice of blood-revenge to the primal groups of humanity. Resentment and revenge as manifestations of the individual. As manifestations of a group. The principle of collective responsibility is involved. Revenge is suppressed within a family circle; when a family feeling spreads so as to include the whole group it is also suppressed within the group. Revenge fits into the evolutionary code of enmity. How revenge was regarded by authors of the Darwinian period. Murder of a tribesman by an enemy is regarded as an injury to the whole tribe. The practice of blood-revenge by the earlier Israelites. The law of retaliation. Blood-revenge is practised in all populations which are divided into separate, independent groups or communities. Head hunting; the effects of suppressing the practice. Natives living under " wild " conditions still retain their zest for life. Revenge, as a tribal practice, is more frequently praised than condemned. The role of resentment and of revenge in bringing about evolutionary change. Duelling as a form of revenge. Why the feelings connected with the code of enmity are unpleasant, while those connected with the code of amity are pleasant.*

IN the four preceding essays I seem to have been swayed by a double purpose—first, to give an explanation of human nature, and, second, of the part played by human nature in the evolution of the groups into which early mankind has been divided. In this essay I am still shadowed by the same duality; I am to assume the existence in early mankind of those mental qualities we name resentment and of its dynamic sequel, revenge; and on this assumption proceed to explain their rôle in group evolution. When it is remembered that these two mental qualities are found in all the higher vertebrates, particularly in those which are akin to man, it is a reasonable assumption to presume their presence in primitive humanity. This assumption is supported by the fact that the human child manifests the feeling of resentment before the end of its eighth month of life; [1] its early appearance may be taken as evidence that the feeling is not copied, but is inborn. Then there is a third source of evidence—that supplied by living primitive peoples of the modern world. Resentment, as a mode of feeling, and revenge, as a mode of behaviour, are to be seen in operation in all native peoples, among whom we may note the part they play in regulating the lives of individuals and of groups. We may transfer, I think, observations made on such communities in the modern world to those which existed in the primal world. Such is the purpose of this essay.

The twin qualities we are discussing may serve the needs of the individual or they may be evoked by the needs of a group. Let us consider, first, the manner in which they serve individual needs. A man's feeling of resentment is aroused when he suffers a deliberate injury to his person, to his mind, to his reputation, or to his honour; it arises when his will is thwarted or his prospects damaged; or it may arise when he suffers an injustice or when he has been outwitted by a rival. The injured man may call reason to his aid, and by strength of will suppress his feeling; or it may pass into hate, and so be postponed. Or resentment may burst into flame and pass beyond control; all the forces of anger are automatically mobilized and the will is forced into physical action. By the infliction of an equal or greater injury, resentment is allayed or gratified. If the act of reprisal is made while the sufferer's anger is still hot and is of a like kind to that received, we name it retaliation; if postponed and urged on by hatred, we call it revenge. In all these cases resentment and revenge serve to give protection, or some measure of justice, to the individual. They may be said to serve an evolutionary purpose.

Resentment may be occasioned, not by an injury done to an individual, but by one done to a group or clan. We have already noted how all the feelings which serve to preserve the individual or to promote his interest become expanded to work for the preservation and welfare of his group. Pride in self becomes pride in group. So it is with resentment; a common feeling comes into existence in all members of a group when their community is attacked, when its honour is impugned, its prospects damaged, or its will thwarted. The sequence of events may be that which I have described in the case of the individual. The result may be an inter-group warfare, for I am of opinion that group revenge was the first form of human warfare. Among the aborigines of Australia, if a tribe is small, all its members are involved in any act of revenge; but if the tribe is large and scattered, the turmoil is confined to local groups; two groups of the same tribe may carry on a vendetta.[2]

There is an important principle underlying the practice of group revenge which I have not mentioned so far. It is the principle of collective responsibility, which works in two ways: it compels the group to avenge a wrong done to any one of its members; it makes the group responsible for trespass committed by any of its members. Group revenge is linked with group responsibility. It is easy to see the advantages which such a linkage will bring to a group: it will give unity of feeling and of action to all its members; it will bring a group its own measurement of justice; and it will restrain unruly and offensive conduct on the part of its individual members. It is not the utility of this group ordinance I am concerned with at this moment, but the circumstances which brought it into being. We get a clue if we consider the conditions which prevail within a primitive family, which I may define as consisting of a man and woman, their children and grandchildren, all living, eating, and sleeping as one company. Now the members of a family are bound together by what is usually described as "natural affection"; the code of amity regulates the conduct of the members of a family towards one another (see Essay V, p. 44). Nevertheless a feeling of resentment does arise between members from time to time, and if allowed to pass into revenge would speedily bring about the destruction of the family. If resentment does pass into revenge in the case of a family, then punishment of the erring member becomes a duty of the family; such punishment is not an act of revenge. We have already seen how the family spirit expands beyond its narrower circles until all families of a group are made into a corporate whole. The family law then holds for the whole group. The duty of punishing crime and wrongdoing falls on the group, so far as its own members are concerned, but if the wrong is committed by someone outside the group, then the law of revenge becomes operative. So we come back again to the action of the dual code—the code of amity which regulates the "home" conduct of a group and the code of enmity which determines conduct in all its "foreign" affairs. Within the group the law of revenge is suppressed; outside the group it is given a rigorous enforcement. Thus the law of revenge nurses enmity between groups, and so serves to maintain their isolation. Isolation, we shall find, has been an important factor in human evolution.

Readers may suspect that the statements I have just made about revenge have been fashioned to fit into the theory of evolution. Let me cite, then, the evidence of polite authors who wrote in pre-Darwinian times. In the fourth essay of a series which Lord Bacon (1561-1626) published in 1626, he said this of revenge: "Revenge is a kind of wild justice, which, the more man's nature runs to, the more ought law to weed it out. . . . Certainly, in taking revenge a man is but even with his enemy, but in passing it over he is superior, for it is a Prince's part to pardon." Bacon's condemnation of revenge relates to life in civilized lands; here we are concerned with the part played by blood-revenge among the uncivilized of the primal world. Adam Smith (1723-96), in the *Theory of Moral Sentiments*, published in 1759 and written while he was still in his "thirties," deals with revenge, not as a vice, but as a virtue with which primitive man was endowed. Here are two of his statements: "Though man be naturally endowed with a desire of the welfare and preservation of society, yet the Author of nature has not entrusted it to his reason to find out that a certain application of punishments is the proper means of attaining this end; but has endowed man with an immediate and instinctive approbation." [3] Elsewhere Adam Smith has this to say of the spirit of revenge: "Nature, antecedent to all reflection upon the utility of punishments, has in this manner stamped on the human heart an immediate and instinctive approbation of the sacred and necessary law of retaliation." [4] The author of the *Wealth of Nations* regarded the spirit of revenge as an inborn constituent of human nature and as an instrument of primitive justice. Thomas Reid (1710-96), who succeeded Adam Smith in the chair of Moral Philosophy in the University of Glasgow in 1765, wrote of resentment and revenge thus: "Nature disposes us to resent injury to self, family, friends, and our community. . . . Resentment is a penal statute, promulgated by nature; the execution of which is entrusted to the sufferer; an uneasy sensation urges the execution." [5] Still earlier in the eighteenth century Bishop Butler (1692–1752) recognized that resentment was " a weapon put into our hands against injury, injustice and cruelty." [6] These eighteenth-century authors were creationists; we who are evolutionists use different terms, but our ultimate meaning is the same—namely, that the feeling or passion we call resentment, and which precipitates the action of revenge, is inborn in man and makes him the executioner of his private sense of justice.

The quotations just given bear upon vengeance as an instrument of law : " Time was," writes Tylor, " when it was every man's duty to take the law into his own hands." [7] The same authority emphasizes the important point that many primitive tribes, such as those of Brazil, regard the murder of a tribesman by an enemy as an injury to the whole tribe. He also illustrates the penalties which overtake the tribesman who fails in his duty as avenger by an example taken from tribal life among the Australian aborigines. " The holiest duty a native is called on to perform is to avenge the death of his nearest relative." [8] His failure is attended by a complete social ostracism, and he becomes a mark of tribal scorn. Among the Nyasa Bantus the clan which fails in the duty of revenge is looked down upon by neighbouring clans; its honour is tarnished.[9] Arab tribes also regard murder of a member as an injury to the whole tribe; " our blood has been spilt," it is said.[10] When a tribe is led by a chief the duties of protection and of vengeance fall on him; [11] with the coming of kings, these duties were transferred to them; from kings it is an easy step to transfer these duties to God himself. Murder came to be construed as an offence against God.

The practice of blood-revenge among the earlier Israelites is illustrated by many passages in the Old Testament. The practice must have been rife when they settled in Palestine, otherwise it would not have been necessary to institute cities of refuge to protect the culprit from the avenger. " The revenger of blood shall himself slay the murderer, when he meeteth him he shall slay him." [12] God's instructions to Noah were : " At the hands of every man's brother will I require the life of man. Whoso sheddeth man's blood, by man shall his blood be shed." [13] The law of retaliation was given by God : " Eye for eye, tooth for tooth, hand for hand, foot for foot, burning for burning, wound for wound, stripe for stripe." [14] In the following passage collective responsibility is recognized, and so is jealousy, as a cause of resentment and revenge: " For I the Lord thy God am a jealous God, visiting the iniquity of the fathers upon the children unto the third and fourth generations of them that hate me." [15] We see the law of revenge at work in the heart of King David as he lay on his death-bed. He entrusted to Solomon the duty of carrying out two acts of revenge he himself had been unable to execute because of an oath—one on Joab the son of Zeruiah, the other on Shimei the son of Gera. As regard the latter the instruction was: " But his hoar head bring thou down to the grave with blood." One other instance from Proverbs [16] is instructive because it illustrates vengeance arising from sex-jealousy on the part of a wronged husband: " For jealousy is the rage of a man; therefore he will not spare in the day of vengeance. He will not regard any ransom." Bacon was right when he described revenge as a form of " wild justice."

The practice of blood-revenge is present in every population that is divided into clans or tribes. The practice springs from, and is allied with, the code of enmity which regulates inter-tribal conduct. Hence the practice is endemic in all those parts of the earth where a tribal or group organization is retained. It prevails in North Africa, in Arabia, and in the Balkans, especially among the Albanians and Montenegrins. The Albanian tribesmen set a higher value on honour than on life; [17] a stain on honour can be wiped out only by blood.[18] When a clan organization prevailed in Ancient Greece, blood-revenge was " an absolute and immediate obligation." [19] How thoroughly the duty was performed is indicated by the old Greek adage: " A man is a fool if he kills the father and leaves the children alive." Among the Highland clans of Scotland there were interminable contentions and rivalries; violent animosities prevailed between their chiefs; the practice of blood-revenge was rampant.[20]

Although the incentives which lie behind head-hunting, the collection of scalps, and the capture of victims for sacrifice, differ from the feeling of resentment which underlies the practice of blood-revenge, yet the results they produce in the relationship between groups are similar. As victims have to be obtained from outside or enemy clans, the result is that the animosity between tribes or clans is heightened and rendered more virulent and lasting, thus assisting to maintain the separation of evolutionary units. Head-hunting is regarded by natives as a proof of manliness.[21] That it gives a zest and excitement to life may be inferred from the change which comes over the mentality of a group when its head-hunting habit is suppressed. Mr. E. W. F. Chinnery,[22] who was a resident magistrate in New Guinea, noted that " the native feels a void in his existence " and that his chief occupation was gone " when the old practice could no longer be followed." Mr. G. Pitt-Rivers declares that " natives deprived of war and head-hunting lose their chief interest in life." [23] Rajah Brooke succeeded in pacifying the head-hunters of his dominion by inducing them to use a " dummy " head instead of a real one.[24] Throughout the whole region of Australonesia magical means are used as instruments of revenge.

The conditions of life described in the two preceding paragraphs, when viewed by civilized eyes, seem so revolting as to be utterly unbearable. Yet those who have visited peoples living under a reign of " wild justice," bring back accounts of happiness among natives living under such conditions. Freya Stark, for example, reported thus of South Arabia : " When I came to travel in that part of the country where security is non-existent, I found the people, though full of lament over their life of perpetual robbery and blackmail, yet just as cheerful and as full of the ordinary joy of living as anywhere on earth." [25] Dr. H. K. Fry had a similar experience among the aborigines of Australia. " A native in his wild state," he reports,[26] " lives in constant danger; hostile spirits are about him constantly. Yet he is light-hearted and cheerful . . . indulgent to his children and kind to his aged parents." My third illustration is taken from the Crow Indians of America, who have been under the eye of Dr. R. Lowie for many years. They are now living in the security of a reserve. " Ask a Crow," reports Dr. Lowie, " whether he would have security as now, or danger as of old, and his answer is—' danger as of old . . . there was glory in it.' " [27] I am assuming that the wild conditions of life I have been describing were those amid which mankind lived through the whole of the primal period of its evolution. It was amid such conditions that man's nature and character were fashioned, one of the conditions being the practice of blood-revenge.

When I count up the opinions which have been passed on the practice of blood-revenge, I find the commendations outnumber the condemnations. Let me deal with the grounds of commendation first. Hobbes commends it in his seventh law of Nature for the reason that " men look not at the greatness of the evil past, but the greatness of the good to follow." [28] Revenge is preventative in its action; fear of fiercer reprisals restrains. It is commended as a test of courage and of the will to duty. It gives solidarity to a group and unity of action. It serves, in the eyes of the participants, to maintain tribal honour and prestige. It gives a sense of collective responsibility to a group, and compels it to restrain its wayward members. On the other side of my account I find the practice of revenge condemned as being savage, brutal, inhuman, a destroyer of peace, filling life with hostility and hatred; it leads to a waste of previous lives; it is a childish passion (Trotter); it is the strongest passion of the savage breast (Machin). The savage has one opinion of the practice of revenge; the civilized man quite another. Certainly the practice of blood-revenge is incompatible with a civil way of life.

How, then, do resentment and—the natural issue of resentment —revenge fit into the group scheme of human evolution? Let us first consider the problem of group selection. We shall find, in a future essay, that isolation is an essential condition for group evolution. The practice of blood-revenge creates a very permanent barrier between neighbouring groups or tribes. If a group refuses, or has not the courage, to defend its members wilfully attacked from without, it will lose, not only its place in esteem, but also its life. If we consider the selection of individuals, which make up a group, the same case holds. The man who shirks his duty when revenge knocks at his door suffers a moral death in the eyes of his community. We who live under the shelter of law may suppress our resentment and so escape, but the tribesman was given no such shelter; he had to be strong enough in mind and body to shoulder his own defence. The strong and resolute were thus favoured in tribal times.

Duelling is a form of revenge; it is a " wild " search for justice conducted according to an accepted set of rules; it is a return of evil for evil between two individuals of the same group or company, one of whom considers that his reputation or honour has been injured. Hobbes gives an excellent account of the conditions which occasion a duel: "A man receives words of disgrace or some little injuries and is afraid, unless he revenge it, he shall fall into contempt, and consequently be obnoxious to the like injuries from others." [29]   Here Hobbes overlooks the fact that duelling, like the practice of blood-revenge, is enforced by the opinion of the company or society to which the duellists belong; unless the duty is undertaken, the duellists or avenger loses his reputation or status in the eyes of his group.   If public opinion had remained adamant, no matter what laws had been enacted, duelling would have still been practised among us.

Why is it that the feelings which accompany the practice of every kind of reprisal or of revenge are painful?   Indeed, all the feelings which enter into the practice of the code of enmity— envy, jealousy, emulation, covetousness, and hatred—are un- pleasant, while all the feelings which support the code of amity are pleasant and abiding.   The explanation I offer is that resent- ment is unpleasant to make sure that it will be put into execution, so giving relief by gratification.   Hume implicitly recognized the pleasantness of the feelings of amity, and the unpleasantness of those of enmity when he wrote: "Gratitude goes out to virtue; revenge to vice." [30]   Here the pleasant feeling of generosity, a component of the code of amity, is made the counterpart of revenge, a component of the code of enmity.   I have sought to prove (p. 62) that the code of enmity is a necessary part of the machinery of evolution.   He who feels generous towards his enemy, and more especially if he feels forgiveness towards him, has in reality abandoned the code of enmity and so has given up his place in the turmoil of evolutionary competition.   Hence the benign feeling of perfect peace that descends on him.

REFERENCES

[1] Duff, Charles, *This Human Nature*, Watts, 1937, p. 41.

[2] Radcliffe-Brown, A. R., *Jour. Roy. Anthrop. Instit.*, 1913, vol. 43, p. 143.

[3] Smith, Adam, *The Theory of Moral Sentiments*, Pt. 2, sect. 1, p. 109 of the Bohn edition.

[4] *Ibid.*, pt. 2, sect. 1, p. 99.

[5] Reid, Thomas, *The Works of*, 7th ed., 1872, Essay 3, pt. 2, ch. 5.

[6] Butler, Joseph, *Human Nature and Other Sermons*, sermon VIII.

[7] Tylor, Sir Edward, *Anthropology*, 1881, p. 414.

[8] *Ibid.*, 1881, p. 415.

[9] Stannus, Dr. H., *Jour. Roy. Anthrop. Inst.*, 1910, vol. 40, p. 235.

[10] Westermarck, E., *The Origin and Development of Moral Ideas*, 1906, ch. XV.

[11] Davie, Professor M., *The Evolution of War*, 1929, p. 214.

[12] Numbers, XXXV, 29.

[13] Genesis, IX, 5, 6.

[14] Exodus, XXI, 24.

[15] Deuteronomy, V, 9.

[16] Proverbs, VI, 34.

[17] Durham, Miss M. E., *Jour. Roy. Anthrop. Inst.*, 1910, vol. 40, p. 465.

[18] See under reference 11, p. 126.

[19] Thomson, George, *Aeschylus and Athens*, 1941.

[20] Browne, James, *A History of the Highlands and of the Highland Clans*, 1852, vol. 1, p. 99.

[21] Carr-Saunders, Sir A. M., *The Population Problem: A Study in Human Evolution*, 1922, p. 194.

[22] Chinnery, E. W. P., *Jour. Roy. Anthrop. Inst.*, 1919, vol. 49, p. 36.

[23] Pitt-Rivers, G. H. Lane Fox, *The Clash of Culture and the Contact of Races*, 1927, p. 43.

[24] Haddon, A. C., *Head Hunters*, 1932, p. 215.

[25] Stark, Freya, *The Times*, 25.11.38.

[26] Fry, Dr. H. K., *The Medical Jour. of Australia*, 23.3.35.

[27] Lowie, Dr. Robert, *The Crow Indians*, 1935.

[28] Hobbes, Thomas, *Leviathan*, pt. 1, ch. XV (p. 79 of Everyman ed.).

[29] *Ibid.*, pt. 2, ch. XXXVII (p. 159 of Everyman ed.).

[30] Hume, David, *Essays and Treatises*, 1772, vol. 2, p. 284.

THE SEARCH FOR STATUS AS A FACTOR IN HUMAN EVOLUTION

Synopsis.—Assumptions made regarding desire for status by primitive man. Ambition is a drive for superiority. Desire for status among animals, particularly among Primates. The urge for status is accompanied by resentment, emulation, jealousy, and competition. The use of force as a means of obtaining status. In human societies the search for status has become widened and deepened. Those who aspire to status in primal societies must observe the dual code. The desire for status develops in childhood and in early manhood, and has an inborn basis. The desire for status promotes the welfare of the group as well as the advancement of the individual. Groups, tribes, and nations are extravagant in their claims for status. The search for power. The role of status in bringing about evolutionary changes. Ambition as a factor. The claims for status are tried and sanctioned at the bar of public opinion. Ordination as an organizing factor. With the coming of civilization, individuals were released from group control and were free to compete against each other for status. Man desires a status outside the animal kingdom.

AT what stage in his exodus from a simian to a human state man began to give names to living and to dead things, we do not know, but I am to assume that in the primal groups of humanity, whose evolution has been discussed in the preceding essays, each individual of a group had a name, and so had each group. I am also to make the further assumption, on grounds to be brought forward in this essay, that each individual of a group was keenly conscious of the place or status he held in his group, and that each group strove for a high place in the rank of groups. My main purpose is to show that this human urge for betterment in place and in rank, on the part of individuals and of groups, is a chief force in keeping the wheels of evolution turning; indeed, there is but one stronger force, the urge for life itself.

We may also assume that in the primal world, as in the present, the strength of the desire for status varied from one individual to another, and from group to group; there were areas where the desire was strong, and others where it was weak. We may be certain those groups in which ambitious men abounded were contentious and competitive in their drive for superiority. Here again, then, we find an element of human nature—the desire for status—serving as a factor in human evolution.

A consciousness of status is not confined to human circles; it is found in all social communities of the higher animals, particularly in the order to which man belongs—the Primates. The Scottish philosopher Thomas Reid (1710–96) observed [1] that in " a herd of black cattle there is rank and subordination. When a stranger is introduced to the herd he must fight everyone till his rank is settled. Then he yields to the stronger and assumes authority over the weaker." My bullocks are continually butting one another to establish their place in the herd. In recent years psychologists have greatly extended our knowledge of the part played by ordination in social groups of all kinds of animals.[2] In a brood of chicks, superiority is settled by " peck-rights "; some, by their courage, pugnacity, and pertinacity, succeed in establishing an admitted dominance, but in most cases the struggle is renewed with varying fortune from time to time.[3] Dr. C. R. Carpenter [4] studied the behaviour of the American Howler monkeys (Alouatta), which were living in a state of nature in their native forest; there were eighteen animals in the group. He observed that each had its rank and place in the group, determined by repeated contest—sex and age being dominant factors. The monkeys of the Old World, especially baboons and macacques, are infinitely more unmannerly and brutal in their fight for status than the gentler monkeys of the New World. The rhesus macacque, for example, seeks to intimidate opponents by means which are " ruthless, cruel, and selfish." Dr. Carpenter also made the important observation that there was a drive for dominance by one group of rhesus monkeys over other groups, the mastery going to the group with daring male leaders.[5] Bullying is the method practised by Old-World monkeys to win rank and dominance, but the use of teeth and nails is less prominent among man's nearest congeners, the great anthropoid apes. Indeed, the orang, the least sociable of the anthropoids, is not interested in status; he is content just to be alive; he seems destitute of ambition.[6] The chimpanzee, the most social of the great anthropoids, lives in groups made up of fifteen to twenty-five individuals of all ages. "The chimpanzee," writes Dr. Yerkes,[7] "resents being laughed at, and occasionally takes revenge." His discomfiture is evident if hoaxed by being offered an inflated food-bag instead of a full one; he shows jealousy when preference is given to companions. Professor Hooton [8] describes the chimpanzee as "a rugged individualist"; he is resentful, jealous, and competitive—qualities which are useful in the search for reputation. The young play at wrestling and fighting, preparatory to the real struggle for rank which is in full swing in groups made up of animals varying from four to six years. In chimpanzee society the male is dominant. In the animals most nearly related to man we find self-consciousness, self-respect, with a desire to be esteemed or valued, in a more or less rudimentary form, whereas we must assume that humanity, even in its pre-human stage, had all these qualities greatly strengthened and, as accessories, a powerful artillery made up of those qualities, such as the spirit of emulation, jealousy, and competition, which vindicate the claims of personal vanity for recognition.

Even among chimpanzees, the most social of anthropoids, rank and reputation are established by the use of physical force. Dr. Yerkes,[9] after noting that the chimpanzee begins its search for dominance in childhood, sums up his prolonged study of this animal by saying that the demand for "priority of rights is almost the major factor in the life of the mature animal" and constitutes a mode of behaviour which "ensures individual effectiveness." Now, it must be admitted that the simian mode of establishing superiority by the use of physical force still prevails in human societies, both civilized and uncivilized. Schoolboys and grown men still resort to fisticuffs to settle "priority of rights." Personal honour, when duels were in fashion, was vindicated by a resort to lethal weapons. In recent years we have seen minor political parties in Russia, Italy, and Germany establish dominance by a systematic exploitation of the brutal methods of physical force. Independent groups, tribes, and nations still use force, in the form of war, as a means to status.

No doubt, the methods of physical force were employed in primal groups of human society, both to settle individual rank within a group and to establish superiority of one group over another.

In a human society, in comparison with one which is simian, the quest for status has entered an altogether new and extended sphere of influence. This has been brought about, first, by the establishment of a bar of group or public opinion, at which questions of individual status are being judged and noted day by day; conduct is being observed; memory has become armed with words. Secondly, within a human society the " code of enmity," so rampantly practised between the individuals of a simian group, is largely suppressed, its place being taken by the " code of amity." The member of a group who would win the good opinion of his fellows must observe and practise the code of amity. In this way a human society is strengthened both morally and physically. The third important difference between a human and a simian society lies in the fact that the antagonism of one simian society to another is passive rather than active, whereas between human societies the opposite is the case— antagonism, obeying the code of enmity, practises warlike deeds. At the bar of group opinion such warlike deeds are judged as honourable. Hence the ideal member of a primitive human group is the thorough-paced dual-codist—the man who wins a reputation for being a lamb at home and a lion abroad.

Some light is thrown on the origin and nature of the human desire for status if we note its manifestations within a family circle. Every child, born in normal circumstances, has to face the bar of family opinion. In a family there is an ordered series of dominance, beginning with the father and descending to the last born. Only by accepting this order can there be peace within a family, yet most children, from the end of their third year onwards, strive to modify family opinion in favour of their own self-importance, by boasts, feats, lies, deceits, and other modes of extravagant behaviour. Blushing and shyness begin to appear in children before the end of their fourth year; [10] both manifestations are evidence that a sense of self-importance, an instinctive desire for status, is awake within them. Seeing the early age at which blushing and shyness appear and the impossibility of acquiring the power to blush by any form of

G

voluntary effort, we must conclude that the desire for individual status is instinctive or inborn. But the forms which this instinctive desire will take depend entirely on the culture, customs, and tradition which a child absorbs from its group. Further, the quest for status is closely linked with sexual life, for it is when the young reach sexual maturity that they become super-sensitive of personal appearance and of criticism, and become emulative, envious, jealous, and competitive.

In this essay I am concerned, not with the psychology of status, but with the part which it plays in securing the welfare and survival of individuals and of groups of primitive humanity. In such primitive societies the search for individual recognition is usually attended by advantage to the group as a whole. This was realized by Hume in the following passage :—

> " Self-love is a principle in human nature of such extensive energy, and the interest of each individual is, in general, so closely connected with that of the community, that those philosophers were excusable, who fancied that all our concern for the public might be resolved into a concern for our own happiness and preservation." [11]

In the pursuit of self-interest a man hopes to establish his standing and reputation in his group. His behaviour and his deeds come up for review at the bar of group opinion; if his action relates to the " home affairs " of the group and conforms to the code of amity, then it is commended and his status is advanced; if a flagrant breach of that code, then he loses status by being disgraced. If his words or actions relate to the " foreign affairs " of the group, then, if they conform to the code of enmity, they are commended and he may be regarded as a hero; if not, then he may find himself treated as a traitor. The co-ordination of a tribesman's care for his own reputation with that of his concern for the name of his tribe is closer and more automatic than has been suggested in the sentences just written.

The tribesman who works to exalt the name and fame of his tribe is rewarded by an advance of his own name and fame. The same bias which makes him exaggerate his own worth, and so gives confidence in himself, leads him to magnify the importance and power of his tribe; pride in self has its counterpart in pride of tribe or patriotism. He is sensitive to criticism of self, and still more to any reflection cast on his tribe. The bias which causes him to lavish praise on his own tribe when turned on an enemy leads him to pour scorn and contempt on all neighbouring and rival tribes. In these, and in many other ways, the search for status, both for the individual and for the group, was, and is, woven into the texture of tribal life, giving zest and urge to activities of individuals and of groups.

The Australian aborigine is vain and fond of praise; [12] with him, precedence counts for much; [13] each tribe claims pre-eminence over all the others. Primitive peoples speak of themselves as being " the people "; the Hottentots, for example, call themselves by a name which means " the men of men " [14] or the " real men," [15] and many similar instances might be cited.[16] The Somalis in Kenya refused to pay taxes unless they were given the status of Asiatics.[17] The children of Israel regarded themselves as " the chosen people "; when their name and fame reached the kings of Canaan " their hearts melted, neither was there spirit in them any more, because of the children of Israel "—an illustration of the power which status can give to a people. The Arabs regard themselves as the noblest nation; all others being barbarians—a self-estimate very similar to that made by the ancient Greeks. A Chinese minister of education exclaimed, " How grand and glorious is the Empire of China, mother of the grandest men in the world." [18] Emerson ascribed " a sense of superiority " to the people of England, a trait in which his own people of the United States are not now lacking. The late Lord Curzon, in 1931, declared that the British Empire was " the greatest instrument for good the world had ever seen," while Joseph Chamberlain held the opinion that " the Anglo-Saxon was to be the predominant race in the history of civilization." [19]

A belief in future greatness is said to be a source of strength to a people. A search for power is the devouring desire of nations as well as of individual men; status, as given by power, is now measured by the number of army divisions a people can muster in the day of battle, but in the springtime of man's evolution the power or status of a group was measured by its manhood. When we note the early age at which the quest for status begins in human life, its innate character, its universal prevalence among all living peoples, civilized and uncivilized, can we doubt its presence and its activity among the primal groups of humanity? The search for power, we may assume, determined the destiny of ancient groups just as it now determines the destiny of nations.

At this present time most philosophers assume that the aim of existence is to permit every child born into the world to develop to the full its inborn qualities amid the circumstances provided by the society into which it is born. We may say the same of human groups; they exist in order to develop their collective qualities as teams amid the circumstances of their time. Now, it has been observed that whenever matters relating to the life or to the welfare of individuals or groups come up for decision human passions are aroused—passions which are felt as being painful. Vital matters refer to the destiny of individuals or of groups, and have therefore an evolutionary significance. The pursuit of status leaves a trail of passion in its wake, as indeed competitions of all kinds are apt to do. Ambition is at the root of man's wish to excel; emulation, jealousy, envy, and covetousness are its attendant furies. "Emulation," wrote Hobbes, "is an endeavour to enforce our ability in competition," while envy is "competition with ill intent." The same author defines ambition as "desire of office or precedent," and notes that it gives rise to the same ill-feeling as covetousness.[20] All these qualities were regarded by the Scottish philosopher Reid [21] as "given by our maker for good ends"; the desire to excel, he regarded as "the god within us." The impulse to compete is strongest in the ambitious, but even in the least ambitious child there is some desire to find a recognized place among its fellows. Seeing how firmly the desire for status is implanted in human nature, and how competitive that nature is, we are justified in ascribing these qualities to primitive humanity, and in saying that in their operation they produced the same kind of results as are seen in modern societies. We may assume that in the ranks of primal groups individuals pursued their quest for reputation and precedence, and that when members of the group met for gossip we may be sure that their favourite topic was a comparison of the merits and demerits of their fellow men and women. In this way was group opinion kept alive, and in such a way were the men and women chosen to guide the destiny of their group. Nor can we doubt that the antagonism and rivalry between the groups of primal humanity were less adamant than those which prevail between groups or nations in the modern world. Nor should we doubt that inter-group rivalries became so acute from time to time that physical force was used to enforce status, leading to brawls—the incipient forms of war. In such ways, so I assume, the search for status in man's primal world determined the destinies of individuals and of groups.

There is another important service which the search for status renders to groups of primitive humanity; it helps to knit the members of a group into an organized unit. Let me illustrate its manner of working by citing a description which W. H. Hudson gave of the organization of a pack of semi-wild dogs :—

> " But from the foremost in strength and power down to the weakest there is a gradation of authority; each one knows just how far he can go, which companion he can bully when in a bad temper or wishing to assert himself, and to which he must humbly yield in his turn." [22]

In a group of human beings, who have to spend their lives as members of the same small society, the search for status leads to the establishment of the relative authority of each individual, and thus knits the society into an organic whole. I do not know of anyone who has made a census of a tribe to discover the distribution of self-assertiveness among its members, but if it were made, I should expect to find a normal curve of distribution—the self-assertives falling to one end of the curve, the " deferentials " or " submissives " to the other end, while the great central area would be filled by those in whom both of these qualities are present in varying degrees. The process of ordination—that is, the search for status—combines these holders of diverse qualities into a workable society.

So far I have been discussing man's desire for status as seen in primitive groups, in which there is no division into class or caste, all being parts of one texture. With the coming of civilization and the detribalization of peoples, individuals became freed from group control, and were thus at liberty to indulge their desire for status to a degree unknown in the primal world. Social conditions in the civilized or post-primal world are well illustrated by the following quotation from the *Wealth of Nations* :—

> " The principle which prompts us to save, is the desire of betterment of our condition, a desire which, though calm and

dispassionate, comes with us from the womb and never leaves us until we go into the grave." [23]

This desire for betterment, aided by the accumulation of wealth and the greater freedom of the individual, led to the stratification of modern populations into classes. Man's desires always turn him towards the class above him and away from the class below him. He is pleased when ranked above his claim, upset when placed below it. The castes of India are of the nature of tribalities; like tribes, they struggle for status, treasure it, and are proud of it.

I have said nothing of the dignity of man, nor of family pride, nor of high birth, although all of them have a place in the search for status. No doubt if men were free to choose they would claim descent from beings which were ranked above them. The ancient Greeks gave their heroes a divine paternity. The people of Japan assigned a divine origin to their emperor. If mankind were guided purely by feeling, it would infinitely prefer the Mosaic narrative of man's creation to Darwin's account of his evolution. Many souls shrink when they think of the number of purely animal functions which are at work in their bodies; they seek to forget such things or to hide them. Nor is this aversion to animality merely a prejudice of the civilized mind; a native will reprove his fellow by comparing his manners to those of a beast. I do not seek to explain this widely spread aversion on the part of men to be classed as an animal; my reason for mentioning it now is that I believe it weighs with some anthropologists when they set out to trace man's evolutionary history. They give him a line of descent which frees it from all entanglements with the lines which lead to anthropoid apes and to monkeys.

REFERENCES

[1] Reid, Thomas, *Essays on the Active Powers of Man*, 1788, Essay 3, ch. 2, p. 175.

[2] Allee, W. C., *Social Life of Animals*, 1939, ch. VI.

[3] *Ibid.*

[4] Carpenter, C. R., *Trans. N.Y. Acad. Sc.* 1942, ser. 2, vol. 4, p. 248.

[5] *Ibid.*, p. 255.

[6] Yerkes, Robert and Ada, *The Great Apes*, 1929, p. 151.

[7] *Ibid.*, p. 292.

[8] Hooton, E. A., *Man's Poor Relations*, 1942, p. 17.

[9] Yerkes, Robert, *Chimpanzees : A Laboratory Colony*, 1943.

[10] Darwin, Charles, *The Expression of the Emotions in Man and Animals*, 2nd ed., 1890, pp. 337, 445.

[11] Hume, David, *Essays and Treatises*, 1772, vol. 2, p. 283.

[12] Westermarck, Ed., *The Origin and Development of Moral Ideas*, 1906, vol. 2, ch. XXXII.

[13] Spencer and Gillen, *Across Australia*, 1912, vol. 1, p. 388.

[14] Westermarck, Ed., see under reference 12, ch. XXXIII.

[15] Smith, E. W., *Jour. Roy. Anthrop. Inst.*, 1935, vol. 65, p. 1.

[16] Davie, M., *The Evolution of War*, 1929, p. 22, and Appendix A.   See also Westermarck, under reference 12, chs. XXXII–XXXIII.

[17] *The Times*, August 13, 1932.

[18] Sumner, W. G., *Folkways*, 1906, p. 14.

[19] *Nationalism : Report of a Study-Group*, 1939, pp. 187, 188.

[20] Hobbes, Thos., *Leviathan*, pt. 1, ch. II.

[21] Reid, Thos.   See under reference 1, Essay 3, pt. 2, ch. IV.

[22] Hudson, W. H., quoted by Dr. Carveth Read, *The Origin of Man*, 1920, p. 45.

[23] Smith, Adam, *The Wealth of Nations*, bk. 2, ch. II.

HUMAN NATURE AS AN INSTRUMENT OF GOVERNMENT

Synopsis.—Primitive humanity has no apparent government. Animal societies are governed by instinct; groups of primitive humanity are governed by human nature, the elements of which are the progeny of instincts. The final aim of group government. To be governed, a people must first be delimited. A group must be held together by social and other bonds. How human nature serves in the protection of a group. The role of fear. The protective machinery also preserves the independence of a group. The significance of independence. The elements of human nature which secure the reproduction and continuation of a group. The group is a " cradle " for the young and has to be protected. The part played by tradition in the government of a group. Tradition is ultimately a product of human nature. The group as a school for the teaching of tradition and custom to the young. How human nature deals out rewards and punishments and compels observance of its ordinances. The duality of man's mentality, a necessity for group evolution. Group behaviour is regulated by the dual code. The form of behaviour implied by clannishness and party spirit is based on the practice of the dual code.

AFTER visiting the natives of Tierra del Fuego in 1832, Darwin reported that " the different tribes have no government or chief; yet each is surrounded by other hostile tribes." [1] If he had made a journey into the remote past of the primal world and examined groups of early humanity, his report would have been drafted in the same terms; no ostensible means of government were to be observed; no proclaimed law, no magistrates, no policemen, no administrators. Yet we must assume that in the early groups of humanity, just as among the Fuegians, a rough sort of order was maintained within each group, otherwise groups would have fallen to pieces. " Look closely enough," wrote Sir

94

Edward Tylor, " and you will find rudiments of government in primitive groups." [2] That is true; the main purpose of this essay is to expound the thesis that a primitive group of humanity is governed by the action and reaction of those inborn mental qualities which are known collectively as " human nature." Nay, my thesis is somewhat more ambitious than I have stated, for I am persuaded that human nature not only supplies the means of group government, but that it has been so evolved as to govern the evolutionary destiny of human groups. What do I mean by " evolutionary destiny "? It is a trite saying that the object of a man's existence is to develop all the potentialities and latent powers that are within him. The student of evolution seeks to explain the existence of a primitive group of humanity in a parallel manner; its chief end is to bring to light the hidden potentialities of its germ-plasm. To do that the group must remain intact and separate, not for one generation, but for an infinity of generations. Human nature is constituted so as to control and regulate the affairs of a group, not only for a generation, but so as to secure its perpetuation over an infinity of generations. In brief, I am to maintain that politics—the art of regulating and controlling the conduct of a community—is part of the machinery of evolution.

Government can be applied only to a community which is sharply delimited from surrounding communities. For purposes of administration modern governments find it necessary to divide their territories into small units, known as parishes, and larger, known as counties. " Tribal law," wrote Bagehot, " could work only on an isolated group." [3] In Essays V and VI we have seen how human nature works to maintain group isolation : first, by the individuals of a group being conscious of membership being restricted to their own group; secondly, by limiting their active sympathy to fellow members; thirdly, by an aversion to all who are not members of their group; fourthly, by a deeply rooted prejudice (patriotism) in favour of their own group and of the territory on which it lives. In such ways does human nature work to secure the condition of isolation which makes the self-government of a group possible.

There are certain other conditions which must be complied with to make a group capable of self-government. Its members must be bound together by bonds of mutual affection and of understanding; they must be known to each other; they must have confidence in each other; they must have those qualities which incline them to mutual service and co-operation. Under the domination of a quest for status (see preceding essay), each member of a group has established a relation with every other member; each has learned how far he may command, and how far he must obey. In assuming that all these conditions were present within the groups of humanity of the primal world, I am fortified by an observation made by Darwin on animal societies while he was still a naturalist on board the *Beagle*. " As we see those animals whose instinct compels them to live in society and obey a chief, are most capable of improvement, so it is with the races of mankind." [4] If discipline and obedience had been instituted in animal societies under the sway of instinct, we need not hesitate in believing that under the rule of human nature, which is the progeny of instinct, they were also present in human groups of primal times.

The safety of the people is regarded by all statesmen as the supreme law; everything must be sacrificed to secure that end. How, then, was the supreme law upheld in a primitive tribe? The machinery of protection was supplied by certain elements imbedded in man's mental nature, but before naming these, and specifying their mode of action, it will be advantageous to recall an important principle which we shall now see in action. The principle involved is that which compels a tribesman to sink his individuality in that of his tribe; so strong is this principle that, in certain circumstances, there is a complete surrender of self for the good of the tribe. Take the strongest of man's prepossessions —the instinct for self-preservation; so strong is the principle of transference that a man, to preserve the life of his group or tribe, will overcome his own most powerful instinct—that of self-preservation—and give his life. Mental qualities which serve for the protection of the individual, such as fear, alarm, anxiety, care, concern, and suspicion, are transferred by the individual to the group and are used for the protection and preservation of the group.

Fear is the agent which stirs the other elements of human nature into action. Fear sharpens eyes and ears into vigilance. " One hardly ever finds a New Zealander off his guard, either by night or by day "; so wrote Captain Cook of the Maoris of his time.[5] Fear serves as an alarm for all social animals, but in man, owing to the high development of his mental qualities, it becomes manifest in a myriad of forms. It may be a mere uneasiness, a suspicion, an anxiety, or it may reach a degree of extreme terror. Fear prepares the way for protection. When danger comes close to the group, alarm passes from mouth to mouth; a feeling of indignation sweeps the group, giving it the comforting feeling of unity of resolution and unity of action. When danger materializes in a threat to the life and integrity of the group, when an injury is inflicted, then the passion of resentment is aroused, a passion which demands reprisal. Anger mobilizes the physical forces of the body and places them at the service of the passion of resentment. Fighting powers, which serve primarily for the defence of the individual, are called forth collectively for the defence of the group. These forces, used for defence and offence, may be under the command of blind, aimless rage, or they may be braced by that strong, resolute, and deliberate form of will known as courage. Such, then, is the manner in which human nature has been organized for group defence. Man is not singular in having his mentality organized for group defence; a corresponding organization is present in all communities of social animals.

Of the dangers which lead to the mental mobilization of a group's defensive powers, there is one of which I have made no mention—namely, a threat to its independence. Now, we say a group is independent when it recognizes no higher authority, but is free to work out its own destiny—that is, its own evolution—under its own government, which, in the case of primitive groups, is the government of the ruling powers resident in human nature. I do not suppose that a primitive group ever made independence the conscious object of its struggle; it fought to maintain its integrity and its separateness from all neighbouring groups, and in so doing secured its independence.

There is a second and very important department of group government which remained, and still remains, almost entirely under the rule of human nature. This is the department which has to do with the reproduction and continuation of the group. A living group is but a link between a dead ancestry and an unborn progeny. It is a government's business to carry out "a partnership, not only between those living, those who are dead, and those who are to be born." [6] The replacement of the existing group is secured by the "imperial passion," the impulse which compels young men and women to "fall in love," to mate, to desire children, and to rear them. "Sex-love," as Thomas Reid has remarked,[7] "has effectually secured these objectives in all ages and in every state of society." The care and upbringing of children has been safeguarded by one of the strongest of inborn emotions—that of maternal love. Maternal care is supplemented by the inborn partiality a father has for his own children. So omnipotent are the parental impulses that they may be said to enslave mothers and fathers for the best part of their lives in the service of their children. Child-rearing may be regarded as the chief industry of every social community; if this industry fails in a group, then that group passes out of existence. The process of evolution permits no balking of the reproductive instincts; the infertile groups are rigorously eliminated, and the fertile perpetuated. The parental duties which prevail among human beings are particularly onerous, owing to the prolonged period during which children must be cared for and fed. Just for that reason human parental impulses have a compelling potency.

A group of primitive humanity may be regarded as a cradle for the young; the cradle is filled by the working of those elements of human nature just specified. The sole duty of group government is to protect the cradle; to this duty a group is always on the alert. Nothing rallies the fighting spirit of a human group with such impetuosity as a threat to its women and children—to its cradle. The duty of protecting the young by a parent or parents is a very ancient ordinance of Nature, but in the human kind this ordinance is carried out by the whole parental group. The cradle is also safeguarded by group opinion, which regards every act that legitimately fills the cradle as good, and therefore a virtue, while every form of conduct which tends to make the cradle empty as bad, and therefore a vice. There is, too, in human nature a desire for perpetuation of name, of family, and of group—an accessory aid to reproduction. In all these ways human nature presides over the reproduction and continuation of a human community.

So far I have been discussing the part taken by the various elements of human nature in governing the affairs of a group of primitive humanity. I am now to turn to the problem of how, within each primitive group, experience became treasured, handed on from generation to generation as an oral tradition, and how this tradition became accepted by the group as an embodiment of its law. I have at this moment a herd of ten bullocks, which, although they met in my fields as strangers, have in the course of a few months organized themselves into a self-governing community. Their organization is entirely the result of the interaction of their inborn mentalities; no ancestral herd taught them how to behave, nor will they 'in turn' hand on their experience to the herd which will succeed them. It was quite otherwise with groups of early humanity; each group was reared under the tuition of an ancestral group; and each in turn handed on its beliefs, its rules of conduct, and its experience to the succeeding generation. I am making the assumption that the primitive men and women with whom I am dealing had reached that point of cerebral development which made it possible for them to make their feelings, their needs, their loves and hates known to each other by means of articulate sounds. Further, I am assuming that the memories of these early men and women had become sufficiently strengthened to serve, not only as treasuries of their own experience, but also to carry all kinds of lore gleaned from the generation in which these men and women grew up. Amid that lore were the proper modes of conduct, habits, customs, and the right attitude to be assumed towards all the forces of Nature by which the group was surrounded; in brief, each group was the carrier of a tradition. But it was more than a mere carrier of tradition; it was a school in which that tradition was taught. Round the family hearth, children drank greedily of the words of wisdom that fell from the lips of parents and of elders. Falling on the receptive mentality of childhood, these words gave the deep impression of being final truths or convictions that had to be remembered and obeyed. Thus the young of every generation grew up with a formulated code of beliefs and convictions which was to regulate their conduct as members of their group.

"Custom is king, nay tyrant, in primitive society," declared the late R. R. Marett.[8] Sir A. M. Carr-Saunders also is of opinion that tradition governs the thought and conduct of a group;[9] if this be so the behaviour of a group is regulated, not by human nature, but by tradition. With this I am prepared to agree, but with this proviso—namely, that tradition itself is codified human nature. Tradition is experience gained under the workings of human nature; unless tradition is consonant with human nature—perhaps I ought to have written group nature—it is powerless to regulate conduct. Thus, in an ultimate sense, primitive groups of humanity were, and are, ruled by human nature.

Up to this point I have been discussing the legislative function of human nature; I now turn to the mode in which human nature enforces its policy and its enactments. Among the Trobriand Islanders, Malinowski [10] observed that conduct was regulated and law enforced by public opinion; a desire for status, love of praise, and fear of blame compelled the islanders to fulfil their contracts and to observe custom. Malinowski's islanders were scarcely primitive folk: they had gardens or plantations; they reaped the harvest of the sea; they exchanged goods by barter; whereas the primitive groups which I have in mind lived on what they could gather or on what they could kill within their nature-clad territories. "The savage," wrote Dr. Marett, "cannot stand up for a moment against an adverse public opinion; so that to rob him of his good name is to take away all that makes life worth living." [11] How is public or group opinion formed? There is nothing so greedily and constantly noted by primitive men and women as the conduct of their neighbours; wherever two or three are met together, the behaviour of the absent is appraised. A tribesman does desire to stand well with his fellows; he dreads their ill opinion. "What is customary is obligatory; a breach of custom calls forth the indignation" [12] of the group. I do not mean to suggest that primitive man was a paragon of virtue, or that his conscience was so sensitive that he could not bear to do wrong; he would not have been human had he not at times risked the gratification of an illegitimate desire if he had a chance to escape the punishment of group condemnation. Nevertheless, group opinion, with its system of rewards and punishments, served to keep order in a primitive community under ordinary circumstances. Major breaches of group law, such as murder or adultery, called forth "retributive moral emotions" [13] of such intensity that the group, assuming the black cap, as it were, inflicted on the criminal its severest penalty, that of ostracism. This, in reality, was a capital sentence, for the man cast out by his group was doomed. In such ways, then, does human nature assume the role of judge, and by enforcing the verdicts of public opinion maintains order in a group, and so serves as an instrument of government.

I have left to the end of this essay the discussion of what I consider to be the most important aspect of human nature as a governing force. I have already noted (Essay VII) that human nature has a dual constitution; it is made up of two parcels of qualities, of two codes. So far as I have gone in this essay, only one code has been discussed—the code which rules in all the "home affairs" of a group, the code of amity. The code which dominates in all "foreign affairs" of the group—the code of enmity—has not been mentioned.

Let me first give a brief enumeration of the chief elements in human nature which go to the working of the code of amity. They are love, affection, sympathy, fellow-feeling, mutual trust, faith, goodwill, mutual service, tolerance, charity, and loyalty. In the enmity or cosmic code are included the qualities which are the converse of those just enumerated—namely, dislike, hate, ill-will, distrust, suspicion, intolerance, deceit, treachery, contempt, envy, jealousy, and malice. The tribal mind is so constituted that no contradiction is felt in the use of two opposite codes of conduct, one towards friends, the other towards enemies; nay, a failure to observe the dual code would be one of the gravest breaches of group custom. The use of the dual code involves the observance of two standards of justice, one standard valid for home affairs, the other for foreign affairs.

How are we to explain the duality of uncorrupted human nature? I know of only one satisfying explanation. If we assume, as we have good reasons for doing, that human evolution has been effected by group contending or competing with group, then we can realize the advantage of a mentality which worked in the interests of a "home group" and against those of neighbour-ing groups. Such is my case for affirming that human nature has been developed, not only as an instrument of government, but also as an instrument of evolution.

Readers may well suspect that my conviction of the truth of the evolutionary process has biased the interpretation I am giving of human nature. I shall therefore cite in my support the evidence of a philosopher who thought and wrote long before Darwin was born. Here is what Hume had to say of human nature :— [14]

" It is acknowledged . . . that human nature remains still the same in its principles and operations. . . . Ambition, avarice, self-love, vanity, friendship, generosity, public spirit; these passions, mixed in various degrees, and distributed through society, have been, from the beginning of the world, and still are, the source of all actions and enterprises which have been observed among mankind. . . . Should a traveller give an account of men who were entirely divested of avarice, ambition or revenge; who knew no pleasure but friendship, generosity and public spirit, we should immediately detect the falsehood and prove him a liar with the same certitude as if he had stuffed his narration with centaurs and dragons."

Therein Hume recognizes the duality of man's mental nature and that those elements which the civilized mind counts as evil are just as essential to its constitution as those qualities which are regarded as good or virtuous. Hume, however, had no explanation to offer of this duality; that became apparent only when the light of evolution fell on it.

It is not usually recognized that the practice of the dual code gives rise to that form of behaviour known as "clannishness" or " party spirit." Clannishness is the application of the code of amity to one's friends, and of the code of enmity to one's enemies. This truth has been recognized by Professor F. H. Hankins in the following statement :—

" In relation to one's own gang, whether tribe, political party, or business group, one must be loyal, honest, truthful and steadfast, charitable and helpful. In relation to the ' out-group ' one becomes meritorious in proportion as one is deceitful, treacherous, lying, vacillating, cruel and destructive." [15]

In this passage Professor Hankins is not concerned with what human nature ought to be, but only with what it has been and still is. He also recognizes that the " spirit of clannishness is both a consequence of, and an aid in, the group struggle for existence."

REFERENCES

[1] Darwin, C., *Voyage of a Naturalist*, ch. X, p. 216.
[2] Tylor, Sir E. B., *Anthropology*, 1881, ch. XVI, p. 428.

[3] Bagehot, W., *Physics and Politics*, ed. 1896, p. 212.

[4] See under ref. 1, ch. X, p. 230.

[5] Cook, Capt., *Voyages of Discovery*, 3rd voyage, Everyman ed., p. 245.

[6] Burke, Edmund, *Reflections on the French Revolution*, 1790.

[7] Reid, Thomas, *Essays on the Intellectual Powers of Man*, 1788, Essay 3, pt. 2, ch. IV.

[8] Marett, R. R. *Anthropology*, 1911, p. 183.

[9] Carr-Saunders, Sir A. M., *The Population Problem: A Study in Human Evolution*, 1922, p. 322.

[10] Malinowski, B., *Proc. Roy. Instit.*, 1925, vol. 24, p. 529. See also *Crime and Custom in Savage Society*, 1932.

[11] Marett, R. R., see under reference 8, p. 198.

[12] Westermarck, Ed., *The Origin and Development of Moral Ideas*, 1906, ch. VII.

[13] *Ibid.*, ch. I.

[14] Hume, David, *Essays and Treatises*, 1772, vol. 2, p. 96.

[15] Hankins, F. H., *Biology in Human Affairs*, edited by E. M. East, p. 42.

H

LEADERSHIP AND LOYALTY AS FACTORS IN HUMAN EVOLUTION

Synopsis.—Leadership introduced a new principle into group government. Evidence which favours the opinion that chieftainship appeared at a very early date in the government of human groups. The first requisite for leadership is that the members of a group must be born unequal in their mental outfit. There must be a just proportion of those qualified to lead to those qualified to follow. Qualities of human nature which fit a man for leadership. The qualities needed in followers. Loyalty and allegiance defined and their mode of action explained. The need for mutual confidence between followers. Leadership and loyalty give strength to a group, and have therefore an evolutionary significance. Conscience; what it is; its value as a factor in social evolution. Repentance and conversion as group phenomena. Proselytism as a factor in group life. Its conversion into missionary zeal. The dual action of conscience.

In the preceding essay I have pictured the primal groups of humanity as democracies living under the sway of "human nature," final decisions resting with the more elderly fathers of the group. This picture is based on what we know of the tribal government among Australian aborigines, but even among them we find a tendency for one man to be given, or to assume, more power than his fellows in settling the affairs of the group, a new principle of government being thus introduced—that of dictatorship or despotism. In Central Australia, Spencer and Gillen noted that there were tribes in which " men not so old, but more learned in ancient lore or more skilled in matters of magic, were looked up to by other members of the tribe, and it was they that settled everything." [1] To this I may add the testimony of Sir E. B. Tylor: " It is common," he wrote, " to find amongst rude tribes such a headman or chief chosen as the most important or shrewdest . . . who gets his way by persuasion or public opinion." [2]   He adds that " government by grandfathers breaks down in wartime." Darwin was of opinion that a primitive tribe gained an evolutionary advantage by adopting the principle of chieftainship. " The perfect equality among the individuals composing the Fuegian tribes," he wrote, " must for a long time retard their civilization. . . . The inhabitants of Otoheite, who, when first discovered, were governed by hereditary kings, had arrived at a far higher grade then another branch of the same people—the New Zealanders, who were republicans in the most absolute sense." [3]   One may hesitate to describe the Maori form of tribal government as republican, but there can be no doubt as to the great power wielded by their tribal chiefs. Writing of Melanesia, Keane has this: " Chiefs exist everywhere, being endowed with religious sanctity in Fiji, where they are regarded as the direct descendants of the tribal ancestors." [4]   Rivers [5] found " leadership at its highest in the Solomons and Fiji," and that the best-led tribes had the strongest hold on life. We may infer, then, that the primal groups of humanity which adopted the principle of leadership had an advantage over those which did not.

Darwin inclined to the belief that even in the earliest human groups government was of the leadership type, otherwise he would not have expressed the view that: " as man is a social animal, it is almost certain he would inherit a tendency to be faithful to his comrades and obedient to the leader of his tribe, for these qualities are common to most social animals." [6]   Darwin's opinion is supported by what we know of the group behaviour of the Primates most akin to man. Dr. Bingham,[7] who studied gorillas in their native habitat, found evidence among them of leadership and discipline, the male gorilla acting as protector of his group. Chimpanzees, which are milder and more variable in temperament than gorillas,[8] have their group affairs managed by several males rather than by one dominant animal. Every troup of baboons has its leader or leaders; [9]   so has every troup of macacques. Dr. C. R. Carpenter had an opportunity of studying macacque societies living at freedom on a small island,[10] and found that when a certain leader was withdrawn from his troup, the troup became less enterprising and its range of territory less extensive. Thus we may presume that the principle of leadership had been evolved in simian societies prior to the date of man's appearance.

There is another reason for suspecting that dominance by a leader must have been, if not the original form of group government, yet of early date. Is not every conceivable form of family rule a government by dominance? Did not most children born within an ancient group come under male dominance during the opening, impressionable years of life? If the mother remained in the home of her family, her children came under the rule of their maternal uncle; if she moved to her husband's home, then they came under the control of the father. The mental qualities which make family life possible are the basal elements of human nature. In the eyes of children the chief male of a family occupies an exalted status; he is submitted to and obeyed with feelings of which love and fear are ingredients. When a youth's sense of family membership expanded into a sense of group membership he was already prepared to obey a form of group leadership. For this reason, and also because of the evolution of leadership among mammals much lower in the scale than man, I am prepared to believe that the office of chief may have been instituted in the very oldest human societies.

I now pass to the consideration of the conditions which must exist in a group to make possible its organization and its government under a chief. The first condition is that men must be born unequal in their mental outfit. While all must be endowed with the same elements of human nature, yet in each individual these elements must be combined in a different proportion. In some there must be a strong competitive desire for position or status, an ambition to lead, to command, to have power. In the majority there must be a lesser development of the " competitive complex," a development which inclines them to accept the place which falls to them in the group rather than to seek for a higher one; content to submit, to obey, to follow, if by so doing they can come by security and ease. " Providence," said Lord Kames, " sends both leaders and followers." [11] This was also the belief of Sir Francis Galton; it was he who realized that for the welfare of a flock, of a herd, or of a human community, leader and followers must be born in the right proportion.[12] Freud bears witness to the truth of this opinion as follows : " That men are divided into leaders and led is but another manifestation of their inborn and irremediable inequality." [13] Another psychologist, Carveth Read, also held the same belief: " A pack or tribe needed enough variability to produce able leaders and enough average ability to follow and support them." [14] We must count Hobbes among the dissentients. He framed his ninth law of Nature thus: " That every man acknowledge other for his equal by Nature," and adds, " The breach of this precept is Pride." [15] Nature breaks the ninth law of Hobbes every time a child is born. Thus we reach the conclusion that for a human community to be easily governed, whether under council of elders, or under a youthful dictator, there must be a just distribution of various elements of human nature among its members. A community made up of ambitious individualists will break up because of internal discord, while one composed of self-denying, unenterprising diffidents will fall a victim to its aggressive neighbours.

What were the mental gifts which qualified a man to become a leader of his group in the primal world of mankind? I assume that they were just the same gifts as make men leaders in the modern world. Let us take some modern instance—that of Josef Stalin, who has made his way from a humble home in the Caucasus to the proud leadership of the United Soviets of Russia. Qualities which have been ascribed to him are: " Had aims and ambitions which he kept to himself but pursued them relentlessly; had plans which he revealed only when he had discovered the wishes of those around him; infinite energy for work; a genius for the management of men." [16] In brief, Stalin had ambition, self-reliance, and an intuitive knowledge of human nature. Let us now take an instance from leadership in the Church. Lord Lang, who had been Archbishop of Canterbury, lamented the death of his successor, Archbishop Temple, in these words : " He had the essentials of leadership—courage, conviction, and confidence." [17] In my opinion, convictions are of great importance; they give the mind a safe anchorage. We now turn to a modern military leader, Lord Wavell, for a confirmation : " No amount of study or learning will make a man a leader unless he has the natural qualities of one; he must have character which is a knowledge of what he wants, and courage and determination to get it." [18] Here emphasis is placed on qualities of the will, for courage and determination express the degree of command a man has over his actions. If I were asked: "Which of all these qualities is the most essential for a leader to possess?" my reply would be: "An intuitive knowledge of human nature." In this I have the support of the philosopher Hobbes, who wrote: "He that is to govern a whole nation must read, not this or that particular man, but mankind." [19] This was also the opinion of Edmund Burke, who held that the first requisite in a statesman is "to know how to manage human nature." [20] Thus I come back to my thesis—namely, that human nature constituted the machinery of government of early groups of mankind, whether rule was centred in a single leader or in a council of elders.

The qualities just reviewed are those of modern leaders; no mention has been made of other qualities which must have been of prime importance in primitive communities. The man who faced dangers with a stout heart and a strong right arm, who defended the group from attacks by man or beast, must have occupied the highest place in public esteem. We may be sure, too, that members of a group responded to the man who, while slaking his thirst for place and fame, worked for the welfare of his group. We may also hazard the opinion that in those early times there were men who carried themselves so that they had only to knock to have the door of leadership thrown open to them, while others had to break down the door by force before they attained their ambition.

I am seeking to build up a picture of the mentality which kept groups of ancient humanity alive and assured their continuance. I have reviewed the qualities which went to the making of leaders; I must now turn to the qualities which go to the making of followers. The most reliable source of information at our disposal is that to be found in family life. Which are the elements in human nature that make children cling to their mother's skirts and dog her footsteps? There is, in the first place, a positive force —the mutual bond of affection or love; in the second place, there is a negative element—that of fear, fear of being separated from the security which the mother's presence gives. We get nearer to the relation of led to leader if we consider the mental attitude which a boy adopts towards his father. Here, too, fear and love are combined, but fear in this case arises not from an apprehension of separation, but from a realization of the power which lies behind a father's command. The father imposes obedience and discipline; his power gives him the means of bringing the recalcitrant under his rule. Between a father and his children there grows up a particular emotional relationship, one which makes his children into his devoted followers. In the eyes of children the father becomes no ordinary man; feelings—prejudices—arise within them which magnify him above all other fathers; he becomes their lawgiver, their pride, and their boast; they regard him with respect, esteem, admiration, even reverence. With this training in the family circle, the youthful tribesman, when he passes into the public life of his group, has already in him the seeds of allegiance to his group and of loyalty to his leader.

Let us consider loyalty first. I use it as a term to designate the feeling which exists between a follower and his leader. This feeling is a mixture of admiration and devotion on the part of the follower, who submits his will to that of the leader, and resolves to follow wherever he may be lead. Loyalty implies more than mere submission; when accompanied by the fervour of enthusiasm, as it often is, it means a complete surrender of self. Admiration may pass into worship, and worship can encircle the head of the leader with the halo of divinity.

Allegiance is of the same mental quality as loyalty—with this difference. It is based on a man's consciousness of being a member of his group, and carries with it a sense of duty towards his group. With the coming of leadership, be it in the form of a chief, of a totem, or of a god, the obligation of allegiance passed into the more intense feeling or emotion we name loyalty. Allegiance was defined by David Hume as " an obligation of obedience " and loyalty as " the feeling towards a ruler." [21]

We have been discussing the mental bonds which link followers to a leader; just as important are those which serve to unite one follower with another. The chief bond between tribesmen is that known as mutual confidence or mutual trust—a bond which permits a man to rely on his fellows for instant co-operation and support in all circumstances. Confidence is of the nature of a conviction—that is, a belief which, being reinforced by an inborn mental predisposition, gives the mind the certainty that a final truth has been reached. To the good tribesman faith or confidence comes in two forms. He must have confidence in himself; he must be self-reliant; he must have faith or confidence in his fellows. The feeling on which the conviction of trust is based is that of brotherhood; there must be brotherly affection between men before the bond of trust can arise between them. According to Thucydides " the most fierce are the most trusty." [22]

Darwin recognized that the group in which leadership and loyalty were strongly developed had an advantage in the contest with other groups. He inferred that a tribe which " included a great number of courageous, sympathetic, and faithful members " would be a victor over one less fortunately situated.[23] Bagehot [24] was of opinion that a " tribe is maintained by loyalty, fealty, authority, bigotry, and observance of custom." Winwood Reade's judgment on clan loyalty merits special consideration because it was based on personal observation of tribal life :—

> " This feeling of fidelity to the clan . . . was based in their hearts; it was a true instinct inherited from animal and ancient days; it was with them an idea of duty, obedience to which was prompted by an impulse, neglect of which was punished by remorse. . . . They have no conscience outside their clan. . . . Within their own communion they live according to the golden rule and would be destroyed by their enemies if they did not." [25]

Thus, in emphasizing the importance of leadership and loyalty as factors in human evolution, I can claim the support of high authority.

What part did conscience play in the group life of early men? I shall try to answer this question by considering the relationship of conscience to loyalty. Loyalty I have defined as an exalted feeling which places the will of a follower at the disposal of a leader. In the passage just cited from Winwood Reade, fidelity or loyalty is described as a " true instinct "; if this were really so the loyal follower would have no choice; uncompromising instinct would secure instant obedience. The better opinion is that, with the expansion of the human brain, all the original social instincts became unloosened and converted into mental propensities or inclinations, so that man could obey them or refuse to obey. Let us suppose that the follower, at the moment when a command from his chief tells him to repair to a certain rendezvous, is engaged on a task of private interest; nevertheless, yielding to his feeling of loyalty, he answers the call, and is rewarded by the gratification of this feeling or sense of duty. But suppose the tribesman yields to his private interest and denies his leader; then his feeling or sense of loyalty is left unsatisfied, and he is punished by being stricken with discomfort or even pain. That feeling of discomfort which follows failure to obey a social impulse is conscience. A tribesman's duties to himself may be safely left in his own hands, but those social duties he owes to his leader and to his fellows, when the bonds of instinct were unloosened, had to be safeguarded and reinforced in the manner just described—by the action of conscience. A tribesman has to satisfy much more than his social impulses; in his childhood he drinks in the oral traditions of his group, its customs, its beliefs, its taboos, and its attitude towards the natural and supernatural. The learning so acquired sinks into the childish mind as final truths, as convictions. Now convictions have the force of instincts; they are safeguarded by conscience; to disobey them gives rise to a painful uneasiness. There could have been no order or government of a primitive human group unless conscience had been at work within it. A group of conscienceless men and women could not endure for even a day. Conscience, then, is part of the evolutionary machinery of social government.

There is one mental state which I have found difficult to fit into my scheme of group evolution—namely, that of individual conversion. Let us take the case of St. Peter. In denying his Lord, he did his sense of loyalty so grave injury that he was left in the state of extreme regret known as repentance. Repentance gives rise to an intensely submissive state of feeling known as conversion. Now conversion implies a complete yielding up of self to the will of a leader, with a resolve never again to harbour a rebellious thought, but to obey him implicitly for ever afterwards. In ancient groups of humanity there must have been men and women who failed in their social duties and suffered from the pangs of conscience. How could they be restored to the ranks of the faithful unless breach of conscience was followed by repentance and conversion? It is in such a way I would seek to fit the phenomena of repentance and conversion into a scheme of evolution.

Besides conscience there is another constituent of human nature which at first sight seems to lie outside any scheme of group evolution—namely, the desire or urge which we find in many men

to convert others to their way of thinking—in brief, to proselytize.
To get unity of action in a primitive group, there must be unity
of conviction. We can understand the utility of aggressive
proselytizers in a primitive community; their efforts would work
towards unity of opinion and of action in their own group.
But how are we to explain the annual exodus of thousands of
enthusiasts from civilized communities, prepared to sacrifice
comfort and life in order that the heathen may be saved? The
evolution of missionary zeal I seek to explain in the following
manner. We have seen (p. 71) that man's social consciousness
has an expanding tendency; consciousness of membership of
family spreads until it becomes group conscious. With the
union of groups to form tribes, and of tribes to form nations,
consciousness of membership expands until tribe and nation are
embraced. It is but a step farther for all mankind to be included
within a common brotherhood. As consciousness of membership expanded, so did the urge to proselytize. It is in this way I
seek to explain the evolution of missionary zeal.

There is one important aspect of conscience of which I have
made no mention—namely, its duality. Human nature has a dual
constitution; to hate as well as to love are parts of it; conscience
may enforce hate as a duty just as it may enforce the duty of love.
For example, conscience has a twofold role in a soldier : it is his
duty to save and protect his own people and equally his duty to
destroy their enemies. Let us take an example from group life.
A tribesman has been injured or slighted by a companion; if he
seeks to satisfy his feeling of resentment by retaliating in kind, he
will find the opinion of his group is against him. He therefore
seeks to slake his resentment by a return to a state of amity, a
return which is made easy if by the repentance of the offender.
But suppose the offender is of another group or tribe; then the
duty of revenge becomes imperative. Conscience, reinforced by
group opinion, will give no rest until the duty of revenge is
accomplished. Thus conscience serves both codes of group
behaviour; it gives sanction to the practices of the code of enmity
as well as to that of amity. It must have been this twofold action
of conscience which made Hume exclaim : " The heart of man is
made to reconcile contradictions." [26]

REFERENCES

[1] Quoted by Dr. R. R. Marett, *Anthropology*, p. 245.

[2] Tylor, Sir E. B., *Anthropology*, 1881, chap. XVI, p. 428.

[3] Darwin, C., *Voyage of a Naturalist*, chap. X, p. 230.

[4] Keane, A. H., *Man: Past and Present*, new ed., 1920, p. 144.

[5] Rivers, W. H. R., *The History of Melanesian Society*, 1914, vol. 2, chap. II.

[6] Darwin, C., *The Descent of Man*, Murray, 1913, p. 167.

[7] Bingham, Harold C., *Gorillas in a Native Habitat*, 1932.

[8] Hooton, E. A., *Man's Poor Relations*, 1942, p. 327.

[9] Marais, E. N., *My Friends the Baboons*, 1939, chap. IX.

[10] Carpenter, C. R., *Trans. New York Acad., Sc.*, 1942, Ser. 2, vol. 4, p. 248.

[11] Home, Henry (Lord Kames), *Sketches of the History of Man*, 1813, vol. 2, p. 50.

[12] Galton, Sir Francis, see his *Life* by Karl Pearson, vol. 2, p. 72.

[13] Einstein and Freud, *Why War?   The New Commonwealth*, 1934, p. 17.

[14] Read, Carveth, *The Origin of Man*, 1920, p. 343.

[15] Hobbes, Thos., *Leviathan*, pt. 1, chap. XV, Everyman ed., p. 80.

[16] Murphy, J. T., *Stalin*, 1945.

[17] *The Times*, October 30, 1944.

[18] *The Times*, February 17, 1941.

[19] See under ref. 15, p. 3.

[20] Burke, Edmund, see his *Life* by Lord Morley, p. 67.

[21] Hume, David, *Essays and Treatises*, 1772, vol. 2, p. 269.

[22] Livingstone, Sir R. W., *Thucydides*, 1943, p. 10.

[23] Darwin, C., see under reference 6, p. 199.

[24] Bagehot, Walter, *Physics and Politics*, ed. 1896, p. 176.

[25] Reade, Winwood, *The Martyrdom of Man*, Watts's reprint, 1934, p. 358.

[26] Hume, David, see under reference 21, vol. 1, p. 65.

MORALITY AS A FACTOR IN HUMAN EVOLUTION

Synopsis.—Statements by Darwin concerning evolution and morality. The importance of group evolution. Under morality the author includes, not only the rules which regulate the conduct of individuals, but also those which regulate the behaviour of groups. Man's dual code of morals. Instinctive control in animals became control by human nature in man. Man's morality is controlled by the elements included under the term " human nature." Human nature and therefore morality has been the subject of the eight preceding essays. If human nature has been evolved, it may still undergo change. The plasticity of human nature is discussed, and the conclusion reached is that it is among the more stable parts of man's fabric. Human nature versus tradition as a factor in moulding morality. Is a sense of justice or " fair play" acquired, or is it inborn ? Man has by nature a dual code of justice; without such duality group evolution could not take place. Individual and collective responsibility in primitive societies. With all its evils, group selection has certain great merits.

WHEN *The Descent of Man* appeared in 1871, it was reviewed by John Morley (later, Viscount Morley), who found fault with certain of its statements relating to the origin of man's moral behaviour. He was rewarded by a letter from Darwin [1] in which the following passage occurred : " I have endeavoured to show how the struggle for existence between tribe and tribe depends on an advance in the moral and intellectual qualities of the members and not merely on their capacity for obtaining food." A second letter ended with this sentence : " Undoubtedly the great principle of acting for the good of all the members of the same community, and therefore of the species, would still have sovereign sway." [2] Side by side with these two statements, let me set one taken from the text of *The Descent of Man*: " We have seen that actions are regarded by primeval man, as good or bad, solely as they obviously affect the welfare of the tribe—not that of the species, nor that of an individual member of the tribe." [3]

From these statements we learn that Darwin was of opinion that each group or tribe of primitive humanity had its own rules of social conduct; that the group which had good rules was more likely to survive than the group which had bad rules; if the rules adopted made for the welfare of the group, then they were good or virtuous; if they had an opposite effect, then they were bad or vicious. It must be obvious to my readers that these statements have a direct bearing on the problems which are being discussed in these essays. I have given my reasons for assuming that early manhood was separated into an immense number of small, independent, local groups, and that the ascent from a simian to a human state was made, not by the competition of one individual against another, but by the competition (and selection) of one human group against neighbouring human groups. Clearly, the group in which the men, women, and children behave towards one another so that there is unity of heart and singleness of purpose will outlast the group in which mutual conduct is such as to give rise to internal strife and a discordancy of aim.

So far I am a follower of Darwin, but now I come to a point where I depart from him. He restricted morality, as most philosophers still do, to the rules which regulate the behaviour of men and women living together within a single group or community, whereas I include within the bounds of morality not only conduct within a group, but the behaviour of one group towards other groups. There is an intra-group morality, and there is an inter-group morality, and of the two the latter is the more important from an evolutionary point of view. It is for this reason that I have insisted again and again in the preceding essays on the duality of man's mental nature; man is not only dual in his nature, he is also dual in his morality. His conduct within his group was regulated by one set or code of morals, while he adopted an opposite code in his behaviour towards " outside " groups. Perhaps it may be said that his " home " conduct was moral while his " outside " conduct was immoral. But we know that savage tribes look upon both these forms of conduct as moral, or right, and we may assume that early man shared in this belief.[4]

All are agreed that the behaviour of social animals is regulated by instinct, and most students of human evolution are of opinion that those inborn mental qualities or predispositions which powerfully incline men towards one line of belief and action, and turn them away from another—qualities known collectively as human nature—are the progeny or representatives of the instincts which guided man's simian ancestors. Human nature, then, having taken the place of instincts, should also take over their function—the regulation of conduct—and we find that this is so. Social animals have within their natures a Mount Sinai which issues commandments as they are required; human nature issues, not commands, but requests, and these are of varying degrees of urgency. Some are imperative, such as, " Thou shalt preserve thy life "; " Thou shalt mate "; " Thou shalt not treat thy friends as thou dost thine enemies." Here I am not speaking of ethics, which is concerned with what man's behaviour " ought " to be, but of morals, which treat of what man's conduct is and has been. Sir Leslie Stephen defined ethics as " the Science of Human Nature "; [5] it is morality rather than ethics which deserves this definition.

In seeking to base man's morality on his inborn mental nature, I have the support of many authorities. I am with Lecky when he wrote : " I shall defend those who believe that our moral feelings are an essential part of our constitution," and am still with him when he added " developed by education." [6] I am with Huxley when he penned this sentence : " In whichever way we look on the matter, morality is based on feeling, not on reason." [7] I have the support of Edward Carpenter : " The theatre of morality is in the passions; virtuous and vicious passions are eternally distinct." [8] McDougall is with me : " Liking and dislikings are the bases of morality." [9] Although the Scottish philosopher Thomas Reid was of opinion that human nature had been " created," while I believe it to have been " evolved," yet we are of the same opinion as regards its relationship to morality. " For that which makes men capable of living in society is that their actions are regulated by the common principles of human nature." [10] Reid has also my wholehearted support in the following paragraph : " There is no active principle which God hath implanted in our nature that is vicious in itself, or that ought to be eradicated, even if it were in our power. They are useful

and necessary in our present state." [11] If I can show that
"instinct" and impulse determine the conduct of human beings
massed in modern societies, then there is all the more reason for
presuming that the behaviour of prehistoric man was also so
regulated. Sumner of Yale declared that : "The great mass of
any society lives a purely instinctive life." [12] Viscount Morley
held a similar opinion. "For the common mass of men," he
wrote, "use and wont, rude or gracious symbols, blind custom,
prejudices, superstitions, are the only safeguards of the common
virtues." [13]

So far I have said nothing about an important matter which
concerns human nature. If it has been evolved and is still subject
to evolution, then it may change, and with that change there
must be a modification in man's behaviour and morality. To
solve this problem I shall call as my chief witness Dr. R. A.
Fisher.[14] "Hereditary proclivities," he affirms, "form the basis
for man's fitness for social life." Hereditary proclivities I take
to be another name for human nature. More to the point is
another of his statements : "Differences in behaviour, whether
due to conscious behaviour or to impulsive reaction, do in fact
determine differences in the rates of death and reproduction.
And behaviour is determined by the constitution of the mind."
Parents in whom the emotion of sympathy is strongly developed
are more likely to bring their children to maturity than parents
who are deficient in this emotion; children of sympathetic
parents are more likely to be sympathetic than those born of
unsympathetic parents. Bagehot gave the same idea a different
expression. "Those children," he wrote, "that gratified their
father and mother most would be most tenderly treated by them,
and so have the best chance to live." [15] Thus the group in which
sympathetic parents abounded should, other things being equal,
outlive other groups in which parents were less solicitous and
sympathetic. In the group struggle, affections are powerful
weapons. McDougall perceived the relationship of morality to
group survival when he affirmed that "the principal condition for
the evolution of moral nature lay in group selection among
primitive societies constantly at war with each other." [16]

In these essays, from the fifth onwards, I have been dealing with
human nature as manifested by groups of primitive humanity, but
until the present essay I have not mentioned morality. If I am

right in maintaining that human nature provides the basis of moral behaviour, then I have really been discussing morality all the while. In Essay V, for example, we found that primitive man limited his sympathy to his own group; that necessarily determined his actions towards those who were members of his group and those who were not members. In Essay VI we found that a man's zeal for his native group and for his native land made his behaviour that of a patriot. In Essay VII man's co-operative and competitive propensities were seen at work. In Essay VIII evidence was brought forward to show how far man's common actions were controlled by bias and prejudice. In Essay IX we saw how powerfully human conduct is influenced by the feelings of resentment and revenge. In Essay X we surveyed man as the slave of status, noting him controlling his conduct so as to win the approbation of his fellows, their respect, esteem, and love. In Essay XI an endeavour was made to estimate the extent to which man's everyday actions are influenced by his nature, while in the essay which precedes this (XII), the behaviour needed to make successful leaders and faithful followers was discussed, and we concluded with a brief dissertation on conscience to serve as a prelude to the present essay on morality. The fundamental fact that underlies all manifestations of human nature is its dual basis. It is based on two potent passions—those of love and of hate. What a man loves he will strive to preserve; what he hates he will strive to destroy. It is so now, and we may presume it was also so in man's primal period.

If it be the case that the mentality of primitive man was radically different from that of modern man, as is maintained by some authorities,[17] then what I have said of human nature would not be applicable to " grouped " humanity of the earliest times. Or if it be true that human nature is plastic and can be " altered out of all recognition," then modern mentality would be no guide to ancient mentality. These two problems, which are in reality but one, must be answered before I proceed farther in my argument. From my portfolios I could bring a cloud of witnesses in support of the plasticity theory of human nature, and only a few who are convinced of its stability. None the less I share the conviction of the minority. Let me illustrate the basis of my conviction by the use of a simile. Ancient man had a taste in foods which he satisfied as best he could by the gatherings from

Nature's table; modern man satiates his desire for food in a thousand ways his remote ancestors knew nothing of. The appetite remains the same; the change has been in the variety of ways it may be satisfied. Or take another basal desire of men— to stand well with their fellow men so as to earn distinction. The opportunities of early man lay within the narrow circle of his group; he could satisfy his ambition only by rendering it some important service; whereas modern man may seek to satisfy his ambition in thousands of ways. The basal desire remains the same; it is the modes of satisfying it that have changed. The modern lover may embroider his courtship with many a new frill, but his passion is that which moved the first of human lovers.

In the preceding eight essays I have enumerated the passions, feelings, predispositions, and desires which I attribute to early man, and have been at some pains to make plain the grounds on which I have made these attributions. I have attributed to early man the same elements of human nature as are still to be found in modern man. Without doubt, selection has been at work on human nature during past æons, strengthening some of its elements and weakening others, but my conviction is that human nature is the least plastic of the qualities which go to make up the fabric of the living human body. So long as man continues to be an intensely social animal, this is likely to remain as before.

To strengthen my case I will cite the evidence of a few expert witnesses. First, this from Sir Henry Maine: [18] "The stable part of our mental, moral, and physical constitution is the largest part of it." Second, from Sir Leslie Stephen: [19] "The great forces which govern human conduct are the same as they always have been and always will . . . a dread of hunger, thirst, cold; a love of wife, child, and friend. Sympathy with neighbours and a resentment of injuries." Third, the answer which Charles Duff has given to the question, " Does human nature change? " His answer is: " The superficial manners of men have changed considerably, but those fundamental instincts and emotions upon which human nature is based have undergone little real change." [20]

I am now to turn to the consideration of a subject which, at first sight, seems to favour the idea that human nature can be quickly and radically changed—namely, that of tradition. Each group of primitive humanity has its own tradition, which is handed on by word of mouth from generation to generation.

I

Tradition represents the accumulated experience and wisdom of a group, and is made up of several items, such as usages, customs, habits, manners, morals, and beliefs concerning events, both natural and supernatural. Such is the impressibility of the young child's mind that the teachings of tradition, as practised by parents or elders, sink home as convictions—as final truths which have to be treasured, obeyed, and, in due course, again handed on. Now, suppose a white child has been kidnapped and adopted by a native tribe of black men. The child will absorb the " black " tradition, its sense of right and wrong, its customs, and its attitude to surrounding groups.[21] Certainly the child has been given a new morality. But it has not been given a new human nature. It is just because the white child has the same human nature as the black that it has been able to absorb and obey the black child's code. It was the white child's moral food that was changed, not its moral appetite.

Marais [22] observed that baboons which had been reared in captivity starved when set free in a locality where wild animals of the same species prospered. This observation seems to imply that wild animals teach their young the art of living and that tradition has a place in monkey communities. John Hunter, the master surgeon of the eighteenth century, has recorded instances of young animals being taught by their dams.[23] Tradition, however, became potent in the living world only when the human brain had attained that degree of development which made speech possible. The brains of human beings who lived early in the Pleistocene period, say half a million years ago, have a conformation which suggests an aptitude for speech, if not its reality. The early groups of humanity, postulated in these essays, I suppose to have lived at this remote period. I have assumed that these early men were already capable of approving and of disapproving, of showing their feelings, of making their wants known, and of putting their simpler thoughts into articulate sounds. In short, I am assuming that at this early period human nature and experience were being codified in the form of tradition. The group with a tradition which inculcated " the rearing of the greatest number of individuals in full vigour and health, with all their faculties perfect " [24] should have been in a stronger position than the group with a more timid tradition. Carr-Saunders is of the opinion that in the struggle for survival tradition is more potent than inborn mental qualities. "A good tradition," he remarks, "has a winning quality." [25] Tradition is important, but I cannot conceive a people nursing and handing down a tradition that is not, or has not been, conformable to their inborn mental qualities. The early Israelites had a distinctive tradition which was inculcated with a religious zeal; [26] an equally zealous observance has carried their children successfully through two thousand years of dire vicissitudes.

The student of human evolution turns with especial interest to that part of tradition in which a group hands down its conception and its rules of justice. The most striking fact he meets with is that every known primitive group transmits two codes of justice, one code for use at home, the other for use abroad. "For that cannot be lawful," said Aristotle, "which is done not only justly, but unjustly also." Nevertheless he was well aware that Barbarians applied one rule of justice to their friends and quite another to their enemies, and in both cases deemed they had behaved justly. Socrates, asking a definition of justice from his compatriots, received two answers: "Justice is doing good to friends and evil to enemies"; "Justice is nothing else than that which is advantageous to the stronger." [27] Both answers were true, not only of the forms of justice practised in Ancient Greece, but are true of every ancient society known to us, and indeed are still true of the justice which exists between nations. Plato was in search of a single principle of justice which would serve the needs of all men at all times, but here we are concerned with only two smaller matters. When did this dual form of justice come into the world? and, why did it come?

We have already seen (Essays V, VII) that in all communities of social animals there is one rule of conduct towards members of a community and another rule for those which are not members. A dual code of justice was in existence long before man came into existence, but in his hands each code became greatly strengthened and the separation between them became more complete. And if it be asked why this most inhumane development took place, the answer is to be found in the mode of human evolution. The mode of human ascent was by means of group selection; the more a group based its code of justice for home use on love and amity, and the more sternly it applied an opposite code to opposing groups, the stronger it became in the evolutionary field. A dual code of justice finds its justification in its evolutionary utility. Bagehot makes the following cryptic remark: " Savages play the game of life with no knowledge of its rules," [28] which can be interpreted only by those who have as intimate a knowledge of human evolution as he had. The " rules " he refers to are the laws of evolution; the savage is their unconscious slave; he adopted a dual code of justice in utter ignorance of its serving any evolutionary purpose.

Moralists are agreed that no human society, ancient or modern, can hold together unless its members observe amiable rules of justice. Has man, then, an inborn sense of justice? Hume was of opinion that justice was an acquired virtue, learned and practised because of its utility.[29] I think that it is more in keeping with the evidence at our disposal to say that man is born with a strong disposition to be just to members of his own group and unjust to those who are not of that group. If we agree that man's inborn feeling of resentment is his reaction to an injustice, and that his inborn display of gratitude is evidence of a consciousness of having been treated with more than justice, then we must admit that he is born with a disposition towards justice. The inborn nature of conscience is also in favour of this view. Children manifest a desire for fair play at an early age. On the other hand, it may be urged that a child's sense of justice may be determined entirely by the tradition it inherits. In the tribal life inherited customs are obligatory (Westermarck). A child absorbs the code or codes of justice taught by its group; but is not its capacity to absorb due to its inborn disposition? Tradition determines only the food on which its disposition feeds.

There is another aspect of justice as practised by groups of primitive humanity that requires mention because of its evolutionary significance. Within a group each individual was held responsible for his words and for his actions. If a man's action rose above a group's standard of justice, it was received with the praise of his fellows; he was rewarded by being advanced in esteem and in status; thus was a desire for status yoked to the chariot of justice. If his behaviour fell below the accepted custom, then he sank in the esteem of his fellows and was punished by a loss of status. If his deeds were of a kind which we now regard as capital crimes, then his group outlawed him, and that, in early times, was equivalent to a death sentence. Individual responsibility held within the group, but in all actions which lay outside the group another principle of justice was imposed—that of collective responsibility. A group was held responsible for every injury which one or more of its members might inflict on neighbouring groups. Such responsibility had a twofold effect: it served to diminish inter-group disturbance and crime, and it also knit members of a group more closely together, thus giving that desirable group quality—solidarity.

My readers may think, after what I have written about the duality of group justice, that the evolutionary method of group selection was altogether evil. This was far from being the case; the system had several outstanding merits. Let me quote a passage which Darwin wrote while discussing the origin of man's " instinct of sympathy ": " Nor could we check our sympathy even at the urging of hard reason, without deterioration in the noblest part of our nature." [30] We are beholden to group selection for that " noblest part of our nature." A group was a nursery of sympathy; the affections which bound parents to childen and children to one another flowed out from the narrow circle of the family to pervade the wider bounds of the group. The group was a school of mutual aid; it could carry not only its complement of fighting men but had room for those who could interpret life and embellish it. It had room for the weak and those in need of sympathy. Early man, like modern man, could be kind, and also he could be fierce.

REFERENCES

[1] Darwin, Francis, *More Letters of Charles Darwin*, 1903, vol. 2, p. 326.

[2] *Ibid.*, p. 329.

[3] Darwin, Charles, *The Descent of Man*, pt. 1, ch. V, Murray, 1913, p. 182.

[4] See discussion of dual code in *Essays on Human Evolution*, 1946, p. 104, by the author of the present volume.

[5] Stephen, Sir Leslie, *The Science of Ethics*, 1882, p. 35.

[6] Lecky, W. E. H., *History of European Morals*, 9th ed., vol. 1, p. 33.

[7] Huxley, T. H., *Collected Essays*, vol. 6, p. 239.

[8] Carpenter, Ed., *Civilization: Its Cause and Cure*, 16th ed., p. 157.

[9] McDougall, Wm., *The Energies of Men*, 1932, ch. XV.

[10] Reid, Thomas, *Collected Works*, vol. 1, p. 451.

[11] *Ibid.*, vol. 2, p. 598.

[12] Sumner, W. G., *Folkways*, 1906, p. 45.

[13] Morley, John, Viscount, *On Compromise*, Watts's reprint 1933, p. 34.

[14] Fisher, R. A., *The Genetical Theory of Natural Selection*, 1930, pp. 182, 178.

[15] Bagehot, Walter, *Physics and Politics*, p. 106.
[16] McDougall, Wm., *The Energies of Men*, 1932, p. 264.
[17] See Levy-Bruhl's *Primitive Mentality*, 1922; Professor John Murphy in *Man*, 1942, p. 37.
[18] Maine, Sir Henry, *Ancient Law*, 1861, p. 10.
[19] Stephen, Sir Leslie, *The Science of Ethics*, 1882, p. 461.
[20] Duff, Charles, *This Human Nature*, 1937, p. 49.
[21] Taylor, J. G., *Popular Psychological Fallacies*, 1938, see p. 243.
[22] Marais, Eugene, *My Friends the Baboons*, 1939.
[23] Hunter, John, *Essays and Observations*, edited by Richard Owen, 1861, vol. 1, p. 53.
[24] Darwin, Charles, *The Descent of Man*, pt. 1, ch. LV, Murray, 1913, p. 185.
[25] Carr-Saunders, Sir A. M., *The Population Problem: A Study in Human Evolution*, 1922, p. 322.
[26] See Deuteronomy V, 33; VI, 6.
[27] Plato, *The Republic*, bk. 1, Everyman ed., pp. 6, 14.
[28] Bagehot, Walter, *Physics and Politics*, p. 127.
[29] Hume, David, *Essays and Treatises*, 1772, vol. 2, p. 247.
[30] Darwin, Charles, *The Descent of Man*, pt. 1, ch. V, Murray, 1913, p. 206.

THE MACHINERY OF EVOLUTION

*Synopsis.—In this essay the author enters another field of inquiry—
the means by which evolution is effected. The methods applied to
the solution of evolutionary problems have greatly changed in the
author's lifetime. The influence of Mendel, Galton, Pearson, and
Morgan. The author assembles an isolated group of Sinanthropes
on which to illustrate his evolutionary creed. A high death-rate and
a compensatory high birth-rate are postulated. The student of evolution
views human beings as carriers of reproductive genes. We are linked
to our simian ancestry by a continuous trail of gene-containing germ-
plasm. The author is a Weismannist. The process of evolution in the
motor-car world compared with that in the world of humanity. The
machinery of evolution is made up of three factors: those of production,
competition, and selection. The triple process as seen in the car
industry and in human communities. The manner in which new types
are brought into existence. Artisans compared to genes. Pearson's
" new theory." Trends explained in terms of genes. The " trend
process " is applied to explain the increase of the human brain. Mutation of genes has played only a minor part in the evolution of human
races. The process of evolution compared to that of legislation.*

It may be well if I notify my readers that in this essay I enter
another field of inquiry. In Essays I–IV I gave my evidence for
believing that early man was divided into small isolated groups,
each of which occupied a delimited territory; in Essays V–XIII
I dealt with the mental qualities which keep members of a group
together and also which turn them away from members of
adjacent groups. In this essay I am to begin an inquiry into the
means by which the men and women of a group change in the
characters of their bodies and minds if they continue to inbreed
over a long period of time. I shall speak of the means and
circumstances which bring about such changes as " the machinery

of evolution." The mere choice of such a term as "machinery" will reveal to the reader what I would willingly have withheld from him—namely, that I am mechanically minded; I can reach results only when I can form concrete images of the means involved. Now, an inquiry into the process of evolutionary change requires an aptitude for, and a training in, mathematics, neither of which I possess. Nevertheless I have not been blind these past fifty years to the results obtained by those gifted individuals who have applied statistical methods to the solution of evolutionary problems. I have seen the statistical methods devised by Sir Francis Galton (1822–1911) developed into a powerful mathematical instrument by Karl Pearson (1857–1936) —an instrument which is undergoing still greater refinements in the hands of modern students of heredity. I have seen grow up, bit by bit, the evidence which leaves us in no doubt that the basis of heredity within each germ or reproductive cell has a particulate form, each particle or gene being exceedingly minute in size, with living potentialities which control the development and growth of the human body. The demonstration by means of the higher powers of the microscope that the hereditary material of the germ cell has a particulate form was a triumphant vindication of the rightness of Mendel's theory—namely, that heredity is particulate in the manner of its operation. Thus the credo I am to apply to the interpretation of man's mode of evolution has been built up as I went along, its Darwinian basis being modified by the teaching of Mendel, Galton, Pearson, T. H. Morgan, and of many others.[1] I know, too, that my credo has but a passing value; as our knowledge of human evolution widens and deepens it will be replaced by one more in accordance with ultimate truth.

In order that we may have a concrete example in front of us, I propose to empanel a group of early humanity, such as existed in China near the beginning of the Pleistocene period; people who lived, according to the most reliable estimate, about 600,000 years ago. It so happened that at this remote date a series of limestone caves became filled in, entombing fragments of the people (now known as Sinanthropes) who then lived in that part of China. They were people who retained certain marks of the ape—namely, prominent eyebrow ridges, receding foreheads, and low-roofed skulls. Fragments of thirty-eight individuals were unearthed; [2] of these, it is important to note, fifteen were under fourteen years of age, and only one was over fifty years; the remainder were between fourteen and fifty. Such figures suggest a heavy bill of mortality. That early man was shorter lived than modern man is also suggested by observations made by Professor Vallois. He brought together the data bearing on the age at death of the Neanderthalians—people who belong to a later date than the Sinanthropes—and found that forty per cent of them had died under eleven years and only five per cent were over forty.[3] I am therefore to assume that in my group of Sinanthropes numbering one hundred individuals the expectation of life was low—not more than twenty years. For convenience of calculation let us infer that our group is made up of individuals at all ages, half of them being males and half females. I make the further assumption that for the bare maintenance of the group we must assign a territory of two hundred square miles, for taking one season with another and one year with another we must allow about two square miles per head for primitive man. I am also making the assumption that our group of Sinanthropes was antagonistic to surrounding groups and maintained its separation from them, as indeed is always the case with a truly primitive human group.

Let us assume that death claimed ten members of our group every year, the chief mortality being in infancy, and that this loss was annually made good by ten births. To see how such a result might be attained we must note the age distribution in the fifty individuals—infants, girls, and women—who made up the female side of the group. Let us divide them into three age classes: (1) those under fifteen years, the number in this class being fifteen; (2) those between fifteen and thirty-five (the years of fertility), for I assume that in primal times women were fertile for only twenty years of their lives. This class I suppose to have kept up an average number of twenty mothers who, one year with another, had to supply ten new lives to make good the loss by death; (3) women who had passed the thirty-five-year mark, numbering fifteen individuals. My scheme involves that each year a maid of the pre-fertile class reaches her fifteenth year and so passes into the maternal class, and that one mother reaches the age of thirty-six and so enters the post-fertile category. Thus every twenty years the mother class is renewed; in the course of a century it is replaced five times. During that period this class, breeding at the rate of ten per annum, has provided the group of Sinanthropes with a thousand new lives to replace the thousand which death has taken from it. With such a turnover of lives, selective agencies are given many opportunities of effecting changes in the constitution of the group. In modern civilized communities it is estimated that sixty per cent of people are the victims of selective agencies, that an eighth part of one generation gives birth to half the succeeding generation,[4] that in the course of a century fifty per cent of families are eliminated and replaced by expanding families.[5] If these things are true of modern societies, we may assume they were equally true of ancient societies. The group which occupied the Sinanthrope territory at the end of a century would thus have differed in many points, both in body and in mind, from the group which held the same territory at the beginning of the century.

So far I have written as if my sole interest had been in the survival of the individual men and women who made up our Sinanthropic group of early humanity. In reality, as a student of evolution my chief concern is not in the survival of the individual men and women, but in the survival of the germinal units or genes contained and carried within the reproductive glands of these men and women. The evolutionist is materially minded; the Sinanthrope who failed to put his genes into circulation within the group and so remained childless is regarded by him as a mere cypher in the chain of descent. The number of genes in circulation within our Sinanthropic group must have been truly enormous; it has been estimated [6] that within the cell which is to give rise to a new human being there are some 25,000 determinants or genes. Our interest, for the moment, is not in the vast population of genes within our Sinanthropic group, but in the relationship between the genes and the living bodies in which they were contained. At a very early stage in the development of a human embryo a parcel of the original gene-containing germ-plasm is laid aside to be handed on in due time to another generation. And so it has been and will be. The genes from which our Sinanthropes arose were the direct descendants of those which at a much earlier period in the earth's history gave rise to ape-like forms. And these same genes which shaped the bodies and minds of Sinanthropes are very probably the ancestors of the genes which circulate in the bodies of the modern inhabitants of China.[7] Thus I have placed my readers in possession of a fundamental part of my anthropological credo—namely, that genes change and evolve, and that evolutionary events in the upper world are determined by what happens in the underworld of genes.

Another part of my credo is my belief in Weismannism.[8] Genes are in the body; they are living and are nourished by the juices of the body, and yet their life is unaffected by that of the body. Nothing a man can think, feel, or do will alter for either good or bad the powers and potentialities of his genes; the habits and the skill he has acquired at the cost of continuous effort leave them untouched. If we could believe with Lamarck and with Darwin that genes can be, and are, influenced by what the body does, how easy would be the solution of many of our evolutionary problems! For example, the lines appear in the palm of the fœtal hand just where the skin is to fold when the hand is clenched. If we believe that the effects of use can be inherited, then we can give a satisfying explanation of the early appearance of suitable lines in the fœtal palm. Yet this simple explanation is rejected by the vast majority of students of heredity; indeed, in my immediate circle there is only one eminent anthropologist—Professor Wood-Jones [9]—who regards the many adaptations of the human body as a result of the inheritance of use and wont.

How, then, do those who believe in the independency of genes explain the ascent of humanity from a simian ancestry and the many wonderful adaptations which characterize the human body? It so happens that during the half-century I have been inquiring into the evolution of the human body I have seen the motor-car or automobile pass from the crude image of a horse-drawn vehicle to the finished products which crowd our modern roads. It will help the reader to understand what I mean by " the machinery of evolution " if I turn aside for a moment and compare the process of evolution as seen in the car world with that which I believe to take place in the world of mankind. In both cases we have a triple process at work—namely, production, competition, and selection. In the car world the buying public serves as the selective agency; it buys according to its needs, its taste, and the state of its purse. The firm which fails to cater for these needs and fancies soon ceases to exist. Com-

petition arises because there are many rival firms which cater for
the same public. We now turn to the group of Sinanthropes and
ask: " Where is the selective agency? And how does competition arise? " The selective agency in this case is power, and
by power I mean every quality that contributes to the strength
and survival of a human group. A group to survive must have
amity and unity at home and a will to resist attack from without.
I have assumed, in our group of Sinanthropes, that births merely
equalled the number of deaths; but let us assume, as we may well
do, that births exceeded deaths, not only in our group, but also
in surrounding groups, and that numbers had come to exceed
what the natural produce of their territories could sustain. Then
there must ensue a struggle, a competition, between our Sinanthropes and neighbouring groups, for territory, for sustenance,
for life. In this struggle it may happen that our group has
proved so powerful that it succeeds in exterminating a neighbouring group, and so is in a position to plant its superfluous numbers
as a new colony or group in the conquered territory. The area
of our Sinanthrope genes will thus have been extended. Such,
then, is what I conceive to have been the chief mode of competition and selection in the primal human world.

I shall now attempt a more difficult feat of comparison—that of
contrasting the production or reproduction of a car with that of
the development of a human child. Our comparison must
explain not only how old types are reproduced, but how types are
introduced, changed, improved, and evolved. To compare with
our Sinanthropic group, let us choose a large factory, one divided
into some ten departments, each department producing a variety
of the same type of car. In the car world production takes place
under one roof, while competition and selection are fought out
in the open, whereas in the human group all three processes take
place, as it were, under the same roof. We have already glanced
at the genes of production in the human world, but where are we
to find them within our car factory? The genes within the
factory are the myriads of skilled artisans and labourers we observe
within each of the ten workrooms of our factory. The car
artisan differs from the human gene in two important respects:
the artisan works outside his material, whereas the gene works
within its material, both gene and material being alive. The
other important difference is that the artisan has to acquire his

skill, whereas the gene, like the worker bee, comes into life with its skill fully developed. To strengthen our comparison let us assume that the artisan, like the worker bee, performs his day's work instinctively and fashions a particular pinion quite unconscious of the end it is to serve. We have to assume, too, that our artisans are divided into teams, each team being engaged on the production of a single car. By the continued co-operation of a team a finished car is made ready for the road. We make a similar assumption in the production of a child; we have reason for believing that within the fertilized human egg there is assembled a vast team of ultra-microscopic genes which co-operate in the production, first, of an embryo, then of a fœtus, and finally of a fully developed babe.

So far as my comparison has gone it has illustrated merely the reproduction of former types; it has thrown no light on how types are changed and improved. Now, in modern factories there are designing brains receiving intelligence of defects in their firm's cars and hints as to what the public is in want of. From such information the designers set to work and, not only remedy the defects, but modify the type so as to make it a more efficient instrument. In the factory which I have just postulated the artisans work purely by instinct; they are deaf to intelligence; they cannot be affected by experience; they can only go on producing their accustomed type. But let us suppose that new teams can be formed, that we can combine half of the artisans engaged on a larger size of car with their opposite numbers derived from a team engaged on a smaller size of the same type of car. Then if we set this new combination of artisans to work, the car which emerges will differ from former products in size and many other details. Such is the method which is actually employed in the genetic scheme of production. In the fertilized human ovum the team of genes has a dual origin : half is derived from the father and half from the mother; each fertile mating thus brings a new combination of genes into being. Each maternal gene seeks out its corresponding paternal gene; human genes are thus duplicate structures. If, then, we are to complete my comparison, we must arrange the artisans of our new team in pairs, each artisan from the larger car being linked with the corresponding workman taken from the smaller car. We must also assume that our artisans, even those who perform the same allotted task, differ in the zest, energy, and even skill with which they set to work; like a gene, our artisan may be energetic and dominant, or may go about his work indifferently, or may be so little skilled as to be counted a mere labourer. Genes of this nature are known in the human world as recessives. Now, two dominant artisans, if they come together, will form a forceful partnership; a dominant artisan, if yoked with one of the labouring grade, will cover the defects of his partner; but if it should so happen that two of the labouring grade become linked, then there will be a piece of defective workmanship which will soon be made apparent when the car takes the road. We may regard our artisans, as we do the germinal genes, as dominant, neutral, and recessive; we may combine them in an almost infinite number of new teams; yet so long as they retain their original inborn natures, they will go on producing mere varieties of the old type; they will fail to produce a new type of car. In the group of Sinanthropes it was assumed that, in the course of a century, a thousand matings had taken place and a thousand new combinations of genes thus brought into existence, and that at the end of a century the group was regarded as differing only in detail from the ancestral group. The mode of radical change to bring about the evolution of a new type has still to be exemplified.

To introduce what may be named the " effective machinery of evolution," let me cite a paper which Professor Karl Pearson published in 1930 and to which he gave the title " On a New Theory of Progressive Evolution." [10] He was then seventy-two years of age, and throughout the greater part of his life had accepted Galton's dictum that in the course of generations exceptional individuals tended to revert or regress towards the mean or average individual of their race. In this new theory Pearson threw Galton's dictum overboard. In 1905 he had commenced the inbreeding of the progeny of a single pair—a dog and a bitch; by 1930 he had reared over 500 specimens of this inbred race and was surprised to find, as he went on, that, far from his breed becoming stable, certain new characters became more and more emphasized. In his new theory he asserts that " if you start with a parentage, however little in excess of type . . . and inbreed, the type, so far from being stable, will progressively alter, without any selection whatsoever." To illustrate his theory he imagines an inbreeding human community containing a number of tall individuals, and proves mathematic- ally that in a group so constituted there is a tendency or trend to an ever rising average of stature in the group.[11] To give a genetic explanation of the Pearsonian theory we must assume that, in the course of matings within a small group, genes with a power to increase stature frequently become linked with genes possessing similar potencies, and that ultimately tall genes prevail within the group.   There is in this case a " trend " to increase of stature, and if stature determined the success of a group in the struggle against other groups, there is no reason why the trend should not go on indefinitely.   Selection, however, has favoured groups having a medium stature, not those made up of tall, lanky men.

Were it necessary I could cite a large number of evolutionists,[12] who have examined the evidence relating to trends and are convinced that, so far as the production of new forms of life is concerned, a gradual rise in power of a combination of genes is the fundamental factor in the process of evolution.   If trend bearers answer the purposes of life, then they are favoured by selection; if they do not, then they are repressed and ultimately eliminated.

To illustrate this thesis as applied to the human species, I again return to my group of Sinanthropes.   About the stature of this early form of humanity we have little to guide us, but something can be said of the size of their brains.   Weidenreich [13] was able to measure the cranial capacity or brain volume of five Sinanthropes; in these five the brain volume varied from 915 cubic centimetres, which is smaller than any brain to be found in most modern races, up to 1,225 cubic centimetres, an amount which places its owner on a lower rung of the modern brain-ladder.   We are justified in assuming that within our Sinanthrope group there were several families which carried genes tending towards the 1,200 mark or beyond it, and that in the course of matings teams of uprising genes came together, and so helped on the upward trend of brain volume.   I am assuming that the well-brained group will be more successful both at home and abroad than groups which are less well equipped.

When we state the rise of the human brain in terms of cubic centimetres, we over-simplify a problem of the utmost com- plexity.   When we remember that in each cubic centimetre of brain matter there may be 20 millions of nerve units, that in a 100 c.c. there are 2,000 millions—which sum represents the total human population of the globe—and that in a modern brain of moderate dimensions (1,400 c.c.) there are some 28,000 million nerve units,[24] then we begin to realize the marvellous organizing powers we are attributing to the genes which regulate the development of the human brain.   Yet we cannot get away from the fact that the vast population of nerve cells which make up the brain are the progeny of a single cell—the fertilized ovum—and that the original regulating power was also contained within that cell.   In the course of development, detachments of the vast army of nerve cells take up allotted stations, form intercommunications, and so the brain becomes an instrument that commands the body and manages its affairs in life.   Yet the problem is not insuperable. Give a commander-in-chief sufficient power and he might succeed in organizing the total manhood of the earth into a single army. To accomplish such a task it must be possible for him to delegate his authority downwards and downwards until it reached all parts of his organizing command.·   I am assuming that the genes which control the development of the human brain have similar powers of delegation.

There is one manner in which changes can be introduced into the development and growth of the human body which I have not mentioned.   A gene may mutate—that is, it may suddenly become changed in nature—and so give rise to an irregular development of that part of the body or brain with which it is concerned.   No doubt geneticists are right when they attribute most of the malformation and defects of the human body to gene mutation, yet I am of opinion that gene mutation has played only a minor part in shaping the modern races of mankind.

Thus it will be seen that I place the productive or creative part of the machinery of evolution in the underworld of genes, while I bring the competitive and selective agencies into the upper world of life where men and women are tested, singly as well as in teams or groups.   The machinery, as I conceive it, has re-semblances to the powers possessed by the Lower and Upper Houses of our British Parliament.   The prerogative of initiating and creating new legislative measures rests with the Lower House, the House of Commons; the House of Lords can but select, accept, or reject what is submitted to it by the Lower House; measures have to pass both Houses before they receive the Royal signature and thus become the law of the land.   Dar-

win placed what he regarded as the supreme power of evolution—
that which he named "Natural Selection"—in the Upper
House, whereas we of a later generation, in the light of increased
knowledge, place the supreme power—that of creation—in the
Lower House.

REFERENCES

[1] For authorities on Evolution see Dr. Julian Huxley's *Evolution: The Modern Synthesis*, 1942.

[2] Weidenreich, Franz, "The Skull of Sinanthropus Pekinensis." *Palæontologia Sinica*, new series, D, No. 10, 1943.

[3] Vallois, Henri V., *L'Anthropologie*, 1937, vol. 47, p. 499.

[4] Pearson, Karl, *The Grammar of Science*, Everyman ed., 1937, pp. 63, 347.

[5] Finot, Jean, *Race Prejudice*, 1906, p. 163.

[6] Huxley, Julian, *Evolution: The Modern Synthesis*, 1942, p. 50

[7] Keith, Sir A., *Nature*, 1936, vol. 138, p. 194; Weidenreich, Franz, *Palæontologica Sinica*, 1943, new series, D, No. 10.

[8] Weismann, A., *Studies in the Theory of Descent*, 1882.

[9] Wood-Jones, Professor F., *Man's Place amongst the Mammals*, 1929, p. 16; *Design and Purpose*, 1942.

[10] Pearson, Karl, *Ann. of Eug.*, 1930, p. 1.

[11] For a criticism of Pearson's theory see Dr. R. A. Fisher, *Nature*, 1930, vol. 126, p. 246; *The Genetical Theory of Natural Selection*, 1930, p. 116.

[12] For literature on Trends see Dr. Julian Huxley's *Evolution*, 1942.

[13] Weidenreich, Franz, *Palæontologica Sinica*, 1942, new series, D, No. 10.

[14] See Constantin von Economo's *Cytoarchitectonics of the Human Cerebral Cortex*, Oxford, 1929, p. 23. This authority gives the number of nerve cells in the cortex of a human brain as 14,000 million; if we include the whole brain this number would probably be twice that sum.

ISOLATION AND INBREEDING AS FACTORS IN HUMAN EVOLUTION

Synopsis.—Darwin ultimately was of opinion that evolution was possible without isolation. His reason for coming to this conclusion. The importance he attached to " conditions " also varied. In the post-Darwinian period Romanes sought to establish isolation as an essential factor in evolution. This is also the author's opinion. Romanes's theory of physiological isolation. His theory of psychological isolation, which is quite different from that formulated by the author. The Descent of Man as a source book. The discovery of genes gave a new significance to isolation. Sewall Wright's opinion of isolation as a factor. Isolation implies inbreeding. Selection of mates is a form of isolation. Some results of inbreeding. The effects of isolation as seen in insular populations. Primal groups were separate by language, custom, tradition, and many other circumstances. Inbreeding lessens the range of variability. The results of inbreeding depend on the nature of the genes concerned. In the Pleistocene period human evolution proceeded at a relatively rapid pace. The author's group theory makes this possible. Social communities of all kinds of vertebrate animals are kept apart by psychological isolation.

IN 1868, eight years after the publication of the *Origin of Species*, Darwin received from Moritz Wagner a brochure [1] which sought to prove that geographical isolation or segregation is the chief means by which a new variety or species is brought into existence. My readers already know that it was the peculiarities of the fauna and flora which had become isolated in the Galapagos Islands that first set Darwin thinking about the transmutation of species. He informed Hooker in 1844 that he was of opinion that " isolation is the chief concomitant or cause of the appearance of new forms "; [2] but later he changed his mind when he observed that the richest sources of new species were to be found on wide continental areas where there were no geographical barriers; hence isolation fell from the high place he had given to it originally. After thanking Wagner for the new facts which he had laid before him, Darwin went on : " But I must still believe that in many large areas all the individuals of the same species have been slowly modified, in the same manner, for instance, as the English racehorses have been improved, that is by the continual selection of the fleetist individuals, without separation." [3]   It does not seem to have occurred to Darwin that although English studs were not " geographically isolated," yet in a very strict sense our race-horses do constitute a separated or isolated community.   Even in the instance he had cited he had not escaped from his dilemma; the moment a breeder begins to select sires and dams for his herd he is bringing into practice a form of isolation.

How, then, did Darwin explain the origin of numerous varieties of the same species on a wide tract of unbroken country?   Let me give his explanation in his own words : " In North America, in going from north to south, or from east to west, it is clear that the changed conditions of life have modified the organisms in the different regions, so that they now form distinct races or even species." [4]   Here Darwin attributes to locality a power of producing new varieties without the aid of isolation.   He is even more explicit as to the importance of the action of conditions in a passage which is taken from *The Descent of Man :* " The races of mankind have been similarly produced . . . the modifications being either the direct result of exposure to different conditions, or the indirect result of some form of selection." [5]   The truth is that Darwin's mind wavered much as to the importance which was to be attached both to " isolation " and to " conditions or environment " as factors in evolution.   Three years before the *Origin of Species* was published he told Hooker that "the conclusion I have come to is that external conditions do by themselves very little," [6] whereas later, as we have just seen, he attached to them a role of the highest importance.   It is his earlier opinion that I, in common with most students of evolution, now accept as true.   The food which a people eat, its richness in vitamins and mineral salts, the climate and mode of life, certainly influence the health and growth of their bodies, but leave their germ-plasm untouched. If we plant an English colony in the heart of Africa, so long as it retains its isolation it will breed true to type, except in one respect.

The tropical climate will favour those strains in the colony which best answer to the new conditions. Conditions, as Darwin usually acknowledged, serve as factors in evolution only when they act as selective agencies. Or we may reverse the experiment and plant a colony of Negroes in a land of white men. If the black genes are kept from mixing with the white, our Africans will breed true to type. Although I hold that external conditions or environment are effective in changing type only in so far as they act as selective agencies, yet I have to admit that the evidence gathered by Boas [7] leaves little doubt that " new conditions " can directly and immediately lead to an increase of stature and a change of head form.

I have just quoted from a letter which Darwin wrote to his friend Hooker in 1856; I return to that letter because it contains a statement which fits in with my own way of thinking. In answer to certain propositions Hooker had pressed on him he replied : " I cannot agree with your proposition that time, altered conditions and altered associates are convertible terms. I look at the first (time) and the last (altered associates) as far more important : time being important only so far as giving scope to selection." This statement, interpreted in terms of human evolution, I take to mean that, so far as primitive man is concerned, the chief " external conditions " were represented by his fellow men, with men of his own group with whom he lived in amity, and with men of other groups with whom he lived in a state of enmity. As Karl Pearson said in 1904 : " It is the stock itself which forms the home environment." [8]

Darwin died in 1882; fifteen years later there appeared a work on isolation,[9] by G. J. Romanes (1848–94). Romanes was a convinced isolationist; " without isolation," he declared, " or the prevention of intercrossing, organic evolution is in no case possible," [10] a declaration which, so far as it concerns human evolution, I accept without reserve. As regards the mode in which geographical isolation furthers the process of evolution, Romanes accepted the explanation which had been given by the Rev. T. Gulick and others—namely, that if part of a species is cut off by a geographical barrier, the colony so cut off will carry characters which are either above or below the average characters of the parent species.[11] In the course of generations the colony so cut off will diverge either in the direction of its excess or of its deficiency. " The very essence of the principle being that, when divergence of type has once begun, the divergence must *ipso facto* proceed at an ever-accelerating pace," [12] a close anticipation of the Pearsonian theory of 1930 (see Essay XIV, p. 132).

So much for geographical isolation; but what of those numerous cases where a species extending widely over an unbroken tract of country has become divided into a series of local varieties? To meet such cases Romanes invented a new theory to which he gave the name of " physiological isolation "; this, in reality, was a theory of infertility. He assumed that along the lines which separated one local variety from another there had arisen a partial infertility which, as it increased, came gradually to isolate neighbouring varieties. Romanes's theory had no foundation in observed fact. Modern biologists are agreed that infertility is not a cause, but a consequence, of the separation or isolation of a species into local varieties.

Romanes mentions also another mode of isolation, to which he gave the name " psychological selection." [12] He defines this mode of selection (which is also one of isolation) as " the tendency of the members of a variety to breed with one another." The following quotation from the *Origin of Species* proves that Darwin also recognized this form of isolation : " I can bring forwards a considerable body of facts showing that within the same area, two varieties of the same animal may long remain distinct, from haunting different stations, from breeding at slightly different seasons, or *from the individuals of each variety preferring to pair together*." [13] He also knew that among horses and fallow deer, when free to do so, there was a tendency for the males to seek out females of the same colour.[14] Galton also recognized that " varieties are separated by mating preferences." [15] In Essay V I have already touched upon the tendency of like to seek out like in mating, but so far as concerns human evolution this form of selection or isolation has played but a minor role.

Now, I am of opinion that isolation is an essential factor in the process of evolution. For these thirty years I have been gathering information from all parts of the earth inhabited by primitive humanity, and everywhere I have found it separated into communities or tribes which are resolute in their determination to remain separate and independent. Why they remain apart I have sought to explain in the preceding essays. My explanation or theory is of a mental or psychological nature, but it is altogether different from that enunciated by Romanes. My explanation of isolation is based on the fact that human nature is dual both in its constitution and in its mode of action. Human nature acts so as to keep the members of a group or tribe together and at the same time apart from other groups or tribes. Human nature is so constituted as spontaneously to attain two opposite codes of behaviour—one, the code of amity, to serve within the group, the other the code of enmity, to serve outside the group. Thus I assume that human groups are isolated from one another by the unceasing action of inborn mental qualities. Another part of my evolutionary *credo* is that human nature has grown up, or been evolved, in the service of evolution.

When I set out to test the truth of my theory that mental isolation has been, and is, a factor in human evolution, it was in *The Descent of Man* that I found most of the corroborative evidence, particularly in Chapters III, IV, and V, which, in reality, deal with the evolution of human nature. Darwin knew that primitive humanity was divided into isolated groups, that members of such groups were sympathetic to one another and were unsympathetic to members of other groups, and that in the evolutionary struggle, group competed against group.[16] Yet nowhere does he suggest that the separation of mankind into groups has an evolutionary significance, nor does he on any page attribute group isolation as being due to a peculiar action of human nature. Such omissions can be understood when we turn to a letter which Darwin addressed to August Weismann in 1872, fully a year after the publication of *The Descent of Man*.[17] Darwin had just received and read Weismann's treatise *The Influence of Isolation on Species-formation*.[18] " I have now read your essay with very great interest," wrote Darwin. " Your view of local races through amixie (inbreeding) is altogether new to me." This is a statement quite unexpected from one who had always insisted that " no breed could be produced if free intercrossing is permitted." A later statement also surprises us. In a letter written in 1878 to another German Professor [19] we find Darwin saying, " Nor do I see at all more clearly . . . how and why it is that a long isolated form should almost always become slightly modified." From these statements we learn that when Darwin wrote *The Descent of Man* he did not regard isolation and inbreeding as important factors in the production of human races, and therefore failed to realize that the separation of early mankind into isolated groups had a high evolutionary significance.

With the establishment of Mendelianism and the discovery that the characters of one generation are transmitted to the next by means of discrete living particles known as genes, the reason for isolation being an important factor in evolution became more apparent. Let us look on a group of primitive humanity as the bearers of an assemblage of genes; that assemblage is cut off from all surrounding assemblages; no strange genes are allowed into the group. With repeated matings the genes which circulate within the group enter into new combinations and give rise to individuals in which old characters are combined in new ways. As we have already seen (p. 133), trends appear in such groups; there is a tendency for certain of the characters to become exaggerated in a definite direction; genes may mutate or change and give rise to new characters within the group. How, then, do such isolated groups behave in an evolutionary sense? Here is Professor Sewall Wright's opinion:[20] "If a given species is isolated into breeding colonies in such a way that there is but little emigration between them . . . in the course of time the species will become divided into local races." Professor Allee[21] agrees with Professor Wright, and so does Dr. R. A. Fisher.[22] In the opinion of Dr. Fisher "partially isolated local races of small size . . . favour progressive evolution and the formation of new species by fission." With the latter's statement Dr. Huxley is in agreement, his opinion being expressed thus: "The smaller the size of a natural population and the more perfectly it is isolated, the more likely is 'drift' to proceed to its limit, resulting either in the complete loss of a mutation from the group, or in its fixation in all the individuals of the group."[23] Thus we may say that isolation now occupies an assured and important place in the "machinery of evolution." It is a condition, not a cause, of evolution. The assemblage of genes within an isolated group of humanity is given an opportunity of developing quickly and effectively all its latent potentialities.

Isolation and inbreeding are, in reality, convertible terms, for if a human group is effectively isolated it must inbreed. It will assist my readers to realize how quickly inbreeding may bring about structural changes if I cite a few illustrative instances. De

Vries crossed two clover plants each of which had a few four-lobed leaves, and by inbreeding produced plants with five-lobed leaves. Guinea-pigs have normally four toes on their front feet, and three on their hind. My friend, Professor C. R. Stockard,[24] mated animals with rudiments of a fourth toe on their hind feet and ultimately succeeded in producing a race with four toes on both feet, and believed if he had gone on that he could have produced a five-toed race. Dahlberg [25] relates that Graham Bell, by inbreeding the progeny of ewes with extra teats, succeeded in producing animals with six teats in place of the normal two.

Populations inhabiting small and remote islands provide opportunities of estimating the effects of isolation and inbreeding. The evidence which is at hand on this matter would require a volume for its adequate treatment, not the short paragraph I am to give it. " Smaller islands," says Julian Huxley, " give quicker changes than large adjacent islands." [26] The islands of the Mediterranean provide many instances of the changes which follow isolation. Keane, in describing the inhabitants of Sardinia, uses these terms : " The Sards would almost seem to be cast in one mould. . . . They have the shortest stature, the brownest hair, the longest heads and the swarthiest complexion of all Italian populations." [27] Many of the populations of the smaller islands of the Mediterranean are characterized by peculiarities of their head forms and blood-groupings. A dominant gene, or combination of genes, such as determine form of head or group of blood, once introduced into an island population may, in the course of repeated matings, infect the whole population, thus transforming a long-headed people into a short-headed one.[28] Dr. Hansen reported thus on the natives of the Faroes : " The fiords and valleys of the islands facilitated the formation of small communities, differing in mental capacity as in bodily form. Such communities could not fail, when removed to small distant islands, to develop into distinct local types." [29] The ancient inhabitants of the Canary Islands were differentiated into island tribes.[30] It is not too much to say that each of the smaller islands in the wide Pacific Ocean has a population which is peculiar to itself. I shall content myself with citing only one instance. Sir William Flower when reporting on a collection of skulls, representing a single tribe of an island of the Fiji group, remarked, " Nothing could be more striking than their wonderful similarity." It was even greater than he had observed among the skulls of Andaman Islanders.[31]

Populations may be isolated in many more ways than those I have mentioned. "A savage tribe," observed Malthus (1766–1834), "surrounded by enemies, or a civilized, populous nation hemmed in by others, is in the same position as islanders."[32] National groups and tribes are isolated by their differing forms of speech. The inhabitants of the Andaman Islands were divided into nine tribes, each having its own dialect. In primal times the speech of offshoots of an expanding tribe became, in the course of a few centuries, differentiated into dialects. In six centuries the English of Chaucer's time has become changed into our language of to-day. Primitive tribes were separated by diversity of interests, by diversity of custom, of tradition, of myth and song, of gods and totems, just as are modern nations. Bagehot explained the separation of early groups thus: "The necessity of forming co-operative groups by fixed customs, explains the necessity of isolation in early society."[33] This explanation places the cart before the horse.

Isolation and inbreeding create a more uniform population; variability is reduced. Is not this a hindrance to progressive evolution? Let us hear what a biometrician, Dr. G. M. Morant, has to say about the extent to which variability is reduced. "The most marked exceptions (in the amount of variability) are found for samples from communities which are known to have been segregated for considerable periods, such as certain island peoples, and for these variation is appreciably smaller than for other peoples."[34] Inbreeding, then, does reduce variability, but not to an extent which prohibits evolutionary change. Professor Karl Pearson[35] estimated that the reduction is not more than twelve per cent. It is not the amount of variation that matters, but its direction; so long as the variations are in the same direction progress will be made.

What of the alleged evils of inbreeding? All depends on the quality of the genes assembled in the group pool; if all are health-giving, then all will be well; but if there be a proportion, even a small proportion, of defective or recessive genes, then repeated mating within a small isolated group will speedily bring defective genes together, so damaging the life of a group. If in small proportion, carriers of evil genes may be eliminated, but if defective members of a group become so numerous that the group is unable to maintain its place in competition with its neighbours, then such a group is speedily eliminated, its evil genes disappearing with it. Thus it will be seen that evolution, as carried out in a human population divided into small, isolated competing groups, gives quick returns; the passage of a number of generations is sufficient to prove whether a new group is to be a hit or a miss.

When we compare the known representative of humanity at the beginning of the Pleistocene Age with the men who succeeded them towards the close of that period, we cannot help marvelling at the rate at which evolutionary changes had been effected—even if we assume that the Pleistocene Age covers a million of years. At first I was greatly exercised to find an evolutionary machinery which could give such rapid results.[36] It was only when the truth of the group theory dawned on me, when I became assured that until the dawn of civilization the total human population of the earth had been divided into a mosaic of small, isolated, competing communities, that I found a machinery adequate for my needs. Nor was I by any means the first to perceive that the division of a population into numerous small independent groups provides exceptional opportunities for a rapid change in racial characters, as is shown by the following passage from a paper written by Professor Metcalf in 1922 : " Human racial diversities, I believe, cannot be maintained now that isolation is about to become a thing of the past." [37]

Human societies, then, are isolated from one another by an instinctive action of human nature. I seem to be alone in regarding human nature as an isolating agency; the reader must judge from my evidence how far I am justified in thinking so. Primitive man was prejudiced in favour of his own community and equally prejudiced against members of other communities; thus was isolation maintained. Nor are such prejudices really dead in the modern world of mankind. Do I, then, maintain that only human groups are kept apart by a mental prejudice? By no means. In Essay V I have already discussed " group consciousness " and the instinctive faculty which all social verte- brate animals have of detecting members of their own community and their aversion to receiving strangers as members of that com- munity. Isolation so maintained is of a psychological nature. Throughout the major part of the vertebrate kingdom the organ of smell serves as the instrument of discrimination, but in birds the organs of sight and hearing are used for this purpose. In the class of Primates, of which man is a member, the eye and the ear are also the organs used in the recognition of group membership. A tribesman knows his fellows by their features, by their gait, and by their speech.

One other objection may be raised to my theory of mental isolation. In the modern world sex passions break across all racial barriers; they have no respect for frontiers of any kind. Would they not have been equally free and roving in primal times? This problem comes up for discussion in the essay which follows.

REFERENCES

[1] Wagner, Moritz, *Die Darwinische Theorie und das Migrationsgesetz*, 1868.

[2] Darwin, Francis, *The Life and Letters of Charles Darwin*, 1888, vol. 2, p. 28.

[3] *Ibid.*, p. 157.

[4] *Ibid.*, vol. 3, p. 161.

[5] Darwin, Charles, *The Descent of Man*, Murray, 1913, p. 281.

[6] Darwin, Francis, *The Life and Letters of Charles Darwin*, vol. 2, p. 87.

[7] Boas, Franz, *Changes in Bodily Form of Descendants of Immigrants*, 1912. See criticism by Morant and Samson, *Biometrika*, 1936, vol. 28, p. 1.

[8] Pearson, Karl, *Jour. Roy. Anthrop. Inst.*, 1904, vol. 33, p. 206.

[9] Romanes, G. J., *Darwin and after Darwin*, 1897.

[10] *Ibid.*, p. 345.

[11] *Ibid.*, p. 111.

[12] *Ibid.*, p. 124.

[13] Darwin, Charles, *Origin of Species*, 6th ed., chap. IV, p. 81.

[14] Darwin, Charles, *The Descent of Man*, Murray, 1913, p. 825.

[15] Pearson, Karl, *Life of Galton*, vol. 2, p. 272.

[16] See Essay V, p. 38.

[17] Darwin, Francis, *The Life and Letters of Charles Darwin*, vol. 3, p. 155.

[18] Weismann, A., *Ueber den Einfluss der Isolirung, auf die Artbildung*, 1872.

[19] Darwin, Francis, *The Life and Letters of Charles Darwin*, vol. 3, p. 161.

[20] Wright, Sewall, *Genetics*, 1931, vol. 16, p. 97.

[21] Allee, W. C., *Social Life of Animals*, 1939, p. 183.

[22] Fisher, R. A., *Eugenics Rev.*, 1931, p. 89.

[23] Huxley, Julian, *Evolution: The Modern Synthesis*, 1942, p. 59.

[24] Stockard, C. R., *Amer. Jour. of Anat.*, 1930, vol. 45, p. 345.

[25] Dahlberg, G., *Race, Reason, and Rubbish*, 1942, p. 61.

[26] Huxley, Julian, *Evolution: The Modern Synthesis*, 1942, p. 238.

[27] Keane, A. H., *Man: Past and Present*, new ed., 1920, p. 461.

[28] Fisher, R. A., *The Genetical Theory of Natural Selection*, 1930.

[29] Hansen, S., *Jour. Roy. Anthrop. Inst.*, 1912, vol. 42, p. 485.

[30] Hooton, E. A., *The Ancient Inhabitants of the Canary Islands*, *Harvard African Studies*, vol. 7, 1925.

[31] Flower, Sir William, *Jour. Roy. Anthrop. Inst.*, 1880, vol. 10, p. 1.

[32] Malthus, Rev. T. R., *An Essay on the Principle of Population*, chap. V.

[33] Bagehot, Walter, *Physics and Politics*, p. 37.

[34] Morant, G. M., *Man*, 1934, p. 103.

[35] Pearson, Karl, *The Grammar of Science*, Everyman ed., p. 346.

[36] Keith, Sir A., *Nature*, 1925, vol. 116, p. 317.

[37] Metcalf, M. M., *University of Buffalo Studies*, 1922, vol. 2, p. 137.

ENDOGAMY, EXOGAMY, AND MONOGAMY AS FACTORS IN HUMAN EVOLUTION

Synopsis.—*The author resumes writing after an interval during which events of great evolutionary significance occurred. Extensive hybridization has taken place in the modern world. How sex passion was controlled and restricted in the ancient or primal world. Group opinion is the restraining power in ancient as in modern times. How mating is controlled* (1) *in anthropoid communities;* (2) *in primitive human communities. Early human communities were inbreeding or endogamous small societies. A form of exogamy was practised by anthropoid communities. There are certain tendencies towards monogamy among anthropoids. This tendency, the author assumes, became developed in groups of early humanity. The evolution of maternal feelings accompanied prolongation of the periods of pregnancy and of nursing. Westermarck and Frazer on mating in primitive human societies. The evolution of "compound" societies. The origin of exogamy in compound groups. The classificatory system. The origin of group marriage. The rise of individual marriages. In human communities exogamy is combined with endogamy. A review of the theories of exogamy. Its purpose and its effects illustrated. Exogamy was a means of consolidating enlarged compound communities. A consciousness of incest arose late in the evolution of human societies. Social effects of incest. The effects of inbreeding.*

AT this point there occurred a break in the writing of these essays which deserves to be noted. The preceding essays were written in the first seven months of 1945, Essay XV being finished in the last week of July. It was while so engaged that a momentous event occurred—the unconditional surrender of the German host to the Allied Nations (7th May, 1945). Essay XV being finished, I had then to devote myself to another task—namely, the revision of my text-book on Human Embryology and Morphology, which occupied the remaining months of 1945. It was while I was so occupied that another event of the first magnitude happened—the unconditional surrender of Japan (14th August, 1945), thus bringing the second world war to an end. And now as I take up my pen to resume essay-writing at the end of the second week of January, 1946, an event of even greater signifi-cance to students of human evolution than the two just chronicled is taking place under my eyes in London. There, representatives of fifty-one nations have assembled to establish a central govern-ment for the whole world. If the United Nations Organization (U.N.O.) succeeds in its Herculean task, then human evolution will have entered a completely new and untried phase. Hitherto evolutionary units (nations) have resorted to war in order to defend or advance their interests; in the new phase co-operation is to replace contention. Hitherto the destiny or evolution of peoples has been decided in the rough and tumble of the world; now man's evolution will have to be planned and *humanized*. Fortunately for me, I need not concern myself overmuch with the future of man's evolution; I am rapidly approaching the eightieth milestone of my life's journey; younger heads will have to unravel the future of human evolution. In the meantime I return in this essay to a consideration of the conditions amid which man made his evolutionary ascent during the long primal period of his history, the period which was succeeded by that of civilization (post-primal) in which we still are.

I picked up the thread of my discourse by returning to the query posed at the end of the preceding essay : " In the modern world sex passions break across all racial barriers; they have no respect for frontiers of any kind. Would they not have been equally free and roving in primal times? " I admit unreservedly the imperious strength of man's sexual passion; of all the mental qualities which go to make up the galaxy of human nature, it is the most difficult to bring under, and keep under, the control of the will. In all the remoter regions of the earth into which men have strayed, singly or in battalion, from the settled homes of the Old World, we find the most ample evidence of the indiscriminate way in which their sexual needs have been satisfied among native peoples. If this is so in the modern world, why was it not equally the case in the primal world? Long-distance migrations which made miscegenation on a great scale possible are modern phenomena;

they became possible in post-primal times when food was produced and ships invented. In primal times every group was surrounded and hemmed in by other groups. More important as a solution to our problem of the restriction and control of the sex passion among primal peoples is a consideration of the manner in which this passion is domesticated and kept within bounds in modern societies. I can best illustrate my thesis by reminding readers of the differing fates which befell the Spaniards and the Englishmen who settled in the New World during the sixteenth and seventeenth centuries.[1] The Englishmen took their wives and their families with them; they established white communities, in which public opinion became all-powerful when moral issues were involved. Marrying natives was condemned and the communities bred white. The Spaniards, for the greater part, left their wives and children behind them; under such conditions white communities could not be established and sex passions demanded, and were given, local satisfaction. I do not claim a stronger sense of race purity for the Englishman than for the Spaniard; all I assert is that the sexual passions of the Englishman were subject to the vigorous and vigilant opinion of his community, while those of the Spaniard were left free of such control. We shall see that in primal communities neither man nor woman could escape from the scrutiny of their group, nor from its condemnation or approval, as the case might be.

If we seek light on the conditions under which primal man mated and begot children, I know of only two sources from which we may obtain it—namely, living communities of chimpanzees and of gorillas—the two anthropoids most akin to man in structure and in mentality—and from such communities of primitive humanity as are still to be found in outlying regions of the earth. To illustrate the manner in which mating and the rearing of young are managed in an anthropoid community[2] let us take a chimpanzee group of fifteen individuals, made up of three adult males, six adult females, and six young animals at various stages of growth. As we have seen (Essays IV, V, XII), such a group represents a " closed " society; it resents with tooth and nail the intrusion of a stranger into its ranks, much as it does the open enemy which threatens injury; it unconsciously seeks to maintain the purity of its stock of seed or genes, and to hand on uncontaminated to a new generation the stock entrusted to it by a preceding generation. Our chimpanzee group thus forms an inbreeding, endogamous—I might truly say an incestuous—society; its members stand in the closest blood relationship to each other; the male chimpanzee, so far as we know, when in search of a mate, makes no distinction between mother, sister, or cousin. There must have been a time in the earlier phases of man's evolution when he, too, was equally unconscious of blood relationship, and when endogamy was the standard practice.

There is, however, a considerable body of evidence which leads us to surmise that among chimpanzees, as in all groups of the higher Primates, a compulsory form of exogamy is practised. As many male as female chimpanzees are born, yet in each group the grown females outnumber the males; there is a missing percentage of males. Further, sex jealousy is strongly developed in male chimpanzees, ending in the death or expulsion of one of the contestant males. All who have studied anthropoids in the jungle have observed stray or "rogue" males; but so far no observer has seen one of those rogues crashing its way into a strange group or seeking to entice females to join him and so form a new group. Yet we are justified in believing that such things do happen, and in this way new seed is introduced to old groups, and so a form of exogamy is instituted, very different, as we shall see, from modern human practice. Among gibbons, it is interesting to note,[3] young females, as well as males, are expelled from their groups.

Monogamy is not an anthropoid practice; matings at most are for a season. Yet it is of interest to note that among the earlier and oldest form of surviving anthropoids, the gibbon, mating is prolonged and both parents share in the care of their young.[4] It may well be that this tendency to prolonged mating had appeared early in the human stem, and so have led the human male to take a "paternal" interest in the progeny of his mate. In captivity the male chimpanzee does, on occasion, manifest a paternal interest in the young. In captivity, too, the chimpanzee has sexual intercourse at all seasons; the female is subject to periods of rut which compel her to seek sexual gratification.[5] Most authorities are of opinion that anthropoids in their native habitat, unlike human beings, are seasonal in their manifestations of sex, intercourse occurring so that the young are born in the spring months of the year.

Before dismissing anthropoid communities from our consideration, it is important that we should note the high development of the maternal " instinct " which is met with among them. As the period of pregnancy increases in length the maternal solicitude of the primate mother increases in power and in duration. The following are the periods of pregnancy in some of the higher Primates : [6] rhesus monkey, 166 days; gibbon, 209 days; chimpanzee, 235 days; man, 266 days. Broadly speaking, there has been an increase of a month in each of these stages leading from monkey to man; and with each increase there has been a lengthening of the period in which the young needs and receives care after birth. The baby chimpanzee remains a suckling in its mother's care for the first eight months of life; at the end of this period she tends it as it learns to climb and to master gradually the anthropoid gait; it needs her maternal care until it enters its fourth year, when the maternal bonds cease to hold and the young chimpanzee takes its place among the juveniles of the group. The chimpanzee child attains a degree of independence in its fourth year which is equivalent to that reached by the human child in its eighth or ninth year; maternal care is prolonged to a corresponding extent; in the human family the maternal bond is never broken, at least this is so in modern human societies. Thus a chimpanzee group or community is really an extended or consanguine family made up of individuals which are closely related to one another in a genetical sense. All the adults are parents of the group; all the young are the children of the group.

I now pass on to review very briefly what is known of mating and matrimony in communities of living primitive peoples. The way has been cleared for me by the pioneer labours of two men—Westermarck [7] and Frazer. [8] Dr. Edward Westermarck died in 1939 at the age of seventy-six; Sir James G. Frazer in 1941 at the age of eighty-seven; both leaving behind them vast monuments of fact and of inference relating to the marital customs of peoples living in a tribal state. From facts cited by them, and from what has just been said about the mating habits of anthropoids, I am convinced that the groups into which primal humanity was separated were inbreeding or endogamous communities. To their inferences there is one I would add here, one relating to the composition of early human groups. It is possible, even at the beginning of the Pleistocene period, when mankind was represented in Java by Pithecanthropus, in China by Sinan-thropus, and in England by Eoanthropus, that mankind was then grouped, just as the gorilla and chimpanzee still are, into single large consanguine families.

About that time, or soon after, I infer that an important change took place in the composition of the primal human group; the group became compound—that is, it was no longer com-posed of a single unit, as among chimpanzees, but was made up of two or more units (consanguine groups). My reasons for making this assumption are two in number. First, we have to account for the fact that the most primitive human groups known to us are really compound in their composition; secondly, the prevalence and power of the factor of aggregation have been so potent throughout the period of human history known to us. By aggregation I mean the tendency of neighbouring units to coalesce, as a result of compulsion or of negotiation, thus obtaining increased security and power by their union. We have records in all historical times of groups being united to form clans, of clans being united to form tribes, of tribes being united to form small nations, and of small nations being united to form great nations. We must never forget the chief enemy which evolving groups of early humanity had to overcome; the main threat to which they were exposed was neither hunger nor wild beasts, but that which came from neighbouring groups of their own species. Under this ever-present danger compound groups of humanity came to be formed. It may be that they arose, not from the union of neighbouring groups, but from the division of overgrown single units, the newly formed group remaining with the parent group instead of separating from it. The idea I have been expounding was known to Andrew Lang, who wrote: " The largest assemblage of individuals . . . living in amity has the best chance of survival." [9]

To trace the origin of out-marriage or exogamy as practised by primitive humanity, I shall assume that we have before our eyes a compound group or clan just formed by the coming together of two consanguine groups which had hitherto been endogamous or inbreeding (incestuous) units. If these two units, living side by side, continue as inbreeders, then their interests must remain diverse; there can be no unity of action, no social unity. But suppose the two groups agree to exchange their marriageable young men, then the two groups become linked by the closest of social ties; they come to have a common, dominant interest which gives collective strength to the compound group. In this way I suppose the practice of exogamy was introduced. It was introduced because it was found to give an extended social security. It will be seen, then, that I am of opinion that the earliest form of human mating or marriage took the form of group exchange. Thus in a compound group, so united, endogamy and exogamy were conjoined in practice.

In support of what I have just written I would cite statements relating to tribes of Central Australia given by Frazer. The Arunta is a tribe whose territory lies to the south of Alice Springs. They now practise exogamy, being divided into eight inter-marrying groups or classes. Their tradition, however, is that at one time they were strict endogamists. "Very different," writes Frazer,[10] "was the state of things in the past, if we may trust tradition, the evidence of which points back to a time when a man always married a woman of his own totem (clan.) The reference to men and women of one totem always living together in groups would appear to be too frequent and explicit to admit of any other satisfactory explanation." Both Westermarck and Frazer give lists of endogamous tribes.

To the south of the Arunta and to the west of Lake Eyre is the territory of the Urabunna tribe, of which Frazer gives the following account :—

> "In Australia we are not left merely to infer the former prevalence of group marriage from the group relationships of the classificatory system, for a form of group marriage persists to the present time in certain of the central tribes, particularly in the Urabunna, and in the Dieri. In the Urabunna tribe, as in all the tribes with which we are dealing, certain groups of men and women are by birth marriageable to each other. . . . And since in this tribe groups of women are thus common to groups of men, it naturally follows that the children born of such unions are also common to the groups." [11]

If we bring together two primal groups of humanity, organized as anthropoid groups are, then group marriage of the sort just described is the most probable sequel. The classificatory system, of which Frazer speaks, implies that all the adults of a group are regarded as parents, while all juveniles of the group are regarded as their children, and therefore as brothers and sisters. On another page [12] Frazer makes this claim: " In short, group marriage explains group relationship, and it is hard to see what else can do so." Here I think the great scholar has placed the cart in front of the horse; the classificatory system was not invented to make group marriage possible; the opposite was the case, group marriage was introduced to fit into the classificatory system, which, as I have indicated, was in existence, at a pre-human level of evolution. Out of the group system of marriage arose the individual practice where mating was arranged between male and female members of linked groups. Later still, in post-primal times, groups were disbanded, and lovers were free to exercise their fancy in the choice of mates. The evolutionary effects of such changes will come up for consideration in a later essay.

Writers are apt to presume that when an enlarged or compound group adopted the practice of exogamy the practice of endogamy or inbreeding was lost. This was not so; the adoption of exogamy but enlarged the group in which endogamy was still practised. Exogamy prospered because of its social effects; it bound together the units of a compound group by marital ties, thus giving it common interests and incentives for common action. A group which practised exogamy would be stronger and more enduring than a neighbouring group whose units retained their endogamous habits; the exogamous groups were selected and survived. Frazer was of the opinion that exogamy had been deliberately introduced as a policy by tribal elders, who were gifted with statesmanlike qualities of mind. That may very well have been the case in later stages of human evolution, but as regards the earlier stages it seems to me that exogamy was forced on primal humanity in search of security rather than by any deliberate choice on the part of its elders.

Let us look very briefly at the explanations which other writers have given of the practice of exogamy by primitive peoples. In Westermarck's opinion [13] the force which drove man to exogamy were the needs of his sexual appetite; it turned away, so he believed, from what was familiar and at hand; it was attracted and stimulated by the strange and distant. Exogamy is strictly regulated and ill-designed to answer the purpose which Westermarck ascribed to it. Frazer shared in the explanation given by L. H. Morgan (1877), which he stated in the following terms: [14] " Morgan held that sexual promiscuity prevailed universally at a very early period of human history, and that exogamy was instituted to prevent the marriage or cohabitation of blood relations." Now, to institute measures against incest, men and women must be conscious of the relationships implied by the terms " father," " daughter," " mother," " son," " sister," " brother." Anthropoid apes know nothing of such terms and relationships. When did mankind come to this knowledge? It could not well have been at an early date, seeing that there are still some peoples who are ignorant of the fact that sexual intercourse is a necessary prelude to conception. If, however, we assume that exogamy was instituted, not to prevent incest, but to give solidarity and strength to a community by uniting its sub-groups by marital ties, then ignorance of blood relationship ceases to be a valid objection.

There can be no doubt as to the intensity of the horror which the thought of incest arouses in the human breast; the dread of it is universal. Is, then, the fear of incest one of man's inborn or instinctive fears? Evidence is against such a supposition; the animals most akin to man know nothing of it; nor did early man. The fear of incest has become inherited as a vital element in the acquired *tradition* of every people. To break rules of exogamy is the most heinous of all crimes known to primitive peoples; the sentence is death, even if the infraction is one which is not accounted incest by civilized peoples. To break the accepted values of exogamy is an injury to the solidarity of a social group.

To get at the root of this matter readers must think for a moment of the conditions which would arise in a community if each family were to mate within itself. A multitude of independent inbreeding units would come into existence, destroying all group cohesion. Such a disrupted community must fall speedily apart. This result has been pointed out by several writers.[15] Nor am I alone in claiming as the chief merit of exogamy its power to link together the sub-groups or clans of a tribe, thus consolidating the social life of such a tribe. " Exogamy," said Sir Edward Tylor, " keeps clans together." [16] Lang and Atkinson [17] were of opinion that Nature aimed at giving a tribe social stability and that the means adopted was the practice of exogamy. Frazer was not blind to the social advantages of exogamy, as the following passage proves: "A system which knit large groups of men and women together by the closest ties was more favourable to social progress than one which would have limited the family group to a single pair and their progeny." [18]

I have been seeking to explain the avoidance of incest and the practice of exogamy on the grounds that they give social integration to a compound group. Westermarck, on the other hand—and most anthropologists have followed his lead—sought for a biological or genetical explanation—namely, that the group which inbred underwent a deterioration. The results of inbreeding were discussed in the preceding essay (p. 143), and the conclusion there reached was that all results depend on the nature of the seed involved: if the seed is sound, then the progeny will be sound; if unsound, then the progeny will be unsound. The smaller the group the sooner will it profit from the merits of its seeds, and the sooner, too, will it suffer from their demerits. Small evolutionary groups favour rapidity of evolution.

In the discussion just mentioned less than justice was done to the opinions held by Darwin as to the effects of inbreeding and of outbreeding; I wish now to make some amends. When writing the *Origin of Species* he gave this opinion: "A cross between different varieties, or between individuals of the same variety but of another strain, gives vigour and fertility to the offspring; on the other hand . . . close interbreeding diminishes vigour and fertility." [19] Against this may be quoted the results of close inbreeding obtained by modern geneticists. Rabbits and rats have been closely inbred for many generations with no loss of vigour, fertility, or size of body; the opposite has been the result; all three qualities were increased. [20] Darwin admitted that "man is not highly sensitive to the evil effects of interbreeding"; [21] he may have had in mind his own case. He married his cousin and had a healthy and gifted family. More to the point of my argument is his statement regarding the speedy production of a new race by close inbreeding. "With our domestic animals," wrote Darwin, [22] "a new race can readily be formed by careful matching of the varying offspring of a single pair, or even from a single individual possessing some new character." In this, modern breeders agree with Darwin; [23] the closer the individuals of a group are inbred the sooner that group is likely to assume a new form. All of which is in harmony with my claim for the group theory—namely, that a multitude of small competing units provides effective means for securing a rapid evolutionary change.

Darlington is of opinion that " parallel inbreeding and out-breeding would give the best racial results." [24] Now, it is this dual form of breeding which rules in anthropoid communities, and which I have assumed to have held also in primal communities of mankind. In a chimpanzee group, for example, the habitual practice is that of inbreeding or endogamy; but this seems to be supplemented by a form of exogamy carried out by the wandering or outcast male.[25] If, then, chimpanzees and gorillas are subject to the most effective form of evolutionary breeding, why is it that they have remained anthropoidal apes, confined to the tropical jungles of Africa, while man's simian ancestry has speeded on to a human estate and multiplied so in numbers that the species now covers the whole earth? In my next essay I shall seek for an answer to this problem.

References for this essay appear on page 160.

HUMAN LINEAGE AS OUTLINED
IN THIS BOOK
❖

GEOLOGICAL PERIODS

Post-Pleistocene Period
18,000 Years

Pleistocene Period
1,000,000 Years

Pliocene Period
7,000,000 Years

Miocene Period
12,000,000 Years

End of Oligocene

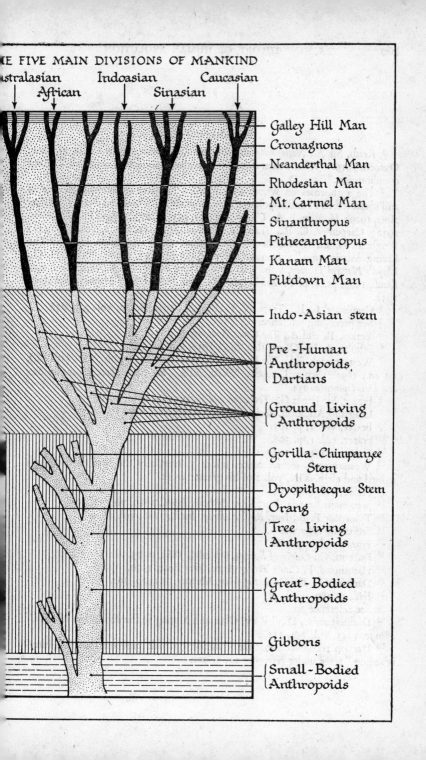

THE FIVE MAIN DIVISIONS OF MANKIND

Australasian   Indoasian   Caucasian
     African   Sinasian

- Galley Hill Man
- Cromagnons
- Neanderthal Man
- Rhodesian Man
- Mt. Carmel Man
- Sinanthropus
- Pithecanthropus
- Kanam Man
- Piltdown Man

- Indo-Asian stem

{ Pre-Human
  Anthropoids,
  Dartians

{ Ground Living
  Anthropoids

- Gorilla-Chimpanzee
  Stem
- Dryopithecque Stem
- Orang

{ Tree Living
  Anthropoids

{ Great-Bodied
  Anthropoids

- Gibbons

{ Small-Bodied
  Anthropoids

REFERENCES

[1] Keith, Sir A., *Nationality and Race from an Anthropologist's Point of View*, Oxford, 1919. What I then named " race consciousness " I now call " group consciousness."

[2] The authorities on whom I have relied for data concerning the sexual and social habits of anthropoid apes are :—Yerkes, Robert and Ada, *The Great Apes*, 1929; Hooton, E. A., *Up from the Ape*, 1931, p. 273; *Man's Poor Relations*, 1942; Carpenter, C. R., *Trans. N. Y. Acad. Sc.*, 1942, Ser. 2, vol. 4, p. 248; Bingham, H. L., *Gorillas in a Native Habitat*, 1932; Coolidge, H. K., " The Living Asiatic Ages " : *Harvard Alumni Bull.*, May 27, 1938; Forbes, H. O., *Lloyd's Natural History*, vols. 1, 2, 1896; Dyce-Sharp, N. A., *Proc. Zool. Soc, Lond.*, 1927, pt. 4, p. 1; Zuckerman, S., *The Social Life of Monkeys and Apes.* 1932.

[3] Carpenter, C. R., *Trans. N. Y. Acad. Sc.*, 1942, Ser. 2, vol. 4, p. 248.

[4] See preceding reference.

[5] Yerkes, R. and A., *The Great Apes*, 1929, p. 256.

[6] Schultz, A. H., *Quart. Rev. Biol.*, 1936, vol. 11, 268.

[7] Westermarck, Ed., *The History of Human Marriage*, 2 vols., 1921 (5th ed.), 1st ed., 1891. See vol. 2, chs. XVIII, XIX. See also *Three Essays on Sex and Development*, 1934.

[8] Frazer, Sir James G., *Totemism and Exogamy*, 4 vols., 1910.

[9] Lang and Atkinson, *Social Origins: The Primal Law*, 1903.

[10] Frazer, vol. 1, p. 103.

[11] Frazer, vol. 1, p. 308.

[12] Frazer, vol. 1, p. 304.

[13] Westermarck, see references under 7, especially the first of the essays named and chap. XIX, vol. 2 of his greater work.

[14] Frazer, vol. 4, p. 104.

[15] Seligman, Brenda, *Jour. Roy. Anthrop. Instit.*, 1929, vol. 59, 368.

[16] Tylor, Sir E. B., *Jour. Roy. Anthrop. Instit.*, 1888, vol. 18, 267.

[17] See under reference 9.

[18] Frazer, vol. 1, p. 287.

[19] Darwin, C., *Origin of Species*, 6th edit., 1885, p. 75.

[20] Hammond, J., *Cairn Terrier Assoc. Year Book*, 1930.

[21] Darwin, C., *The Descent of Man*, Murray, 1913, p. 292.

[22] *Ibid.*, p. 280.

[23] See reference 20.

[24] Darlington, C. D., " Race, Class and Mating in the Evolution of Man," *Nature*, 1943, vol. 152, 315.

[25] Darwin recognized that the " wandering male prevents too close interbreeding "; see under reference 21, p. 901.

THE CONTRASTED FATES OF MAN AND APE

Synopsis.—This essay seeks to explain why the evolutionary fate of man differs so greatly from that of his co-descendant, the chimpanzee. A clue to this problem is provided by a study of the evolution of the erect or orthograde posture. How the author became drawn into the study of posture. A brief account of the hypothesis he formulated in the last decade of the nineteenth century. The modifications of the orthograde posture in the gibbon, orang, chimpanzee, gorilla, and man. Geological epochs and their estimated duration. So far the earliest evidence for the existence of the orthograde posture comes from the Lower Oligocene. The author's original hypothesis has had to be altered in several respects, but he still holds that the human stock did not separate from that of the great anthropoids until late in the Oligocene period. It was then that postural modifications appeared which gave man and the great anthropoids their respective modes of progression. These modifications confirmed the arboreal adaptations of the great anthropoids, while they set man free from them, thus permitting him to become a ground form. The parable of the postural genes. Evidence that the gorilla and chimpanzee have become less human and more simian in their structural characterization.

WHY, then, has evolutionary fate treated ape and man so differently? The one has been left in the obscurity of its native jungle, while the other has been given a glorious exodus leading to dominion of earth, sea, and sky. Of the four surviving forms of anthropoid apes, the gibbon, divided into many species, inhabits those forest lands which lie between Assam and Java; the orang is confined to certain jungle tracts of Borneo and Sumatra; while the chimpanzee and gorilla, which are nearly akin in a structural sense, have their home in the tropical belt of Africa. Students of evolution are of opinion that, at no remote period, as geologists reckon time, anthropoids and man were represented by a single ancestral stock, and that the forms set out upon their evolutionary journey from the same starting point, all equipped with germinal potentialities drawn from the same common stock. We have seen that anthropoid groups are just as well organized for evolutionary progress as are primitive groups of humanity. How, then, has it come about that the human population of the world now numbers about 2,000 millions, while the anthropoids, if assembled together from the jungles of the East and of the West, would be found to number under, rather than over, one million? What has made man an evolutionary success and his cousins, the anthropoids, numerical failures? If we knew how man came by his great brain, and why the anthropoid brain falls short of the human measure, we should be in a better position to return an answer. We are far from being in a position to explain the rise of the human brain or the comparative failure of the anthropoid brain, but there is another character which may provide the clue we are in search of—namely, that of posture. If we could give an acceptable account of how the anthropoids came by their varying modes of progression and posture, and how man came by his, then we should be able to throw light on why they have remained in the jungle, while he had succeeded in escaping into the open. I am the more willing to follow up this clue because of two circumstances: first, because the evolution of posture in the higher Primates is a subject to which I have devoted much attention, and, secondly, because in tracing the evolution of man's posture, I shall have opportunities of sketching in outline phases in the historical evolution of man and ape.

This is how I became involved in the study of posture. The spring of 1889 (I being then in my twenty-fourth year) found me medical officer to a mining company which had established its camp right in the heart of a Siamese jungle.[1] In the neighbourhood lived several communities of gibbons and groups of various kinds of catarrhine monkeys, of which I shall mention only one sort, a semnopitheque, or langur, cousin to the Hanuman, or sacred monkey of India. My attention was soon drawn to the fact that the gibbon held his body, and moved his limbs in climbing, quite differently from the method adopted by the langur and other catarrhine monkeys. While in movement in the trees, the gibbon assumed an upright or orthograde posture; when running along a branch, the animal grasped it with its feet, used its hands and arms for support from overhanging branches, and thus carried its body at right angles to its plane of progression. It used its arms in the manner of a gymnast on a trapeze. When making its daring leaps from branch to branch, or from tree to tree, the arms were used as the instruments of propulsion. In contrast to this, catarrhine monkeys, such as the langur, move in quite a different way. Running along a branch on " all fours," they hold their bodies parallel to the planes of progression; their posture is pronograde. When making their leaps, they plunge heavily from tree to tree or from branch to branch; the instruments of propulsion are the hind limbs, combined with a sudden extension of the lumbar part of their spines.

When I began a systematic course of dissection, the anatomy of the gibbon came to me as a revelation; the muscles of its back were disposed, not as in pronograde monkeys, but as in the human body; they were modified to maintain the upright or orthograde posture. So, too, with its body; the thorax and thoracic organs, the abdomen and the abdominal organs, all were closely similar to the condition I was familiar with in the human body. Then, as now, the gibbon was regarded as the most primitive and, in a geological sense, the oldest of all the anthropoidal forms. I therefore supposed that Lamarck, and also Darwin,[2] had been in error when they imagined that the upright posture had come by an ape getting up on its hind limbs; the case of the gibbon seemed to indicate that the erect or orthograde posture came in a downright way—namely, by some form of monkey using its arms as the chief means of support and of progression.

Some years later, when I had made many more dissections and taken a census of the structural characters of anthropoids, both great and small, as well as those of the human body, I framed an hypothesis [3] to account not only for the modes of progression to be observed in these orthograde forms, but also to explain how each of these—man, gorilla, chimpanzee, orang, and gibbon— had come by the assemblage of structural characters to be found in their bodies. In my theory I assumed that the erect or orthograde posture had come into the primate world with the evolution of the gibbon (Hylobates). I assumed, and I had geological evidence to support me, that from the hylobatian or gibbonish stock there had emerged, at an early period, a stock of anthropoids which differed from all which had gone before by their great size of body; this group I named provisionally the " giant Primates."

Living representatives or descendants of this giant group are man, the chimpanzee, the gorilla, and the orang; many members of this stock have become extinct. The chimpanzee, which at one time bore the generic name of Troglodytes, seemed to me the truest living representative of the stage of evolution passed through by the giant Primates, so I named this stage of evolution "troglodytian." Thus it will be seen that my theory postulated three stages in the evolution of the orthograde posture in man and the great anthropoids; first, they passed through a gibbonish or hylobatian phase, then a troglodytian stage, from which man, the gorilla, the chimpanzee, and orang emerged with the particular posture which is now characteristic of each of them. The orang, like the gibbon, has his arms greatly modified to serve as the chief means of support and progression; man, on the other hand, has had his feet, his legs, thighs, and pelvis profoundly modified to serve for this purpose; the chimpanzee uses upper and lower limbs to an equal degree; while the gorilla employs his lower extremities more than his upper in arboreal locomotion. While the anthropoids retain the foot as a grasping organ, man has lost this common heirloom of the Primates; but that at one time his foot did pass through a grasping stage there is ample evidence.

The theory of posture just outlined was formulated in the closing years of the nineteenth century; with the twentieth century came new facts and new considerations necessitating amendments to my working hypothesis. It is with these amendments I now want to deal, but as they involve us in excursions into the geological past we must have a geologist's scale of time for our guidance. The geological ages which concern us, with estimates of their depth of strata and of their duration in years, given in the following table, are based on data provided by Professor Arthur Holmes and other geologists and compiled by my friend Rear-Admiral Beadnell.[4]

Geological Epoch	Depth of Strata in feet	Duration in years
Pleistocene [5]	4,000	1,000,000
Pliocene	13,000	7,000,000
Miocene	14,000	12,000,000
Oligocene	12,000	15,000,000
Eocene	20,000	25,000,000
	63,000	60,000,000

The background of time, in which we are to work, is provided by the last or Tertiary era of the earth's history; the total duration of this era is estimated at sixty million years and is divided, as the above table indicates, into five epochs or periods. In the Eocene no fossil trace of the catarrhine stock has been found—the stock which gave birth to the lines which led on to man, anthropoids, and the monkeys of the Old World. We have to traverse the opening half of the Tertiary era—a period estimated at thirty million years—and so reach the Lower Oligocene, before we find a trace of the beginnings of the catarrhine stock. So far we have had only one glimpse of it—in the Lower Oligocene deposits of the Egyptian Fayum. By 1911 jaws and teeth, representing four Primates of small size, had been unearthed from these deposits.[6] One of these early Primates, Propliopithecus, in characters of teeth and mandible had clear claims to be regarded as ancestral to the gibbon. Although no bones of its body were recovered, there are good grounds for assuming that when they do come to light they will prove that this Primate had evolved, or was evolving, into an orthograde posture. On this somewhat slender basis we assume that the evolution of the orthograde posture was coming into existence some thirty million years ago. Another of the Fayum fossil forms, Apidium, has dental characters which foreshadow those of the pronograde monkeys of the Old World; we assume that it retained the pronograde posture of its Tarsioid ancestor. Two other Fayum forms, Parapithecus and Moeripithecus, have intermediate dental characters and may have been intermediate in their posture. Such, then, is the evidence which permits us to infer that the Lower Oligocene saw the differentiation of the catarrhine stock into orthograde and pronograde forms.

We have to ascend from the Lower Oligocene to a point well within the Miocene, involving an elapse of some twelve or fifteen million years, to reach our next zone of evidence. Here we find the gibbon fully evolved in the fossil form of Pliopithecus; great anthropoids abound, chiefly of the Dryopitheque family. So far, India has proved the richest source of Miocene anthropoids,[7] but Europe and East Africa have provided several representatives of the family.[8] The evidence, scanty as it is, suggests that giant orthograde apes were in process of evolution in the Upper Oligocene, reaching the zenith of their development in the Upper

Miocene and Lower Pliocene. Unfortunately we have to base our knowledge of these great Miocene anthropoids on a study of their teeth and of their jaws; only in a few instances are fragments of fossil limb-bones available to give us guidance as to posture. It has to be confessed that fossil teeth and jaws may mislead us, for teeth which are human in conformation have been found in the fossil anthropoids of South Africa; [9] while teeth of an anthropoid conformation have been found in an early form of man.[10] It is possible that teeth and jaws we are ascribing to Miocene anthropoids may turn out to belong to ancestral forms of man.

The early Pleistocene form of man which Dubois discovered in Java (1892–93), and to which he gave the misnomer of Pithecanthropus, still provides the earliest definite evidence that by the end of the Pliocene period man had attained his full plantigrade mode of progression. From the beginning of the Miocene to the end of the Pliocene epoch, according to our time scale (p. 164), involves the passage of some nineteen million years. It was during this long period, so my theory assumed, that the great anthropoid stock became differentiated into the lines which led to the forms now represented by man, the gorilla, chimpanzee, and orang. There is, however, one recent piece of evidence bearing on the evolution of the plantigrade posture which demands consideration. In 1925 Professor Dart [11] announced the discovery of fossil remains of a great anthropoid in South Africa; since then Dr. Broom has found fossil bones of two other kinds of the same type. All are attributable to the Pleistocene, although one may be of late Pliocene date. The South African anthropoids had larger brains than the gorilla or chimpanzee; their teeth were more human than anthropoid in character; fragments of limb bones have been found, and from them it has been inferred that in their posture and in manner of progression these anthropoids were more or less plantigrade. If this latter inference proves to be valid,[12] then we have in these South African anthropoids creatures which were intermediate to man and ape in characters of brain and of teeth, as well as in posture. The South African discoveries throw no light on the date at which man's plantigrade posture was evolved, but they do suggest that man came by his posture while his body was still anthropoidal in its characterization.

Such, then, was the theory I formulated to account for the structural composition of man and ape. Let me now turn to the

" facts " and " considerations " which have led me to alter my original theory. First, there was the recognition that the hylobatian progression of the gibbon was not primary but an extreme specialization evolved out of an earlier and simpler form, in which both upper and lower limbs were used equally in maintaining the orthograde posture. My theory now assumes that the early orthograde Primates of the Oligocene will prove to have been dualists in the use of their limbs—making an equal use of both upper and lower limbs. Secondly, I had to account for the human hand. Man must have separated from the anthropoid stock before their hands had been transformed into grasping-hooks with greatly reduced thumbs. We may safely assume that in the early Oligocene Primates the hands were not modified into grasping-hooks, but had well-developed thumbs and a proportionate development of fingers. It is therefore tempting to suppose that the human stock parted from the primitive orthograde forms of the Oligocene period while that stock had small bodies and hands which still retained their grasping qualities, and that as man's lower limbs became more and more his organs of support, his hands were free to preserve all their more primitive characters. But if we make man's stock break away thus early—some thirty million years ago—we are brought face to face with a difficulty. It is not only size of body that links man to the great anthropoids; he has a large number of other important characters in common with them, such as a prolonged period of pregnancy, of nursing, and of infancy. His brain, although larger and more powerful, is still framed on anthropoid lines; and he shares with them many special structural features. If we assume that the stock which ultimately gave rise to the human form broke away from the primitive orthograde stock in Lower Oligocene times, then we must suppose that man and anthropoids have come independently by the set of structural and functional qualities just enumerated. It seems to me far more probable that man and the great anthropoids remained united in the same stock until late Oligocene times, when a stage was reached characterized by a relatively great size and strength of body. It was as this stage was being approached that I now believe postural differentiation to have been effected. We may safely assume that the early orthograde stock of large-bodied Primates was divided into numerous competitive groups, all of them adapted to an orthograde arboreal

M

mode of life. In the group ancestral to the chimpanzee and gorilla, upper and lower limbs served equally in the maintenance of posture; in the group or groups ancestral to the orang, the upper limb became the more important means of support, while in the groups ancestral to man, the lower limbs underwent modifications to serve as the chief, or perhaps the sole, means of support and progression. While anthropoids became more and more adapted for an arboreal existence, our pre-human anthropoid ancestry underwent modifications which fitted it more and more for a life outside the jungle.

The stock of large-bodied orthograde Primates we assume to have come into existence in late Oligocene times, and their place of evolution was more likely to have been in the tropical forests of Africa than in those of Asia or of Europe. If a zoologist had been there to examine them, he would have classified them among the large anthropoid apes. He would have noted, too, that in the isolated communities into which this Oligocene stock had become divided there were incipient changes in posture. He would have drawn the inference that the genes which regulate the development of postural structures were in a plastic state.

With this stock of Oligocene anthropoids in our mind's eye we are in a position to answer the question posed at the beginning of this essay: Why has evolutionary destiny dealt so differently with man and the chimpanzee, co-descendants of the same ancestral stock of large-bodied Oligocene Primates? The parable of the talents [13] points the way to an answer. In this ancient case talents were represented by the germinal potentialities which are handed on from generation to generation by means of genes. When a stock becomes separated into isolated, inbreeding groups, there is never an equal distribution of genes. To one group fall potentialities which are denied to other groups. To the pre-human groups fell that set of genes which were biased towards making the body and brain dependent on the lower limbs for support and progression, and to deprive the hands and arms of their locomotory function and make them the domestic servants of body and brain. The pre-chimpanzee groups were less fortunate in the " draw " for genes. To them fell postural genes of a more conservative nature, genes which worked on developing arm and leg, on hand and foot, so as to make them better adapted to an arboreal life. Thus the postural adaptations which fell to the chimpanzee confine its species to a life in the jungle, while those which fell to man fitted him to become a denizen of the whole earth.

Man has changed greatly since Oligocene times, but it must not be supposed that the chimpanzee has stood stock-still; it, too, has made evolutionary progress. The Miocene deposits of Kenya have yielded the fossil remains of a large anthropoid which may very well be, as Hopwood [8] has supposed, ancestral to both the gorilla and chimpanzee. One can conceive the teeth and mandible of this fossil anthropoid being moulded into the forms now found in living chimpanzees and gorillas. Especially noteworthy in the mandible of the Kenya anthropoid are certain features which are also met with in the mandible of early forms of man. These humanoid features have disappeared from the mandibles of the gorilla and chimpanzee; their mandibles have become more and more simian in their characterization. While the chimpanzee has retained a moderate size of body (65 kilos, 145 lb.), the gorilla, particularly the male, has increased in size and strength, the male often attaining a weight four times that of a man or of a chimpanzee. His characters indicate a vigorous action on the part of the pituitary gland. Especially noteworthy, as compared with the chimpanzee, is an increased adaptation of the lower limb for the purposes of support and progression.

REFERENCES

[1] For a more detailed account of my early inquiries into the orthograde posture, see *Amer. Jour. Phy. Anthrop.*, 1940, vol. 26, 251.

[2] Keith, Sir A., " Six Lectures on Man's Posture; Its Evolution and Disorder," *Brit. Med. Jour.*, 1923, from March 17 to April 21. Lecture 1 gives an account of the opinions formulated by Lamarck and by Darwin.

[3] See *Nature*, 1911, vol. 85, p. 509; *Revista di Antropologia*, 1916, vol. 20, p. 3. (Lo Schema Dell' Origine Umana.)

[4] Beadnell, Rear-Admiral C. M., *A Picture Book of Evolution*, 1934, p. 63. Rear-Admiral Beadnell died in 1947 at the age of 76. He was president of the Rationalist Press Association.

[5] I here give the longer estimate of the Pleistocene favoured by geologists, although I think the evidence as it now stands supports Zeuner's shorter estimate of a little over half a million. The estimate given of the Pleistocene includes also the post-glacial (post-Pleistocene) period, which had a duration of about 12,000 years.

[6] Schlosser, Max, " Ueber einige fossile Saugetiere aus dem Oligocene von Egypten Fayum," *Zool. Anz.*, 1910, vol. 35, p. 500; Gregory, W. K., *The Origin and Evolution of the Human Dentition*, 1922, p. 286.

7 Pilgrim, G. E., *Records Geol. Survey, India*, 1915, vol. 45, p. 1; Black, Davidson, "Asia and the Dispersal of the Primates," *Bull. Geol. Soc. China*, 1925, vol. 4, p. 133.

8 Hopwood, A. T., "Miocene Primates from Kenya," *Jour. Linnean Soc.* (Zoology), 1933, vol. 38, p. 437; MacInnes, D. G., *Jour. East African and Uganda Nat. Hist. Soc.*, 1943, vol. 17, p. 141.

9 For an account of the earlier work on South African anthropoid see my *New Discoveries relating to the Antiquity of Man*, 1931.

10 Keith, Sir A., *The Antiquity of Man*, 1925, vol. 2, p. 687.

11 Dart, Raymond, *Nature*, 1925, Feb. 7, p. 193.

12 Broom, Robert, and Schepers, G. W. H., *The South African Fossil Ape-Men; The Australopithecinæ*, Transvaal Museum Memoir, No. 2, 1946. The discovery in 1947 of the pelvis of one of the fossil anthropoids confirmed the view that their posture was human. (See Broom and Robinson, *Nature*, 1947, vol. 160, p. 153.)

13 St. Matthew, XXV, 14.

SEX DIFFERENTIATION AND SEX HORMONES AS FACTORS IN HUMAN EVOLUTION

Synopsis.—The individuals of a primitive evolving community are specialized in body and mind for three forms of activity: (1) for the production of new lives; (2) for the care and nourishment of the young; (3) for the protection of mothers and children. Groups are selected according to the efficiency of these three forms of activity. Doubt as to the innate nature of man's paternal feelings. Sex differences in anthropoids compared with those in man. Differences in cranial markings, in canine teeth, in stature, and weight of body. Stress is laid on the sexual difference in size of brain. The correlation in the development of body and brain as illustrated by the increase and reduction in size of the canine teeth. A quotient expressive of the degree of sex differentiation. The overlap of sexes in point of differentiation. The degree of differentiation determined by group selection. The action of sex hormones on body and brain. The effects of castration. The action of the male hormone on the female body. The mental qualities attributed to women and to men. The action of such qualities in primitive societies. The significance to be attached to the preponderance of the male size of brain. Women retain longer the joyousness of youth. The relationship between the various forms or kinds of human affection.

In this essay we are concerned with three essential activities carried on by members of every evolving community, whether that enclosed community is made up of anthropoid apes or of primitive human beings. The first of these activities is destined to secure a due mixture of the seeds or genes which circulate within the group. This end is attained by the separation of the individuals composing a community into sexes; in the male, during embryonic development, the parts immediately concerned with reproduction are modified in one direction; in the female the same parts are modified in another direction. With the differentiation of the sex organs there is also a correlated change in mental organization; the brain of the male is so constituted that when puberty is reached an urge towards the opposite sex becomes imperious; equally compelling are the calls which sex makes on the mentality of the female. If sex passion fails within a community or tribe, then that tribe comes to an end.

The activity just named secures the creation of new lives within a community. The second activity with which we have to do is that which assures the conception, bearing, nourishing, and nursing of these new lives. Here, too, the brain as well as the body of the female, be she ape or be she human, are modified, the breasts to give milk and the brain to give succour. The passions of the mother are so biased that she will sacrifice her own life to save that of her child. "Natural affections," declared Reid,[1] "spring up in the mother's heart . . . as the milk springs up in her breasts." Whether the mind of the male has a corresponding inborn bias is still a moot point. There is credible evidence that among the most primitive of surviving anthropoids, the gibbons, the male shares the care of the young with his mate, but the evidence that affirms the same of the male chimpanzee is much less reliable. For a male chimpanzee to recognize his progeny from that of others he must be monogamous, and of this the chimpanzee seems to be incapable. His habits are definitely polygamous, and, so far as our evidence goes, the same was true of early man. Yet I think there can be no doubt that modern fathers are innately biased in favour of their own children. There is a letter which Darwin wrote when his first child was born that reveals such bias.[2] A passage from this letter runs as follows: " I had not the smallest conception there was so much in a five-month baby. He is so charming that I cannot pretend to any modesty. You will perceive from this that I have a fine degree of paternal fervour."

The point just discussed—whether or not man comes of a stock in which the males were endowed with paternal feelings—bears on the third of the communal activities we are now considering. This third activity concerns the defence of a community, particularly of its mothers and children, which constitute the core of every live community. To carry out this activity both bodies and brains of males have been modified; their bodies have come by bone, brawn, strength, and mass; their mentality is biased so that when the need arises, they will sacrifice their lives to save those of mothers and children. They have to varying degrees a fighting spirit born in them; to sustain this spirit they have come by an increase of courage and of a blind and passionate resolution to do or die. Thus I presume that the greater physical strength and fighting prowess of the male have come into being, and been selected, not as Darwin thought, to give one male victory over another in the contest for a female, but arose primarily for group defence. But I also admit that " the law of battle " has tended to strengthen the special characters of the male.

The success of any tribe or group, whether composed of anthropoids or of human beings, will depend on how efficiently and spontaneously these three services are carried out by its members. Sexual passions must be strong and healthy; maternal affections must abound; security must be guaranteed by the prowess of the protectors. The group which is rich in all these qualities will outlast a group less well endowed; such qualities will be favoured and strengthened by " group selection." The extent to which the sexes are differentiated will depend on how far males and females have become adapted to carry out their communal duties. Over-differentiation or under-differentiation may be equally inimical to the life of a group.

To what extent were the sexes differentiated in the simian stock which ultimately gave origin to man? A partial answer to this question may be obtained if we consider the extent to which sex differentiation has been carried in the surviving anthropoid apes, seeing that they are man's collaterals in descent. I have had a long experience in " sexing " the skulls of anthropoids and men, so I turn first to the cranial characters which distinguish the skulls of adult males from those of adult females. In all anthropoid skulls the bony crests which give attachment to the muscles of mastication and of the neck are so strongly developed in males that I cannot remember ever coming across a case which left me in doubt. This is particularly true of the muscular cranial crests of the male gorilla and of the male orang. In the skulls of chimpanzees and gibbons sex differences are less, but always recognizable. It is otherwise when one comes to deal with collections of human skulls; in every hundred specimens there are always some fifteen or twenty which are so poorly marked that one is left in doubt about their sex. So far as concerns cranial characters, sex discrimination is least marked among modern races of mankind and most in gorillas and orangs. As to the degree of separation of sexes in the earliest forms of man so far discovered, little can be said because the specimens available are so few in number and often so fragmentary in nature. The same handicap prevents any definite statement being made as to the degree of sex separation in fossil forms of anthropoid apes.

The cranial crests of anthropoid apes may be used as indications of fighting power, for their size is largely determined by the development of the anthropoids' chief weapons of offence—the canine teeth. These reach their largest size in the males of the gorilla and orang. In the male gorilla the lower canines rise to a height (in the average) of 9 mm. above the level of the teeth immediately behind them; in the female to a height of 5 mm.; the sexual difference is 4 mm. This sexual difference may also be regarded as a measure of the ferocity of the sexes. In the orangs the canine measurements are identical with those in gorillas, but in chimpanzees the measurements are decidedly less, the canine heights in males being 5 mm., in females 3 mm., the sexual difference being 2 mm. In gibbons, although the canine of the male is the stouter tooth, in height both are alike—namely, 9 mm. This is consonant with the known fact that the female gibbon is as ferocious as the male. In modern races of mankind, although the canine of the male is usually the stouter tooth, there is no difference as regards their degree of projection; in both sexes the canines share the level of their neighbours. Thus we reach the conclusion that, so far as concerns canine development, the sexual difference is least in man and greatest in the gorilla and orang.

Now, it is assumed by many authorities that man has inherited his small canines from his early Oligocene ancestry, and that at no time did he share in the caninization which overtook the anthropoid apes. I, on the other hand, am not alone in holding the opinion that man, in the simian stages of his evolution, had canine teeth which, in point of development, were equal at least to that seen in chimpanzees. Man's canines are formed in the same anomalous position as the large canines of anthropoid apes; [3] projecting canines have been observed in two fossil human types—at Piltdown and in Java. [4]

If we believe that in the earlier stages of his evolution man had large canines, then we are confronted by a problem which is both interesting and intricate. Why did man's canines become reduced? How was the reduction in their development brought about? The first question is the more easy to approach. When man's hands became free and his brain had reached that degree of development which enabled him to become a weapon-user, he would have depended no longer on his canine teeth as his chief weapons of defence; their reduction would then have become advantageous to him. The second question remains: How was this reduction brought about? I do not believe that mere disuse brings about a developmental atrophy; nor do I believe that it can be accounted for by " natural selection " working by itself. We have to presume a factor, of which as yet we have no direct evidence—a factor which works during the development of the embryo and brings about changes in the organization of the brain in correspondence with evolutionary changes in the body. With the decay in man's brain of the physical substratum which supports the instinct to use the teeth as weapons of offence, I presume there also came about a reduction in the bodily structures so used.

After this somewhat abstruse discussion I now turn to the simpler matter of sex differentiation in size and strength of body. In a primitive community, such as is to be found in Central Australia,[5] the mean stature of women is 126·2 mm. (5 ins.) less than that of the men. A woman's stature is 94 per cent of the man's; the sexual difference is 6 per cent. As regards weight the difference is much greater, the average male weighing 125·2 lb. (57 km.), the female, 95·7 lb. (44·8 km.); the female weighs 76·4 per cent of the male, the sexual difference being 23·6 per cent. Anthropoid and human statures are not comparable, but weights are; unfortunately our knowledge of anthropoid weights is still defective. Of the anthropoids, the chimpanzee stands nearest to man in size and strength of body. The adult male weighs from 60 to 65 km.; the female 45 to 50 km.; the sexual difference being about 6 per cent. The sexual difference among gorillas is very much greater; the adult female weighs about 72 km., while the male weighs twice, thrice, or even four times the weight of the female.[6] The sexual difference in size is thus of a high order. The sexual difference among orangs, although less than among gorillas, is very much higher than among chimpanzees. Although the female gibbon has a slightly longer body than the male,[7] the mean weight of the female is only 91 per cent of the mean weight of the male (5·9 km.). The sexual difference is thus 9 per cent. In the extent to which the male body is differentiated in size from that of the female, man finds a place between the chimpanzee and gorilla, his differentiation being much less than in the gorilla, but greater than in the chimpanzee.

The most reliable, as well as the most interesting, index of the degree to which sexes are differentiated is to be found in weight of brain, or, in the absence of such information, the volume of the cranial cavity which contains the brain. Let us take a sample of modern Europeans first.[8] The mean weight of the male brain in this sample was 1410 gm.; that of the female 1250 gm. The female brain is thus 88·6 per cent of the male amount; the index of differentiation is 11·4 per cent. In Negroes, although the brain is smaller, the index figure is practically the same as in Europeans. Turning to the aborigines of Australia as representatives of primitive man, we have to deal, not with weights of brains stated in grammes, but with the capacity of the brain chamber stated in cubic centimetres.[9] The mean cranial capacity of the male Australian [10] is 1287 c.c. (with a range from 1040 c.c. to 1630 c.c.); that of the female is 1145 c.c. (with a range of 1010 c.c. to 1280 c.c.). The volume of the brain of an aboriginal woman is 89 per cent of that of the male; the sexual difference (or index) is 11 per cent. The constancy of an index of 11 per cent for all three races is noteworthy. Taking the chimpanzee as a representative of the great anthropoids, we find that the mean cranial capacity [11] of the male is 420 c.c., that of the female 390 c.c., the female capacity being 93 per cent of the male. The index of sex differentiation is thus 7 per cent, compared to 11 per cent for the Australian aborigines. The cranial capacity of the male chimpanzee varies from 350 to 480 c.c., compared with a range of 1040 to 1630 in male aborigines; the range for female chimpanzees is from 320 c.c. to 450 c.c., compared to that of 1010 c.c. to 1280 c.c. in the aboriginal women of Australia. In gibbons the sex quotient is 7·2—nearly the same as in chimpanzees—whereas in gorillas it is 12, being somewhat greater than in human races, while the maximum of sexual differentiation is reached in orangs, with a quotient of 14.

I have gone into the degree of sexual differentiation revealed by a comparison of cranial capacities for several reasons. We learn from them that man, the gorilla, and the orang represent a group of the great Primates in which there is a high degree of sexual differentiation, much more than in the chimpanzee and gibbon, which I infer to stand nearer to the early orthograde ancestry in this character. If we arrange the capacities given for male and female chimpanzees into a continuous series, it will be seen that many males fall short of the female capacities and that many females exceed those of the male. The same is true of a combined series of aboriginal capacities; the sexes overlap. The same overlap is seen if we group the sexes together according to size and strength of body; at one end of the series are those moulded towards the small ultra-feminine frame of body; at the other end of the series those of a robust and ultra-masculine type; between these extremes is a myriad of intermediate types of men and women. One can readily perceive, in the competition of a primitive human group with other groups, that conditions might arise which favoured the group which was strong towards the masculine end of the scale, masculinity being thus selected. Or, opposite conditions might favour feminine qualities of body. In either case it is evident that the sexual balance of an evolving group is determined by the result of the competition of that group with other groups; the group with an optimum sexual balance is a winner. Under the conditions in which humanity was evolved in the primal world, the optimum degree of sexual differentiation is represented by the amount by which the mean cranial capacity of women falls short of the mean capacity of men—namely, by 11 per cent. Whether this will continue to be the optimum amount under modern conditions is a matter which will be discussed in a later essay.

Sex differentiation is fundamental; a boy became a boy at the moment when the egg from which he sprang was fertilized, and so with every girl. If, however, we pass on to the period of puberty, we find certain special factors at work. I shall touch very briefly on the part taken by these factors in determining sex characters. If the testes are removed from a boy, the growth of both body and mind become altered. His voice does not break; if he belongs to a hairy race, he remains beardless; hair does not grow on the usual sexual sites; his skin changes in texture; his muscular development is lessened; his bones become changed in shape and length. He becomes indifferent to the presence of women. He is devoid of sexual jealousy; he has no spirit to compete, to struggle, or fight. Why should the removal of the testes bring about, not only a suppression of sexual characterization of the body, but also lead to the appearance in it of new features? It has to be remembered that the chemical substances or hormones thrown into the circulation by the testes do not act directly on larynx, skin, hair, and muscle, but produce their effects by acting on the pituitary gland, which is the chief source of the hormones which regulate the growth of sexual and other characters of the body. With the removal of the testes, the pituitary, escaping from the control of the testicular male hormone, changes in its structure and in its action. Thus the non-development of the secondary sexual characters of the body is due to a pituitary failure. One may suspect, too, that the mental changes are also due to a pituitary defect, for the pituitary gland is near to, and closely connected with, the nerve centres of sex. Presently, when we come to deal with the differentiation of mankind into races, the evolutionary importance of the hormonal system will become increasingly apparent.

There is a lack of precise information of what happens to women when their ovaries are removed in girlhood; the effects produced are much less apparent than those which occur in castrated boys. We do know, however, what happens to young women when, as a result of disease, their systems are brought under the influence of the male hormone. Broster [12] has studied many of these cases of " virilism " in young women. Their bodies assume the outward marks of the male; men no longer attract them; maternal affections vanish; they lose all interest in feminine pursuits and duties. Healthy ovarian action is essential for the full manifestation of femininity.

The most complete analysis of the sexual differentiation of men and women known to me is that made by Havelock Ellis. [13] Let us apply his list of female traits, not to women in general, but to members of a primitive society, so that we may realize the social significance of such traits in early times. When he says that women are more conservatively minded, I take this to mean that they are upholders of tribal traditions, seeking to hand them on to their children just as they received from their own mothers.

Women are said to have an intuitional aptitude in discerning character; such a faculty makes them apt in deciphering the thoughts and motives of their social fellows. They are said to be more susceptible to praise and to blame than men; it would be equally true to say they are more ready to praise and to blame; more given to criticize social behaviour. In this way they establish and uphold tribal opinion. They are said to excel in acting, which I take to imply that they can behave so as to hide their true thoughts and motives—a trait which would be particularly useful in a society of masterful males. Women's nature is said to be more susceptible of suggestion, more docile, easier of domestication, more responsive to instinct, and of greater emotionality. All these qualities fit women to be the staid element of society. " Women," said Darwin, " are more tender and less selfish "; they have the warmer hearts.

It would take me too far afield to tabulate the prevalent traits attributed to men by Darwin and by Ellis. Suffice it to say that they are the characters of mind and body needful for those who are responsible for the protection and welfare of their tribe. They are the qualities which make them successful lovers. In the anthropoid world the male establishes his dominance by the free use of physical force, and this policy, one may suspect, also held in the early world of mankind. One minor trait of the sexual morality of men may be noted here. While they impose a single code of morality on their women, that of chastity. they regard breaches of this code by themselves with a lenient eye. In this respect men are dual codists, while they are single codists as regards their mates.

Readers may have detected two omissions in my discussion of sex characterization. I have given no explanation of the preponderating weight of the male brain. Much of this is due to the greater mass of the male body; the bigger the frame the larger is the administrative outfit in the central nervous system.[14] I do not think that this factor accounts for the whole of the difference. I suspect that a certain part of the male preponderance is due to the specialization of his brain for functions which fall to the lot of the protective male. The other omission refers to changes in mentality which comes with age. Women tend to retain the joyousness of youth to a greater degree than do men. The male anthropoid, when he reaches adult years, turns sedate, taciturn, and sulky, while the female behaves more as the young do. A corresponding change is often to be noted in men.

Here seems the proper place to devote a paragraph to the discussion of one of the many abstruse problems which dog the footsteps of the student of human evolution. What is the relationship between the mental bonds which link a mother to her child, a lover to his lass, and those which bind together the children of the same family or the members of the same community into a social whole? Have each of these bonds been evolved separately, or is one of them the parent of the others? Westermarck [15] accepted Freud's explanation—namely, that the passionate self-surrender of lovers represents the basis from which the two other forms of instinctive affection arose. Sutherland [16] and many other authorities regard the maternal affections as the evolutionary basis of all the others. There remains a third mode of interpretation—namely, that the special affections of the mother and of the lover are but exaggerations of the social affections. I am inclined to accept the third explanation. When the sex glands are removed in childhood the social aptitude remains, but the mother's love and the lover's passion are no longer developed. This fact is in favour of the primacy of social feelings.

Perhaps the greatest mental difference between man and ape is the exaltation of the faculties which wait upon man's quest of sex. "Love," said Hume, "is cloaked parenthood." [17]

REFERENCES

[1] Reid, Thos., *Essays on the Active Powers of Men.*

[2] Darwin, Sir Francis, *The Life and Letters of Charles Darwin*, vol. 1, p. 300.

[3] Keith, Sir A., *The Antiquity of Man*, 1925, p. 675.

[4] Weidenreich, Franz, *Anthrop. Papers Amer. Mus. Nat. Hist.*, 1945, vol. 40, pt. 1.

[5] Campbell, T. D., and others, *Oceania*, 1936, vol. 7, p. 101.

[6] Schultz, A. H., *Quat. Rev. Biol.*, 1934, vol. 2, p. 259.

[7] Schultz, A. H., *Amer. Jour. Phys. Anthrop.*, 1944, N.S., 2, p. 1.

[8] Pearl, R., *Biometrika*, 1905, vol. 4, pts. 1, 2.

[9] For relationship between brain-weight and cranial capacity see article by the author in *Jour. Anat.*, 1895, vol. 29, p. 282.

[10] Basedow, H., *Zeitschr. Ethnol.*, 1910, p. 124.

[11] Hagedoorn, A., *Anat. Anz.*, 1926, vol. 60, p. 117.

[12] Broster, L. R., and others, *The Adrenal Cortex and Intersexuality*, 1938.

[13] Ellis, Havelock, *Man and Woman*, 2nd ed., 1897.

[14] Darwin, Charles, *The Descent of Man*, Murray, 1913, p. 857.

[15] Westermarck, E., *Three Essays on Sex and Development*, 1934.

[16] Sutherland, Alex., *The Origin and Growth of the Moral Instinct*, 1898.

[17] Hume, David, *Essays and Treatises on Several Subjects*, 1772, vol. 1, p. 237.

SEXUAL SELECTION AND HORMONAL ACTION AS FACTORS IN THE DIFFERENTIATION OF MANKIND INTO RACES

Synopsis.—Darwin called in " sexual selection" to explain racial differences. His conception of the manner in which it acts. Sexual selection in a chimpanzee community. Love-making and mating in a primitive human society. Even in a civilized society mating is mainly local. Westermarck's dictum. Sexual selection favours the survival of the instinctively minded. How far " like will to like" is true. Lovers show a great diversity of taste in their choice of mates. Taste is environmental in its judgment. The problem of sexual jealousy and of marital jealousy. The triple process concerned in bringing about evolutionary change. The production of racial characters by hormone action. The discovery of hormones. Starling's forecast. Examples of hormone action. The pituitary gland. It can bring about orderly as well as disorderly changes in the body. Much still awaits elucidation. Hormones and genes. Even in inbred societies there is a wide individual variation, and hence opportunities of sexual choice. Sexual selection is a minor factor in human evolution. The first step in the differentiation of a new race.

The Descent of Man was published on 24th February, 1871, soon after its author had entered on his sixty-third year. At the end of Part 1, in which he summarized his evidence in support of man's evolutionary origin, he had to confess that none of the means he had postulated explained the racial differences which separate Negro from Mongol, or Mongol from European or Caucasian. " We have now seen," he admitted, " that the external characteristic differences between the races of man cannot be accounted for in a satisfactory manner by the direct action of the conditions of life, nor by the effects of the continued use of parts, nor through the principle of correlation . . . but there remains one important agency, namely Sexual Selection, which appears to have acted powerfully on man, as on many animals . . . it can further be shown that the differences between the races of man, as in colour, hairiness, form of features, etc., are of a kind which might have been expected to come under the influence of sexual selection." [1] Thereupon he proceeds to Part 2, which is an exposition of his theory of sexual selection.

Darwin used the following simile [2] to illustrate his conception of how sexual selection brings about evolutionary change: " If during many years two careful breeders rear animals of the same family, and do not compare them together, or with a common standard, the animals are found to have become, to the surprise of the owners, slightly different." This, he explains, is due to each owner selecting, and thus modifying, the animals to answer to his own taste or standard. A similar effect will be produced, so he inferred, if the males of a community choose their mates, over a long series of generations, according to the standard of taste which prevails in their community. He notes that:—

> " the men of each race prefer what they are accustomed to; they cannot endure any great change; but they like variety, and admire each characteristic carried to a moderate extreme. Men accustomed to a nearly oval face, to straight and regular features, and to bright colours, admire, as we Europeans know, those points when strongly developed. On the other hand, men accustomed to a broad face, with high cheek-bones, a depressed nose, black skin, admire these peculiarities when strongly marked." [3]

If the Negro steadily sought for a mate with the blackest and glossiest of skins, with thick and pouting lips, with eyes of charcoal, and with the woolliest of hair; if the Mongol sought his bride according to the degree her eyes were of the almond shape, her cheek-bones high, with root of nose duly submerged and hair black and straight; if the European lover were constantly partial to the feminine features portrayed by the sculptors of classical Greece, then sexual selection would be a powerful factor in bringing about the divergence of human races. How far modern evidence supports Darwin's theory will come up for discussion as we proceed. Meanwhile, the extracts just given will place the reader in touch with the main features of his theory.

N

To begin our inquiry, let us note first the manner in which courting and mating are carried out in a chimpanzee community. Such a community, as we have already seen (p. 149), is a closed society; intruders are driven off. Young chimpanzees are thus limited in their choice of mates; they have to be content with what is produced at home. There is, however, the exceptional case of the " rogue " animal; it may be that he has escaped from his home circle to search for a mate abroad; more probably he has been defeated by a rival male, and so outlawed. Although no one has seen a contest between males for a mate in a jungle community, it is very likely that such contests do occur. The male chimpanzee is an aggressive and imperious lover when in captivity, forcing his embraces several times daily on reluctant females.[4] Only when he has received, or expects to receive, favour from a female does he show a preferential treatment towards her.[5] To this degree the male may be said to be a lover. Nevertheless, there is selection in the choice of mates, for preference and aversions are persistently manifested by the younger female animals; such animals seek to make themselves sexually attractive by stamping and whirling movements which may be regarded as incipient forms of dance.[6] The female begins to menstruate in her ninth year; before then her vulval parts become greatly swollen and tumid; at the mid-menstrual phase, when the ovum is shed, this swelling reaches its maximal development; [4] it is then that the female obtrudes herself unashamedly on the male. Yet Yerkes [6] observed a pair seek seclusion before embracing. In chimpanzee communities love is a naked passion dominated by instinct.

In primitive human societies a lover's choice was restricted to his home community, just as much as is the case with chimpanzees. Even in the myriad of living tribal people, where the practice of exogamy is carried out with rigour, a young man's choice of a bride is limited to the young women of his allotted group; often his bride has to be a cousin; nevertheless he has a choice, even if it is restricted. If he selects the bride which seems most attractive to him, thus exercising his taste, his act of selecting will serve in moulding a local type, as Darwin postulated.

Even in modern civilized societies choice of mates is limited by many circumstances—by locality, by class, by nation, by language, and by race. It would take me too far afield to tabulate the evidence which reveals the extent to which mating still remains local; a few instances will suffice. My first witness is the late Professor Karl Pearson.[7] " In the Yorkshire dales from which my ancestors came . . . nearly everyone was my fourth cousin or was more nearly related." To give such a result, mating in those dales must have been local over a series of generations. " Fancies of young people," said Galton, " are so incalculable and so irresistable . . . yet ninety-five per cent marry according to the custom of their nation . . . each pair within their own place and circle." [8] " In German villages," according to Boas,[9] " fifty per cent of marriages have common ancestry." Gobineau said the same thing of the villages of France. Hocart [10] relates that of fifty-three marriages celebrated within a commune in Egypt, thirty-one were between inhabitants of the same village or commune, thirteen with neighbouring communes, only ten marrying outside the district. Local marriages tend to produce a distinctive local population, but this result must be ascribed to inbreeding rather than to sexual selection.

The evidence I have touched on is altogether against Westermarck's dictum that " proximity creates aversion," [11] and therefore lovers seek their mates outside their native communities. Yet it has to be admitted that there is a degree of truth in Westermarck's contention. Men who go abroad often marry women of foreign nations; they are stimulated by the strange and novel. Here we meet another example of the strange duality of human nature; a man who is most partriotically attached to his native land may yet, in certain circumstances, turn emigrant. A tribesman's mentality changes as he passes from his own into a neighbouring territory. Men are sometimes tempted to do a thing just because it is forbidden. It is in this manner I seek to explain Westermarck's dictum. The " rogue " chimpanzee may have been impelled to seek a mate abroad because of " an aversion to the familiar " of his own group.

Sexual selection became free when men entered civilized life and ceased to live in circumscribed tribal communities. Only under modern conditions are men and women at liberty to mate in the manner postulated by Darwin; even under modern conditions, as we have just seen, their choice is limited by many circumstances. Although sexual selection has played only a minor part in the production of human types and races, there is a sense in which it is of the utmost evolutionary significance. If it is really true that love is " cloaked parenthood," as Hume supposed, and if those in whom love abounded mated in a larger proportion than those in whom it was less developed, then the highly sexed, the children-producers, would be favoured, and the founts of fertility would be always full to overflowing.

Love may abound and yet lead to childless marriages; love may be prostituted. But in such cases there is elimination—elimination of the stock of those who have voluntarily dissolved the bonds which link love to parentage. In this way sexual selection secures the perpetuation, as well as the reproductive health, of a community. As regards sexual selection, it is the instinctively minded parents, rather than the rationally minded, who hand on their reproductive qualities freely to the next generation.

In this paragraph I am to tie together in a single bundle a number of minor matters connected with selection of mates. Does the rule " like will to like" hold in a lover's choice? Darwin believed it was so among certain animals,[12] and Julian Huxley [13] has cited the case of a white (albino) community of Indians in Panama who, being denied partners by neighbouring coloured communities, were left to find mates among themselves. The latter is an instance, not of selection, but of rejection, and is paralleled in civilized communities by those cases where the maimed, the deformed, and the grossly diseased are left un-courted and unwed. The tastes of lovers are infinite; there is the utmost diversity of mind and body among women, yet there are very few that fail to answer to some lover's ideal. " Love is blind," it is said; if not blind, it is certainly strongly prejudiced; bystanders never see lovers as lovers see each other. A lover's taste is based, not on any standard which has been born within him, but upon the faces and fashions on which his infant eyes opened and amid which he grew up. Taste is a local tradition; a white child reared in a black community, or a black child brought up among whites, will model its taste on the faces and manners of those by whom it is surrounded. A lover's taste, then, usually works within the limits of a community, and so diverse are its ideals that it tends to produce within that com-munity, not a single type, but a great diversity of the local type. In brief, sexual selection is but an adjunct of the evolutionary machinery which works so as to give differentiation to the members of a local community.

Why is love so often accompanied by jealousy? We have seen (p. 58) that competition is an essential part of the machinery of evolution; jealousy is the spur or whip which urges competitors on towards their goal. It is the painful passion which seizes contestants when they fear their ambition is to be frustrated, urging them on to obtain by foul means what they cannot win by fair dealing. Jealousy is deaf to reason; it gives the strongest of biases to thoughts and feelings. Under free conditions sexual selection is a contest between lovers for the same desirable bride. Being a competition for sole possession, it is naturally attended by jealousy on the part of contestants. It is not a passion peculiar to man; all through the animal kingdom jealousy arises wherever there is a contest for attention, for affection, or for sole possession; but the high organization of man's emotional nature renders his pangs of jealousy far beyond those felt by other animals. Jealousy, then, is the spur which urges lovers on, so that the fittest may receive his reward.

When the mating contest is over and the competition ended, why should husbands (and wives) become jealous? The contest is, in reality, not over; former rivals still exist; the husband may find his mate exchanging glances with other men, which, by rights, ought to have been his. Darwin, in the following passage,[14] states his belief that marital jealousy is inherent in man's nature: "The most probable view is that man lived aboriginally in small communities each with a single wife, or if powerful, with several whom he jealously guarded against all other men." Against Darwin's view we have evidence that the practice of "wife lending" was widely spread among primitive peoples; the Eskimo and Todas[15] are said to be devoid of marital jealousy. It seems to me more probable that the ban against unchastity, like that against incest, is part of a domestic tradition, instituted to prevent disruption of families, and has no instinctive basis in human nature. This is supported by the fact that the most highly civilized peoples (who are also the most competitive) are those in which marital jealousy most abounds. I agree with Hume that:[16] "Chastity would never have been thought of but for its utility in safeguarding the interests of the children." Darwin called in sexual selection to explain the origin of the diverse varieties or sub-species into which mankind has been demarcated.   We have seen (p. 129) that the evolutionary process is carried out by the simultaneous action of three factors. First, there is *production*—the production of new hereditable traits of body and of mind.   Secondly, there is the *competition* between individuals and between communities.   Those in which new characters have appeared may be stronger than those devoid of them.   Thirdly, there is *selection*, the increase, spread, and survival of those best fitted to meet the needs of life, as well as the decrease and, ultimately, the elimination of those less well fitted.   So far I have considered only two of the factors concerned in the evolution of races by the action of sexual selection—namely, the competitive and selective factors.   We have now to inquire into the productive factor, the means by which races have been given their distinctive features of face, body, skin, hair, and brain. This involves a brief exposition of the modern and still very defective doctrine of hormone action.

Early in the twentieth century, some twenty years after Darwin's death, the discovery of hormones and of their action threw a new light on the origin of racial characters.   Such a discovery would not have taken Darwin by surprise, for when discussing the possible origin of such characters in *The Descent of Man* [17] he wrote as follows : " We must not be too confident in deciding what modifications are of service. . . . It is also well to reflect on such facts as the wonderful growth of galls on plants caused by the poison of an insect."   What Darwin here calls a poison came to be recognized as a hormone—a chemical substance which has the power to induce or cause growing tissues to assume new forms.   The tissues of the same plant can be made to produce galls of many kinds.   " Many forms of gall-producing insects," writes Julian Huxley, " are distinguished solely or mainly by the type of gall to which they give rise." [18]

It was Ernest Starling [19] who gave the name hormone to chemical substances which control the physiological actions of the body.   His, too, is the first clear enunciation that hormones control growth as well as function.   In evidence of this I cite the following passage from his Croonian lectures of 1905 :—

"If, as I am inclined to believe, all the organs of the body are regulated in their growth and activity, by chemical mechanisms similar to those I have described, an extended knowledge of hormones and of their modes of action cannot fail to add largely to that complete control of the body which is the goal of medical science." [20]

Each year which has gone by since 1905 has brought evidence in support of Starling's forecast; it became clear that the racial characterization of the human body is under the control of hormone action.[21] The effects of castration, as was mentioned in the preceding essay, have been known from earliest times, but it was the discovery of hormone action that revealed the means by which such effects were produced. In 1885 Dr. Pierre Marie of Paris gave the name of " acromegaly " to a disordered growth of the human body, a disorder which, in the course of a few years, transforms the external appearance of the men and women who suffer from it. In all such cases it was found that the pituitary gland, at the base of the brain, normally small in size, had undergone an irregular enlargement. The explanation of this disorder came with the formulation of the doctrine of hormones. The pituitary gland has proved to be the headquarters for the production of the hormones which control growth. Then, later, from 1924 onwards came the knowledge that chemical substances akin to hormones control the development of the embryo.[22] In this way anthropologists of the twentieth century were given a clue to the origin of racial characters.

Disorders of the pituitary affect stature; they give rise to giants and also to dwarfs; they can strengthen the brow ridges, alter the shape and size of nose, chin, and face; they can alter the texture of skin and of hair; they can alter the proportion of limbs to trunk. These alterations are due to disorderly action of the pituitary, but there are many instances of orderly increased action. For example, the majority of the characters wherein the gorilla differs from the chimpanzee can be traced to an exaggerated action of the pituitary.[23] Evidence of this is to be seen in the gorilla's great jaws, his bar-like supraorbital prominences, his enormous cranial crests, his large teeth, his massive body, and his extreme strength of muscle. Evidence carrying the same implication is met with in certain human families and also in some human races. Much still remains to be explained. There are forms of dwarfs such as those who are the subjects of achondroplasia [24] and those suffering from "mongolian" idiocy which we are justified in regarding as examples of disordered hormone action, but the exact nature of the disorder remains obscure. In the achondroplasiac dwarf we meet with the flattened, retracted nasal bridge which prevails in peoples of the Mongolian stock. We have reason to believe that the formation and deposition of pigment in the skin are under hormone control, but exact evidence is still lacking.

Such, then, is the present state of knowledge regarding the production of the external characters of the body, which, of course, include those which discriminate one race of mankind from another. How far can sexual selection alter the production of such characters and thus change a race? Let us suppose we have before us an isolated human community of early primal times. Within such a community there is a certain stock of genes, among them those which hand on the determiners of hormones. Seeing that it is an inbreeding community, it might be expected that all members of the community would be cast in the same mould. This is not so. Only in the case of identical twins, which arise from the same ovum, do we meet with approximate identity. In a large family, born to parents who are cousins, we note that brother differs from brother, and sister from sister, although all may show a degree of resemblance. No two eggs, even of the same parents, receive the same allotment of the genes which determine the external characteristics of the body. Thus in our primal community there is still variety on which a lover's choice can be exercised. If that choice were uniformly to fall on a particular kind of face, then in the course of generations that type of face would prevail in the community. As we have seen (p. 186), the lover's taste is not uniform but rather indiscriminate in its action. Sexual selection cannot by itself bring about a discrimination of mankind into races, although it may assist in the differentiation of local breeds.

In another essay I shall have to go more closely into the manner in which new races of mankind are produced. There is a preliminary step in my inquiry which I may profitably take now. Let us suppose that the primal group mentioned in the preceding paragraph has greatly increased in numbers, so that part of it, to get enough to eat, has to seek a new home and territory. The genes which the colonists carry with them is a sample of the stock of genes circulating in the parent community. It is but a random sample of that stock, and is likely to be richer in certain genes and poorer in others than the mean of the parent community. Thus in the setting up of a colony we have a new assortment of genes and hence the production of men and women who differ in details of form from those of the parent community. The essential factor in the production of races is not sexual selection, but the differentiation which goes on in endogamous communities.

REFERENCES

[1] Darwin, C., *The Descent of Man*, Murray, 1913, p. 307.

[2] *Ibid.*, p. 909.

[3] *Ibid.*, p. 890.

[4] Schultz and Snyder, *Johns Hopkins Hosp. Bull.*, 1935, vol. 57, p. 193.

[5] Hooton, E. A., *Man's Poor Relations*, 1942, p. 39.

[6] Yerkes, R. and A., *The Great Apes*, 1929, pp. 256, 542.

[7] Pearson, Karl, *Annal. Eugenics*, 1930, vol. 4, p. 13. In the author's opinion Pearson was the deepest student of evolution of his period.

[8] Pearson, Karl, *Life of Galton*, vol. IIIA, p. 233.

[9] Boas, F., *Asia*, 1940, p. 231

[10] Hocart, A. M., *Nature*, 6 March, 1937, vol. 139, p. 415.

[11] Westermarck, Ed., *Three Essays on Sex and Marriage*, 1934.

[12] Darwin, C., see under reference 1, p. 825. See also *Variation of Animal and Plants under Domestication*, 1864, vol. 2, p. 100.

[13] Huxley, Julian, *Nature*, 1924, vol. 114, p. 464.

[14] Darwin, C., see under reference 1, p. 901.

[15] Frazer, Sir J. G., *Totemism and Exogamy*, 1910, vol. 4, p. 88.

[16] Hume, David, *Essays and Treatises*, 1772, vol. 2, p. 271.

[17] Darwin, C., see under reference 1, p. 91.

[18] Huxley, Julian, *Evolution: The Modern Synthesis*, 1942, p. 299.

[19] Starling, Ernest H., Professor of Physiology, University College, London, b. April 17, 1866, died May 2, 1927.

[20] Starling, E. H., *Lancet*, 1905, (2), p. 583.

[21] Keith, Sir A., *Lancet*, 1911 (1), 993 (Studies in Acromegaly); *Lancet*, 1919 (2), 553 ("The Differentiation of Mankind into Racial Types"); *Johns Hopkins Hosp. Bull.*, 1922, vol. 33, pp. 155, 195 ("On the Evolution of Human Races in the Light of the Hormone Theory").

[22] Keith, Sir A., *Human Embryology and Morphology*, 1947, ch. IV.

[23] Keith, Sir A., *Nature*, 1927, vol. 120, p. 314.

[24] Keith, Sir A., *Jour. Anat.*, 1913, vol. 47, p. 189 (Achondroplasia).

FŒTALIZATION AS A FACTOR IN HUMAN EVOLUTION

Synopsis.—*There is a stage in the development of the chimpanzee foetus when the distribution of hair is similar to that of the human body. Hairlessness in man has come about by the retention of a foetal stage of his development. The law of recapitulation is invalid for such characters. To the process which leads to the retention of foetal characters Louis Bolk gave the name of "foetalization." In the development of the human body new characters are interpolated with the old. Examples of foetalization. The palato-cerebral ratio. The movements of the foramen magnum. Man's orthognathy. Man's skull retains foetal characters. Certain traits of the Mongol race are of foetal origin. The influence of endocrines or hormones. The correlation in development of man's brain and body. The process of foetalization also affects mental qualities. The prolongation of the periods of life. A definition of these periods. In man the period of active brain growth has been greatly extended. The prolongation of the " preparatory phase " of life. In this phase new and untried features make their appearance. These may, or may not, have a survival value. There is a similarity between the " progress " made by man under conditions provided by civilization and the advance made in the evolution of his brain and body under conditions afforded by the preparatory phase of his existence.*

IN the year 1908, when I was entrusted with the care of the Museum of the Royal College of Surgeons of England, there was exhibited in one of its galleries a specimen which had been added in the time of my predecessor, Sir Richard Owen. It was the foetus of a chimpanzee in the seventh month of development and therefore within a month of term, the period of pregnancy in chimpanzees being eight months.[1] Most visitors passed it by with merely a casual glance, believing it to be an example of a human fœtus exemplifying one of the darker-skinned races, for the skin was *café-au-lait* in colour and apparently bare. The head was of goodly size and crowned with hair such as is seen in the scalp of a newly-born child. In the final month of development the chimpanzee fœtus becomes clad with hair, and is born a hairy animal.[2] The face, which was small, was turned down on the breast, while the lower limbs and feet were tucked against the belly. Those who looked critically at the specimen were surprised to find that the feet were provided with great toes which had the shape of thumbs.

The lack of interest displayed by visitors in the specimen may have been due to a belief which was widely prevalent at the end of the nineteenth and at the beginning of the twentieth centuries—namely, that all the characters to be seen in a fœtus are repetitions or recapitulations of ancestral traits. Darwin so regarded them.[3] Haeckel [4] formulated this belief in his " biogenetic law," which read as follows: " Ontogeny, or the development of the individual, is a shortened recapitulation of phylogeny, or the evolution of the race." [5] If the law of recapitulation represented the whole truth, then we should have to suppose that the chimpanzee comes of a hairless human-like ancestry which later put on a hairy dress. Such is an impossible interpretation, for hairiness is one of the most ancient of mammalian characters, and all the records of the rocks are against it. The fœtal chimpanzee, in its hairless stage, is not repeating an old or ancestral feature, but is exhibiting a new one. The stages passed through by a developing animal are not only retrospective; they are also prospective. In the development of the body new characters are interpolated with the old.

Man being a Primate, we must assume that he shared at one time in the universal hairiness of his Order. We may also assume, seeing his structural affinity to the chimpanzee, that he, too, in fœtal life passed through a hairless stage. In his later fœtal stage—that is, during the eighth and ninth months—man retains this hairless state, and thus we have an acceptable explanation of how man came by one of his most peculiar characteristics. The hairless state is only one of the many fœtal traits which have been retained, and so have become incorporated in the structure of adult man. The passage of fœtal characters into adult life was named " fœtalization " by my friend Louis Bolk (1866–1930), who held the chair of Human Anatomy in the University of Amsterdam. He began his investigations in 1900, but was by no means the first to recognize that many of man's special characters are fœtal in nature; anatomists before his time were familiar with the idea.[6] One example will suffice. Havelock Ellis [7] after comparing the infantile characters of ape and man ends with this passage: "We see, therefore, that the infantile condition in both apes and man is somewhat alike and approximates to the human condition. . . . We might say that the fœtal evolution which takes place sheltered from the world is in an abstractly upward direction." Nevertheless, it was the inquiries and publications made by Bolk during the first three decades of the twentieth century which compelled students of human evolution to recognize that the majority of man's structural peculiarities have come into being during the fœtal stage of his existence and have been carried over to adult life by the process he named "fœtalization."

The hairless state of man's body, the character just discussed, is one which appears in a fœtal stage in the development of the anthropoid body, but in man's body is carried over from the fœtal stage to the adult. There are many other characters which show a similar transference. Man is remarkable for the large size of his brain and the small size of his face; this, too, is a feature of the anthropoid at birth. To give precision of statement of the relationship of brain to face, I have been in the habit of using a formula which is constructed as follows: [9] The volume of the cranial cavity, stated in cubic centimetres, is employed to express the size of the brain; the area of the dental palate, stated in centimetres square, is taken as an index of face development; the palato-cerebral formula gives the relationship of palatal area to brain volume. Thus in the skulls of European men it is quite common to meet with a palate of 25 cm.^{2} combined with a cranial capacity of brain volume of 1500 c.c. In such instances 1 cm.^{2} of palate corresponds to 60 c.c. of brain; the palato-cerebral ratio is 1 : 60. In Australian aborigines the palate is larger and the cranial capacity smaller than in the European, the ratio being 1 : 40. Turning to the male chimpanzee, we find a palatal area of 46 cm.^{2} conjoined with a cranial capacity of 390 c.c.; the palato-cerebral ratio is thus 1 : 8·5. In the adult male gorilla the ratio is even less—namely, 1 : 7. But if we turn

to the ratios of these anthropoids at birth, we find an approximation to the human ratio. At birth a chimpanzee has a palate
measuring 13 cm.², a cranial capacity of 260 c.c.; its ratio is thus
1 : 20. In the gorilla at birth the ratio is 1 : 22, while in the new-
born child it is 1 : 50. Thus we may ascribe the smallness of
man's face and the largeness of the brain-containing part of his
head to a tendency to prolong an infantile stage into adult years.
We note, too, that man's infantile stage is an exaggeration of that
seen in the young of anthropoid apes.

In the newly-born monkey and ape the great foramen in the
base of the skull, by means of which the cranial cavity communi-
cates with the spinal canal, is situated near the centre of the base.
Man is the only Primate which retains this central position. This
may be described as a fœtal inheritance. In all other Primates, as
the permanent teeth erupt and the jaws and face grow, the opening, by a series of complicated growth changes, is moved backwards until it comes to be situated at the hinder end of the base.[10]
There is a certain degree of movement in a backward direction
in primitive human skulls, a greater movement in that of the
female chimpanzee; it reaches its maximum, so far as orthograde
Primates are concerned, in the skulls of old male orangs and
gorillas. A suckling monkey, clinging to its mother's breast,
has to carry its head in the human position; hence the central
position of the foramen magnum in the skulls of newly-born apes.
Movement of the foramen sets in when the suckling period is
coming to an end. This infantile stage has become permanent
in man.

Another growth movement, closely associated with that just
described, gives man another characteristic feature—namely, his
face. This is attached to the front part of the base or floor of the
skull and descends more or less vertically from that base, whereas
in all the anthropoids it passes to a greater or less degree in a
forward direction. Man is orthognathous; the anthropoids are
prognathous. At an early stage of development the face in all
monkeys and apes is bent backwards under the base of the skull,
owing to the part of the base to which the face is attached being
bent downwards. As development goes on in the skulls of
fœtal anthropoids, the anterior flexure of the base is undone, the
face thus assuming its forward or prognathous position, whereas
in man the fœtal flexure is retained to a greater or less degree, thus

giving an orthognathous position to the human face.[11] Here again we have an instance of fœtalization.

Fœtal and infantile anthropoids have bulging, prominent foreheads, devoid of ridges. With the eruption of the permanent teeth, the forehead of the chimpanzee becomes transformed. Great supraorbital ridges are developed; the frontal bone is remodelled and becomes low and receding. In man, and also in the orang, the forehead retains the fœtal characters to a greater or less extent. The forehead of women is usually more fœtal in its characterization than that of men. In the extinct Neanderthal race, and in some other ancient races of mankind, the forehead went through changes similar in kind to those seen in chimpanzees and gorillas; in the more civilized races the infantile form of forehead is often retained.

Many other human characteristics of body make a transitory appearance during the fœtal life of anthropoid apes. Three further instances may be cited now. Round-headedness (brachycephaly) appears in the earlier stages of fœtal development of the great anthropoids and also in those of man.[12] In the orang and in many human races this character is retained in the adult. Then there is an example on which Bolk laid great stress.[13] In the face of a typical Mongol there is a combination of three features : (1) the nasal bridge is low and retracted; (2) a fold of skin, the epicanthic fold, passes from the root of the nose upwards to join another fold above the upper eyelid; (3) the eyeballs are protuberant. In Mongolian peoples only does this combination of fœtal characters persist into adult life; they put in a temporary appearance in the fœtal stage of a certain proportion of Europeans; seventy per cent of Hottentots retain them. The third instance I am to cite concerns the prominent bony crests which are developed on the skulls of anthropoid apes and give attachment to the mighty muscles of mastication and to those of the neck which move the head. In the fœtal and infantile stages of anthropoid development these bony crests are absent; the cranial bones are smooth and relatively thin; the muscles just named expand over the surface of the skull, bony crests being thrown up for their increased attachment. Crest formation goes farthest in the male gorilla, to a much less extent in the female chimpanzee, while man passes little beyond the stage reached in the infancy of the ape.

The example just cited is both interesting and instructive for the following reason. In the subjects of acromegaly the jaws again begin to grow, the muscles of mastication and those of the neck to expand their origins, and prominent bony ridges are formed.[14] These changes are brought into being, or stimulated, by a hormone or a combination of hormones thrown into circulation by a disordered pituitary gland. We may justly infer, then, that the development of cranial crests is controlled by a hormone or hormones formed in the pituitary gland; and that delay in the development and growth of bony crests is due to a reduced hormonal action. The various roles played by the pituitary hormones in the development and characterization of the body are handed on from parents to children by means of genes. These genes, we must infer, can undergo changes in the course of evolution. In the male gorilla, for example, the genes responsible for crest-development have undergone changes which lead to a more durable and more vigorous hormonal action, while in man gene changes have limited this action both in the time of its application and in the strength of its effects.

In the evolution of man there has been a great increase in size and in power of the brain; there has also been a reduction in size and in strength of the teeth and jaws. In peoples living under civilized conditions, if there is no indication that the brain continues to increase in either size or power, there is evidence that teeth and jaws tend to a reduction. We may say that the process of fœtalization goes on in civilized communities, but such an explanation leaves this question unanswered: Why is increase of brain accompanied by a reduction of all parts connected with mastication? These changes are somehow correlated; there must be a factor, or a combination of factors, at present unrecognized, which during embryonic development correlates the organization of the brain with that of the body. As we have seen (p. 86), the brutal anthropoid has a disposition to attain his desires by the use of physical force, whereas the disposition of modern man, in whom the process of fœtalization has wrought its full effects, is to settle his quarrels not by force, but by the milder means of understanding and stratagem. Changes in man's body have been accompanied by co-related changes in his mentality.

The process of fœtalization is applicable not only to characters of the body, but also to those of the mind. Apes, in their early youth, like children, are full of life and play. The adult anthropoid, particularly the old male, is serious, morose, and short of temper. In mankind there has been a tendency to carry the joy of youth and the carefree spirit into adult life; the retention of a youthful mentality is commoner among women than among men.

Man is the most slowly growing of all the great Primates; there has been a prolongation of all his periods of life within the womb and outside the womb. This matter is related to the subject just discussed; fœtalization is a prolongation of fœtal or infantile structures into adult life. The subject we are to consider now is the prolongation of life—of all periods of life—and the bearing of this prolongation on new developments in the evolution of man.

The life of man may be divided into four periods. There is first the intra-uterine or fœtal period of 266 days (9·5 lunar months); secondly, the infantile period extending from birth to the eruption of the first molar, the earliest of the permanent teeth, a period of six years; thirdly, there is the juvenile period, one of fourteen years, extending from the sixth to the twentieth year, during which time the permanent dentition comes into use; fourthly, there is the adult period, covering in favourable cases a space of fifty years. The first thirty years of the *adult period* covers the years of female fertility; the later twenty years, the time of decline. The duration of the corresponding periods in the chimpanzee is as follows:— [15] Intra-uterine, 235 days (8·4 lunar months); infantile, three years; juvenile, eight years; the adult some thirty years, the first twenty of which are believed to be the fertile years of the female. Thus, compared with the chimpanzee, man's intra-uterine period has been extended by one month; the infantile, three years; the juvenile, six years; the adult, some twenty years. We may take the rhesus monkey as representative of the smaller and earlier primate stock and compare its periods with those of the chimpanzee. In the rhesus the intra-uterine period is 166 days (6 lunar months), two months less than in the chimpanzee; the infantile period, 1·5 years, half the length of the anthropoid; the juvenile period, 6·5 years, being 1·5 years shorter than in the chimpanzee; the adult period, some twenty years, ten years less than the estimate for the anthropoid. With the evolution of the large-bodied orthograde Primates there came a prolongation of life periods, a trend which reached its climax in the evolution of man.

Man is remarkable, not only for the prolongation of his life periods, but also for the prolonged period of *active* brain growth. In the gibbon, and the same is true of the rhesus monkey, the active period in the growth of the brain is reached at the time of birth. Their brain has then attained about seventy per cent of its adult size. After birth their brains grow at a rate which has a correspondence to body growth. Man, on the other hand, is born with his brain only twenty-two per cent of its adult size. There is a rapid increase during the first and second years of life, the seventy per cent figure being reached early in the third year. Thereafter the tempo of increase bears a relationship to the growth of the body. In the chimpanzee and gorilla there is a brief period of active growth of brain after birth, the seventy per cent phase being reached early in the first year. Thus the period of active brain increase in the rhesus monkey lasts for only six months, in the chimpanzee for eleven months, while in man it is extended to thirty-six months. Herein we see that an important, if not the most important, feature of human evolution—namely, the time taken to assemble and to organize the myriads of nerve cells and of nerve tracts which enter into the structure of man's brain exemplifies the law of fœtalization.

The opening part of this essay was centred on characters which appeared in fœtal life and later became transferred to adult life. In their fœtal and infantile stages the young of man and of ape are large-brained and small-faced. It must be noted, however, that in these stages neither the utility nor the efficiency of brain and face is tested. In the fœtal stage the mother's body supplies nourishment, warmth, and protection. Both brain and jaws are idle; they have no duties to perform. In the infantile stage the needs of the young are supplied by parental care. The fœtal and infantile periods make up what may be named the " preparatory phase " of development, the phase in which structures are being built up before they are brought into use. In the rhesus monkey the preparatory phase is short—namely, about two years; in the chimpanzee it has been nearly doubled (three years and eight months); in man it has again been doubled (six years and nine months). Now, although it is in the preparatory phase of development that new features of the body become

manifest, it is not then that they really came into being.   Their
presence in the fœtus has been " determined " or preceded by
changes in the germinal seeds or genes which are responsible for
their development.   In the preparatory phase new characters of
many kinds may make their appearance; they may be useful or
useless, necessary or superfluous; as long as they are not lethal
the fœtus and infant survive.   On entering the maturation or
juvenile phase these new characters are " tried out," but it is only
when the adult phase is entered that their fate is known.   If
such characters are useful and increase the chances of survival,
then they are preserved; if not, then they are finally eliminated.
Man's prolonged preparatory phase provides increased opportunities for the " try-out " of new characters arising from gene
mutations.

An instructive parallel may be drawn between the " progress "
made by man under the conditions provided by civilization and
the " advance " made in the evolution of his mind and body under
the conditions which mark the long preparatory phase of his
development.[16]   Civilization was made possible by the accumulation of " capital."   It was capital which gave men leisure to
think, to invent, to decorate life, and thus enhance its value.
Capital permitted men to explore and bring into use those latent
gifts and faculties of their brains which, having no utility value,
were left unexploited in primal times.   During the preparatory
phase of life the fœtus and the infant live on capital.   The fœtus
lives on capital provided by the mother's body; the infant on
capital supplied by parental care.   The conditions which prevail
in the preparatory phase of human life make evolutionary experi-
ments possible on a large scale.   The results of this experimenta-
tion, the alterations of structure and the modifications of function
so introduced may, or may not, have a utility value; they may
represent the first stage of a process which is valueless until the
final effective stage is reached.   It was under the conditions
provided in the preparatory phase that man came by the great
potentialities of his brain, potentialities which he exploited in
more modern times amid the opportunities provided by civilization.   It was in the preparatory phase that the more recent
modifications of man's body came into being, modifications which
were carried into adult life by the process of fœtilization.

REFERENCES

[1] Schultz, A. H., *Quart. Rev. Biol.*, 1936, 11, pp. 259, 425.

[2] The chimpanzee fœtus mentioned in the text was described along with four others by Dr. Schultz in the *Amer. Jour. Physical Anthrop.*, 1933, vol. 18, p. 61.

[3] Darwin, C., *Origin of Species*, sixth ed., 1885, p. 396; *The Descent of Man*, Murray, 1913, p. 923.

[4] Haeckel, E., *Generelle Morphologie*, 1866.

[5] For a criticism of the law of recapitulation see an article by Dr. W. K. Gregory in the *Amer. Jour. Physical Anthrop.*, 1925, vol. 8, p. 375.   The history of the recapitulation theory is told by Professor A. W. Meyer, in the *Quart. Rev. Biol.*, 1935, vol. 10, p. 379.

[6] Kohlbrügge, J. H. F., *Die Morphologische Abstammung des Menschen*, Stutgart, 1908.   This author cites authorities who recognized fœtal characters as a source of adult characters.

[7] Ellis, Havelock, *Man and Woman*, 1897, p. 25.

[8] For a summary of Professor Bolk's investigations, see *Proc. Kon. Akad Wetensch. Amsterdam*, 1925, vol. 29, p. 465.   See also *Amer. Jour. Physical Anthrop*, 1929, vol. 13, p. 1.

[9] Keith, Sir A., *The Antiquity of Man*, 1925, vol. 2, pp. 524, 659; *New Discoveries of the Antiquity of Man*, 1931, p. 105.

[10] Keith, Sir A., *Jour. Anat.*, 1910, vol. 44, p. 251.

[11] Bolk, L., *Proc. Kon. Akad. Wetensch. Amsterdam*, 1922, vol. 25, p. 371.

[12] Schultz, A. H., *Quart. Rev. Biol.*, 1926, vol. 1, p. 465.

[13] Bolk, L., *Proc. Kon. Akad. Wetensch. Amsterdam*, 1927, vol. 30, p. 320.

[14] Keith, Sir A., *Lancet*, 1926, vol. 1, p. 490.

[15] Schultz, A. H., *Quart. Rev. Biol.*, 1936, 11, pp. 259, 425.

[16] Keith, Sir A., " Capital as a Factor in Evolution," *Rationalist Annual*, 1925, p. 10.

CROSSING THE RUBICON 'TWIXT APE AND MAN

Synopsis.—The bearing of the discovery of extinct forms of anthropoid apes on the problem of human origin. An account of the discoveries. The evidence produced by Dr. Broom proves that the South African anthropoids were more akin to man than the author had originally supposed. The chief characters of the South African anthropoids. The difficulty in distinguishing man from ape. Darwin held that no line could be drawn between them. The author proposes to use the size of brain as a mark of distinction. The test applied to the hominids of Java and to the South African anthropoids. An imaginary group is followed across the frontier which separates ape-dom from man-dom. The instincts of the anthropoid (anthropoid nature) became the instincts of man (human nature). The relation of intelligence to instinct. The mental changes which accompanied an increase of the brain in mass and organization. The beginnings of speech. Man's emotional nature was enriched as his power of understanding increased. Why such an enrichment was rendered necessary. The place of the South African anthropoids in Dr. Broom's scheme of human evolution. Their place in the author's scheme of evolution.

MY argument had reached its present point when, in the spring of 1946, there came to me from South Africa a monograph entitled *The South African Ape-Men: The Australopithecinæ* by R. Broom, F.R.S., and C. W. H. Schepers. The senior author, Dr. Robert Broom, is my friend and contemporary; we were both born in the same year, 1866; we were both bred as medical men in Scotland; both of us have developed, as a main interest, a study of extinct forms of life known only by their fossil remains: his chosen field lying in the transitional forms which lead on from reptile to mammal; mine in the narrower field which leads from ape to man. In one sense I was the more fortunate; my office provided me with my opportunities, whereas he had to pitch his medical tent in such parts of the earth as supplied his fossil needs. Hence he established himself in medical practice in a village in the southern part of the Transvaal to be near the fossil beds of the Great Karoo. In the year 1934, when Dr. Broom was in his sixty-eighth year, there came to his village two distinguished South African statesmen—General Smuts and the Hon. J. H. Hofmeyer. They begged him to accept a post in the Transvaal Museum, Pretoria, in order that he might be free to devote his genius to the untrammelled exploitation of his chosen field of study. Dr. Broom gladly accepted their offer.

Long before Dr. Broom went to Pretoria he was interested in discoveries which were being made in a great lime-pit at Taungs, which is situated outside the south-western corner of the Trans- vaal and within British Bechuanaland. From that pit there came, in 1924, along with many other fossil remains, mostly of a Pleistocene date, a fossil skull which Prof. Raymond Dart, of the Witwatersrand University, Johannesburg, announced [1] to be that of a very young but altogether new kind of anthropoid, much more akin to man than any living or fossil form then known. Dart's announcement was questioned by many of us; [2] we were of opinion that the fossil anthropoid, to which the discoverer had given the name of Australopithecus, would turn out to be, when its adult state was discovered, a member of the family group to which the living African anthropoids belonged—the gorilla and chimpanzee. Dr. Broom took Dr. Dart's point of view and, when he went to Pretoria in 1934, determined to follow the matter up. In 1936 he was rewarded by the discovery of the fossil skull of an anthropoid which at first he believed to be the adult form of that found at Taungs, but later came to the conclusion that it differed so much from that described by Dr. Dart that it deserved a separate generic name—Plesianthropus. Then in 1938 fortune again smiled on him; the fossil bones of a third kind of South African anthropoid were discovered. To this third form Dr. Broom gave the name Paranthropus. The calcareous deposits which yielded these new forms to Dr. Broom were of the same nature as those at Taungs, but were situated within the Transvaal, near Krugersdorf, some twenty miles to the north-west of Johannesburg. Meantime, on the strength of the evidence which had been accumulating, Dr. Broom believed that the antiquity of the South African anthropoids was greater than had been originally estimated, that the Taungs form might be mid-Pliocene in date, the others Upper Pliocene or Lower Pleistocene.

In the monograph which has now come to me Dr. Broom assembles the evidence which bears on the nature of the anthropoids which roamed across the velts of South Africa in prehistoric ages. The evidence is dead against those of us who believed they would prove to be members of the gorilla–chimpanzee group. They differ from all living anthropoids in three important respects : first, their teeth are human ; if only the teeth had been found, they would have been accepted as evidence of the existence of man ; their canine teeth were not prominent and tusk-like. Second, such fragments of the lower limbs as have been recovered are human in shape ; if these only had been found, they would have been accepted as incontrovertible evidence of human existence ; the South African apes must have walked as men do. Third, the fossil fragments from their upper limbs were also shaped as in man ; the arm and hand no longer served in locomotion as in all living anthropoids, but were free to serve the needs of the body. The anatomical evidence suggests that the South African anthropoids were also human in this respect— their chief means of offence and defence were provided, not by great canines, but by means of improvised weapons wielded by the hand.

Are we, then, to regard these extinct races of South African beings as men or as apes? This is how Dr. Broom sums up the situation : "It seems immaterial where we draw the line, and whether we regard the Australopithecines as sub-human or human. What appears certain is that the group, if not quite worthy of being called men, were nearly men, and were certainly closely allied to mankind, and not at all nearly related to the living anthropoids " (p. 142). Dr. Broom is thus of opinion that if we are to give a status to these extinct South African forms, we must place them among men, not among apes. Dr. Broom's junior partner, Dr. Schepers, who deciphered the brain equipment of these extinct forms from casts taken from the interior of their skulls, demands a human status for them in the most positive terms. " The least we can say," writes Dr. Schepers, " is that these fossil types were capable of functioning in the erect posture, of using their hands in a limited sense for skilled movements not associated with progression, of interpreting their immediately visible, pal-

pable and audible environment in such detail and with such discrimination that they had the subject matter for articulate speech
well under control, and of having developed motoric centres for
the appropriate application; they were also capable of communi-
cating the acquired information to their families, friends, and
neighbours, thus establishing one of the first bonds of man's
complex social life.   With all these attributes they must have been
virtually true human beings, no matter how simian their external
appearance may have remained" (p. 253).   In brief these extinct
forms of South Africa were truly human, but were dressed in the
garb of anthropoid apes.

The discovery of extinct forms of man-like apes in South Africa
brings us face to face with a situation which Darwin had foreseen
as he wrote *The Descent of Man*.   How are we to distinguish ape
from man?   As the following passage shows, Darwin was of
opinion no line of demarcation could be drawn.   " In a series of
forms," he wrote, " graduating insensibly from some ape-like
creature to man as he now exists, it would be impossible to fix on
any definite point when the term ' man ' ought to be used." [3]
There is the same difficulty in deciding when an infant becomes a
child, yet it is useful to distinguish the one period from the other.
The eruption of the first permanent molar teeth provides a convenient mark for determining the end of infancy and the beginning of childhood.   In the chimpanzee the first permanent
molar cuts at the end of the third year; in the human infant in the
seventh year.

What sign can we use to mark the end of apehood and the
beginning of manhood?   The essential mark of man lies neither
in his teeth, nor in his postural adaptations, but in his brain, the
organ of his mentality.   How big was the brain when it became
capable of sustaining a mentality which may be called human?
In search of an answer to this question let us turn first to a primitive race of mankind, the aborigines of Australia.   Professor
Wood-Jones [4] found that the brain volume in aboriginal women
may be as low as 855 c.c., and as high as 1470 c.c. in men.   The
mean brain volume for the race is approximately 1200 c.c.   The
gorilla is the largest-brained of living anthropoids; in females the
brain volume may be as low as 390 c.c. and in males as high as
650 c.c.; [5] the mean for both sexes, 470 c.c   The Rubicon between
apehood and manhood, so far as concerns brain volume, lies some-

where between the sum for the highest gorilla (650 c.c.) and the lowest aborigine (855 c.c.). On the strength of such evidence as is available to me at present I would say that the Rubicon lies somewhere between 700 c.c. and 800 c.c.; to be more precise, I would say that any group of the great Primates which has attained a *mean brain volume* of 750 c.c. and over should no longer be regarded as anthropoid, but as human. Let us test such a standard on the earliest men of Java, whose remains have been found in the oldest deposits of the Pleistocene period (see p. 225). The brain volume of one of the Javanese fossils regarded as a female has been estimated at 750 c.c., while that of another, regarded as a male, 950 c.c., the mean for the two being 850 c.c.[6] These early Pithecanthropi, then, have crossed the Rubicon as regards volume of brain, and all who have made a special study of casts taken from the brain-chambers of their skulls agree that the essential human features of the brain can be detected on them.

Let us now apply this test to the brain volumes of the extinct South African anthropoids. The largest-brained is the form named by Dr. Broom, Paranthropus; the individual studied had a brain volume estimated at 650 c.c.; in two individuals of another genus (Plesianthropus) the estimated volumes were 435 c.c. and 560 c.c. Let us take the case of the Taungs child; its brain volume is 500 c.c., its first permanent molars are cut, and it has therefore attained eighty per cent of its full size of brain; if it had lived, its brain would have been about 650 c.c. In contrast, let us consider the case of the oldest of the fossil skulls of Java. It is that of an infant about two years of age, and should therefore have attained about seventy per cent of its full size of brain. The brain volume of this infant is 650 c.c.; if it had lived, it should have reached a volume of 845 c.c., thus almost reaching the Australian minimum. In brain volume, then, the extinct South African anthropoids fall short of the Rubicon; they are anthropoids, but of a kind which in structure of body and in form of brain come much nearer to man than do any of the living forms.

I have given details relating to the brain volumes of extinct forms of anthropoids and of men because of a special object I have in view. I want to envisage, in imagination, a social group of these South African anthropoids and to follow it through long æons while the brains of its individual members grew in mass and in organization, until the Rubicon that lies between ape-dom and man-dom had been crossed.   What are the changes in mentality which would have occurred at the crossing?   From what we know of living anthropoids, we may infer that the chief mental activities of the group will be three in number—namely, those concerned with mating, maternity, and social behaviour.   Each group will be attached to a territory and maintain its isolation. In living anthropoids, as we have seen (Essay XIV), all these activities are under instinctive control; the members of a group followed a policy of which the ends or object were quite unknown to them.   The structure of their brains was so organized as to secure the instinctive carrying out of such a policy.   We know, however, that even in living anthropoids instinctive control is far from being rigid; [7] they have the power of learning from experience; that power they owe to the extent of their cerebral cortex.   We may assume, therefore, that in the more highly-brained group, whose progress we are following, instinctive urges, when they rise within the field of consciousness, may not be given their appropriate responses; these responses may be modified in the light of experience.   When our group has safely crossed the mental Rubicon and passed well within the realm of humanity, it has carried with it all the instinctive urges which served on the other side.   The sole change lay in this : an increase in mass and in specialization of the cerebral cortex gave a higher degree of control over the inborn urges or impulses.   Thus it was, as Darwin had declared, there was no point in the passage from ape to man at which a bystander could have said : here simian mentality ended and there human mentality began.   The important fact for the student of human evolution to note is that man brought with him, out of ape-dom, the entire anthropoidal outfit of instincts, but had obtained an increase of cerebral cortex to enable him to control them.

The relationship of intelligence to instinct has been discussed by many authorities.   I need cite only a few of their statements. First, there is that of the philosopher-surgeon of the eighteenth century, John Hunter.   "Man," he wrote, " has the instinctive principles of every animal, with this difference, that he chooses or varies the mode of putting these principles into action." [8]   Then there is the opinion of a philosopher-physician of the twentieth-century, Wilfred Trotter, which he worded as follows : " Intelligence leaves its possessor no less impelled by instinct than his simple ancestor, but endows him with the capacity to respond in a larger variety of ways." [9]   " Intelligence and instinct are inseparable," is the opinion of a modern psychologist, C. S. Myers.[10] Professor Drever holds that " if there is emotion or interest, then there is instinct." [11]   To these may be added Herbert Spencer's statement that " Memory becomes necessary as instinct becomes intelligence." [12]

The anthropoid ape has no means of treasuring and of transmitting its experience from generation to generation.   The mother chimpanzee knows her child but has no name for it;   the child knows its mother but has no name for her;   each member of a group knows every other but has no names for them;   they know the things which are good to eat but these things remain nameless. The facts of birth and of death are beyond their comprehension. Such sounds as they use are expressive of their feelings and moods. When did man begin to be vocal—to apply names to things, and thus become capable of handing on experience?   It was when certain cortical areas of his brain underwent extension and specialization, especially changes which affected the frontal lobes of his brain.   The circumstances which gave rise to these cerebral additions remain a mystery, but there can be no doubt as to the advantage they gave to the group or groups in which such cerebral additions made their appearance.   Dr. Schepers claims to have detected the beginnings of the cerebral basis of speech in the cranial casts of the South African anthropoids.   However wrong this may prove to be, there can be no doubt of their presence in the hominids of Java;   they were alive at the beginning of the Pleistocene period, which, on our present crude geological scale of reckoning, is given an antiquity of about a million years. How much earlier the brain became an organ fit for speech we cannot tell, but when it did become fit man had indeed crossed the ape—man Rubicon.

The great increase of cerebral cortex in early man was accompanied by certain changes in his mentality.   His powers of memory became greatly increased.   His field of consciousness became widened and more brightly illuminated.   He became capable of discriminating—of comparing in his field of consciousness one thing with another;   of detecting wherein they agreed and wherein they differed.   Public opinion, which in an anthropoid group is but a rabid exhibition of temper, became in early man a vocal criticism expressed by significant sounds. What he regarded as good had one vocal sound given to it; what was disliked was given another. Morality became codified.

As the powers of understanding increased in early man, as his tree of knowledge flourished more and more, he became exposed to a grave danger—that of disillusionment. What would have been the fate of a primitive community if its members, as they began to understand the stark realities of life, came to share the opinion expressed by the preacher in Ecclesiastes? " Therefore I hated life; because the work that is wrought under the sun is grievous unto me; for all is vanity and vexation of spirit." [13] Hume was of opinion that man was kept alive by a prejudice, and this may be accepted as true if we agree that the instinct of self-preservation may be regarded as a prejudice. In the passage from the ape stage to the human stage there was introduced in the instinctive centres of the brain a magical texture which made all connected with life seem not only desirable but beautiful. This was so, not only with the " prejudices " which make us cling to life, but with all the urges connected with sex, with motherhood, and with homeland; all became shot with a new radiance. What the nature of the neural changes which gave the human brain these magical qualities may have been we do not know, but they made him see beauty in what entered his sensorium by the eye, to hear music in what entered by the ear, and turned the drab offices of paternity and of maternity into soul-satisfying ordinances. These marvellous changes belong to the obscure period which marked the rise of man's emotional system. Suffice it to say that as man's faculty of understanding grew so did his power of enhancing all that was felt, seen, and heard.

How am I to fit the fossil anthropoids which were alive in South Africa during the Pliocene and Pleistocene ages into the scheme of human evolution outlined in Essay XVII? These animals, although anthropoidal in appearance and in size of brain, were yet human in their dentition and in carriage of body; their habitual life was no longer led in the trees but on the ground. My scheme assumes that up to the end of the Oligocene period (see p. 158) the great anthropoids (the gorilla, chimpanzee, and orang) and man were represented by a common ancestry, all being strictly arboreal in habit. It was during this stage, my scheme assumes, that the anthropoidal group which was ultimately to evolve into humanity became separated from the groups which were to remain anthropoids. The limbs and bodies of the common ancestry were then undergoing postural modifications, the lower limbs of the pre-human group or groups becoming more and more the chief means of support in climbing and, at the same time, becoming better fitted to serve as organs of progression on the ground. In the groups destined to remain anthropoid, on the other hand, both upper and lower limbs became more and more adapted for an arboreal life. In the ancestral anthropoid groups the canine teeth became more and more developed as weapons of defence and offence, while in the pre-human group the canines fell into abeyance. My scheme assumes that before the end of the Miocene period the lower limbs of the pre-human groups had become completely adapted for a life on the ground; they were thus no longer confined to a life in the jungle, but were free to roam in the open country and thus to have the whole earth open to them. The South African anthropoids seem to me to represent the stage reached by our human ancestry in the Miocene period. That representatives of this Miocene phase of man's evolution should have survived into the Pleistocene period in South Africa does not seem to me an improbable assumption.

Dr. Broom's scheme of human evolution, and the place of the South African anthropoids in that scheme, differs from that I have just outlined. He holds that man's lineage separated from that of the great anthropoids at a much earlier geological epoch than that postulated by me; he regards the separation as having taken place in the Lower Oligocene period, while the Old World Primates were still at an initial stage of their evolution. Here is a significant passage from his text (p. 142) : " And we may regard it as almost certain that man arose from a Pliocene member of the Australopithecines (South African anthropoids), probably very near to Australopithecus itself, and that the resemblances between the higher anthropoids and some types of man are merely due to parallel developments and do not indicate any close affinity."

In the most important point Dr. Broom and I are in agreement; of all the fossil forms known to us, the Australopithecines are the nearest akin to man and the most likely to stand in the direct line of man's ascent. We differ in two matters: (1) he places the phase of evolution represented by the Australopithecines in the Pliocene, whereas, for reasons to be unfolded in the next essay,

I think it necessary to attribute it to an older geological period; (2) he attributes the structural resemblances of the Australopithecines to the living anthropoids as due to parallel evolution. I attribute these resemblances to a common inheritance. The points of structure which man shares with the living anthropoids are too numerous and too intimate to be attributed to anything else than an inheritance from a common ancestry.

REFERENCES

[1] Dart, Raymond, *Nature*, Feb. 7, 1925.

[2] Keith, Sir A., *ibid.*, Feb. 14, 1925; see also *New Discoveries relating to the Antiquity of Man*, 1931, chaps. I–VI.

[3] Darwin, C., *The Descent of Man*, Murray, 1913, p. 279.

[4] Wood-Jones, F., *Man*, 1932, no. 45; *Jour. Anat.*, 1934, vol. 68, p. 323.

[5] Hagedoorn, A., *Anat. Anz.*, 1926, vol. 60, p. 117.

[6] Koenigswald, G. H. R. von, *Proc. Kon. Akad. Wetensch. Amsterdam*, 1938, vol. 12, p. 185.

[7] Yerkes, R. and A., *The Great Apes*, 1929; Koehler, W., *The Mentality of Apes*, 1925.

[8] Hunter, John, *Essays and Observations*, edited by Richard Owen, 1861, vol. 1, p. 39.

[9] Trotter, W., *Instincts of the Herd in Peace and War*, 2nd ed., p. 97.

[10] Myers, C. S., *Lancet*, 1926, (1), 1183.

[11] Drever, James, *Instincts*, ch. VII.

[12] Spencer, H., *Principles of Psychology*, 4th ed., 1899, vol. 1, p. 432.

[13] Ecclesiastes, II, 17.

THE ANTHROPOIDAL ANCESTORS OF MANKIND SPREAD ABROAD

Synopsis.—The author summarizes the argument developed in the preceding essays and outlines the course it is to take in succeeding essays. Africa is postulated as the centre of dispersal of the anthropoid ancestors of mankind. Darwin's description of a migratory tribe. The spread of the Maoris in New Zealand. Although anthropoid apes and early hominids inhabited ancient China, they failed to reach the New World. Man's late arrival in America. The American Indians cannot be derived from any of the Asiatic peoples now living in the neighbourhood of Bering Strait. Nevertheless, the migratory movements of the Northern Tungus help us to understand how the original settlement in Alaska was made. The original immigrants from Asia to America had a peculiar assortment of blood-genes. How this anomaly may be explained. The author attempts a reconstruction of the dispersal movements which carried the original settlers from Alaska to Tierra del Fuego. Clans and tribes multiplied in numbers; so did forms of speech. Each new clan represented a new assortment of genes. An estimate of the number of "evolutionary units" ultimately formed in America. The anthropological effects produced by the introduction of agriculture. Later arrivals from Asia. Exogamy.

MY argument has now reached a point when it is necessary for the sake of the author, as well as for that of the reader, to look back and survey the road along which we have come and again to note the milestones we have passed to reach our present position. It may be convenient, too, at this point to glance foward along the path our footsteps are to follow and mark the heights we hope to attain.

First, then, let us look back and see how far our argument has carried us. Essays I–III were devoted to an exposition of the group theory of human evolution; thereafter we entered on a detailed account of the factors concerned in group evolution. It may have surprised the reader—it certainly did the author—to find how deeply "human nature" was implicated in the process of group evolution. Essays IV–XIV are concerned with the part played by mentality in group evolution: the attachment of a group to its territory; its consciousness of community; its patriotism or devotion to community affairs; its co-operative and competitive complexes; its prejudices; its resentful and revengeful nature; its continual search for status and power; its loyalties; its morality—all these being manifestations of "human nature." Essay XIV provided an interlude during which a brief survey was made of the factors which bring about functional and structural changes in man's body and brain. We found that in bringing about these evolutionary changes three factors were concerned— namely, production, competition, and selection. In the essays which follow XIV such factors as group isolation, inbreeding, mating, marriage, sex differentiation, and sexual selection, which, at first sight, seem to be remote from the influence of human mentality, turn out on closer analysis to be very closely connected with it. Thus our main effort, so far, has been to set up what may be called the machinery of evolution; now we are to study the effects produced by that machinery. Two of the preceding essays, however, have a direct bearing on the steps we are now about to take. In Essay XVII (the contrasted fates of ape and man) a geological scale of time was set up in order that we might be in a position to give approximate dates to the evolutionary events which have to be mentioned and described; in that essay, too, an opportunity was taken to discuss the bearings of genetics on the processes of evolution. Then, in Essay XXI man's anthropoid ancestor was set on his feet and brought to the mental Rubicon which has to be crossed before the term "human" can be claimed or admitted.

Such is the point in human evolution we have reached. In this essay we have now to follow the pre-human groups as they spread abroad from the centre or centres where they made their first appearance. We shall have to confess that, as yet, we have not the evidence which permits us to trace the spread of these forerunners of man from region to region of the Old World; but we do know that by the end of the Pliocene the status of humanity had been attained and that races of hominids were to be found in all the continental masses of the Old World. Later we shall have to inquire how each continent came by its own kind of humanity and how these kinds became separated into local varieties. Then we shall have to discuss the rise of the modern races of mankind and the building of nations and empires. Nationalism and racialism will have to come up for discussion, and the bearing which these human passions have on statesmanship and on anthropology. If the theory of human evolution which is being expounded in these pages is well-founded, it should help us to understand how beings which were at first purely simian in nature became ultimately human; it should throw a new light on the problems which perplex the modern world; it should permit us to make a reasoned forecast of what the future has in store for mankind. So much, then, for the programme which lies in front of us.

Meantime, we have to return to the spreading abroad of the ground-living forerunners of mankind, such as are represented by the extinct anthropoids of South Africa. Where are we to pitch the centre of dispersal? The evidence, as it stands to-day, favours Africa. It is in that continent we find the living anthropoids which are most akin to man in structure of body and of brain; it is there, too, that ground forms of anthropoids lived; the oldest and most primitive of orthograde forms lived in the lower valley of the Nile. If we may select one region as more likely than another, then our choice falls on the uplands of Uganda and Kenya; during Upper Miocene times this area was the home of numerous anthropoids, one of which was akin to the gorilla and chimpanzee and yet in certain features more human than either.[1] If the spread was towards the north, the continent of Asia was open to the migrating groups, for at that period there was no Red Sea, Arabia being joined to Africa and India united with Arabia. Northern India, in Upper Miocene times, had a rich fauna of anthropoid apes, and it may have been, as Dr. Davidson Black[2] maintained, that the spread was from Asia to Africa, and not as I have postulated. Nevertheless, the evidence favours an African source, so, until we know better, I am to regard the uplands of East Africa as a centre for the dispersal of man's anthropoid forerunners. Nor should it be forgotten that at the date of which I write—Upper Miocene—Europe also provided a home for several forms of anthropoid apes. Thus, some ten or twelve million years ago, on the time scale we are using (p. 164), the great anthropoids had spread throughout the tropical jungles of the Old World.

First, let us turn to passages in which Darwin gives his conception of how the process of dispersal was carried out. His descriptions refer to early humanity, not to the more primitive forms which I have in mind; in all stages of evolution the process of spread is likely to have been similar. Here is Darwin's chief passage :—

> " As it is improbable that the numerous and unimportant points of resemblance between the several races of man in bodily structure and mental faculties should all have been independently acquired, they must have been inherited from progenitors who had these same characters. We thus gain some insight into the early state of man, before he had spread step by step over the face of the earth. The spreading of man to regions widely separated by the sea, no doubt preceded any great divergence of character in the several races; for otherwise we should meet with the same race in distinct continents; and this is never the case." [3]

Here Darwin assumes that differentiation into races followed dispersal. In another passage concerned with dispersal Darwin ascribes differentiation into races as a result of sexual selection, whereas modern anthropologists ascribe racial characterization to the action of hormones (see Essay XIX, p. 189). A passage from *The Descent of Man* [4] reads thus :—

> " Let us suppose the members of a tribe, practising some form of marriage, to spread over an unoccupied continent. They would soon split up into distinct hordes, separated from each other by various barriers, and still more effectually by the incessant wars between all barbarous nations. . . . The hordes would thus be exposed to slightly different conditions and habits of life, and would sooner or later come to differ in some small degree. As soon as this occurred, each isolated tribe would form for itself a slightly different standard of beauty, and then unconscious selection would come into action. . . . Thus the differences between the tribes, at first very slight, would gradually and inevitably be more or less increased."

P

An instructive example of the manner in which a primitive people effects dispersal in a new homeland is provided by the traditional history of the Maoris. Somewhere about the fourteenth century A.D. a few boatloads of Maoris reached the North Island of New Zealand, and married with the aborigines, the Moriori, whom they ultimately exterminated or expelled. Here is Elsdon Best's account of their spread :—

> "As the northern parts of the North Island became more populated by increasing numbers of the mixed Maori folk, inter-tribal quarrels became frequent, and weak tribes were often compelled to seek new homes elsewhere. The general direction of their movements was southwards, and so, in the course of centuries, many such peoples were pushed southwards to Weirarapa, the Wellington district, and the South Island. As the population increased, so, apparently, did hostile conditions and isolation, for inter-communications between tribes would tend to decrease as dissensions and fighting became more common." [5]

These pioneering groups of a spreading people formed inbreeding communities, thus permitting a full development of their germinal potentialities.

Although anthropoid apes were living during the Pliocene period in that part of Asia which is now known as China, they never made their way into the New World. More surprising is the fact that the early hominids who inhabited China at the beginning of the Pleistocene period never reached the virgin continent; all authorities are agreed that there is no evidence of the existence of man in the New World until the closing phase of the last glaciation—that is to say, about 10,000 years ago.[6] Anthropologists agree that the conjoined American continents were populated by one breed of mankind, and that this breed came from the north-eastern part of Asia, and entered their new home by the ice-pack which forms a natural and easy bridge to the north of Bering Strait.[7] The inhospitable conditions which mark the approach to the Bering Strait on the Asiatic side seem to have repelled all early inhabitants. Even Japan, which is 2,000 miles distant from the Strait, was not inhabited until the Neolithic Age; no trace has been found in it of Palæolithic inhabitants.[8]

The peoples who now live in the north-east corner of Siberia cannot be regarded as representatives of the ancestral stock which gave birth to the pioneers who settled the New World; all of them have full-blown Mongolian features; in the pioneers these facial traits were still in an incipient stage of development. Although this is the case, yet much concerning movements, migrations, and spread of primitive peoples can be learned from the Tungus tribes who now inhabit the bleak and mountainous country along the upper reaches of the Lena and the lower reaches of the Amur valley. We shall not greatly err if we apply what we learn from the northern Reindeer Tungus to the movements and migrations of the pioneer immigrants. A distinguished Russian anthropologist, Dr. S. M. Shirokogoroff,[9] made a prolonged and detailed study of the Reindeer Tungus, and this is what he has to say about their migratory habits:—

> " The Tungus have migrated ever since the early ages. . . . Clans like the Samagir, Mamugir, Kindigir, and many others under certain circumstances have broken up into two or more territorial and exogamic units. . . . So if the unit is too numerous, it divides into two or more new units; if too small, it joins any other clan. . . . The process of division and absorption of clans is especially intensive during periods of changes and migrations."

And further it is of particular importance for our present object to note that " in the process of migrations two clans bound by marital exogamous relations usually separate, and the new group may continue to maintain endogamy" (p. 367). Thus a clan on the move is an endogamous, inbreeding, small community, made up of some fifty to a hundred families. " Every clan member is proud of belonging to his clan and is interested in its future success " (p. 189). " The fruit of the hunting does not belong to the hunter but to the clan " (p. 195). Such are the customs and habits of a modern migratory Tungus clan; we shall not be far wrong if we attribute to the group or groups of Palæo-Asiatics who made their way to Alaska and laid the foundation of the entire Amerind population of the New World the habits, customs, and clan organization still retained by the northern Tungus.

In one respect the pioneer immigrants differed from all the peoples who now live in N.E. Asia; all of these are rich in a particular blood group, that known as " B "; whereas this group is unrepresented in the Amerind population of the New World.[10] Apparently in the germinal outfit of the pioneer group or groups the gene for " B " was absent. Now, the population of Asia is noted for the high proportion of the " B " group and, we infer, always has been. How, then, are we to account for the absence of this blood element in a people which was undoubtedly derived from Asia? I account for it in this way. An inbreeding group or community may differ profoundly in its blood groups from a neighbouring group or community, although both may be members of the same tribe. For example, Dr. Shanklin [11] examined various sections of the Rwala tribe of Arabs; in one section he found the " B " group unrepresented, while in another section of the same tribe the " B " and " AB " groups were represented by 14.8 per cent of its members. Dr. Bijlmer [12] found a similar state of matters among adjacent communities in the island of Ceram. I assume, therefore, that the clan or clans of Palæo-Asiatics, who first succeeded in reaching the New World, were inbreeding communities in which there were no bearers of the " B " gene, but only those which carried the " O " or " A " gene; I further make the bold assumption that the whole Amerind population of America, from Bering Strait to the Strait of Magellan, is the progeny of the original pioneer group or groups. Certainly the American Indians differ in appearance from tribe to tribe and from region to region, but underneath these local differences there is a fundamental similarity. This, too, is in favour of descent from a single, small, ancestral community.

The pioneers who broke into Alaska had before them such limitless prospects as had never before fallen to the lot of any human community in the long history of mankind. Before them lay two virgin continents with fifteen million square miles of land, representing one-third of the total inhabitable area of the earth's surface. We may safely assume that the pioneers retained their clan organization; as the original clan became of swollen size, it divided, the daughter clans spreading into new territories. And so the process of dividing and re-dividing went on; there must have been what we may call a " growing edge " of population advancing towards the south, advancing very slowly at first, but ever more rapidly as the number of clans and tribes increased. It took the white settlers two centuries and a half to spread across the United States from east to west, a distance of 3,000 miles. It is about 12,500 miles from Bering Strait to that of Magellan. The spread of the white man was fostered and fed by emigration from Europe, whereas that of the Indian was a result of native increase, and would therefore be much slower—say one-fifth of the white rate. At such a pace it would have taken the descendants of the pioneers some 5,000 years to reach Cape Horn.

As daughter communities broke away and became isolated from their parent communities, the parent speech underwent modification after modification, so that by the time Cape Horn was reached thousands of dialects and scores of "families of speech" had come into existence. The more the forms of speech multiplied, the more effectively were the Indian communities isolated from one another. Experts estimate that about 150 different groups of speech have been used and evolved by the native communities of America.[13] The theory I am upholding assumes that these 150 separate linguistic families have been evolved from the tongue of the original group of pioneers. If this is so, then these tongues, which seem unrelated, must have been united by a host of languages which are now extinct. Speech is infinitely more plastic to the impact of evolution than is the living human body.

In the advance from the north to the south, groups, clans, and tribes must have divided and re-divided a very great number of times, new swarms passing out to form separate communities. Those who have not considered the matter may be of opinion that each new swarm carried away a fair sample of the genes circulating in the parent tribe. This is not so; an inquiry by Dr. G. Morant [14] serves to illustrate the inequality of such division. He tabulated the stature of 700 soldiers recruited in Lanarkshire, taking hundred by hundred in the order of recruitment. Each hundred differed from the other in the distribution of stature and, we may presume, in the hereditary genes which control stature. If each hundred of these recruits had been members of a separate swarming group, then each of the new groups formed would have had its own individuality of stature. And so with every other feature of the body, such as shape of head, form of nose and face, colour of skin and texture of hair.

North and south of the chain of lakes of North America there were evolved large tribes of tallish, finely made, but fierce men with heads varying on each side of the line which separates long

heads from round; such men provided the warriors of the Iroquois, the Algonkins, and Sioux; although of different tribes,
these men were much alike in physical appearance. In South
America we again meet with the tall type in the pampean plains
and also forming a separate community in Brazil, but the pre-
dominating type in South America is short in stature, with choco-
late tint of skin and, most frequently, round of head.[16] But
underneath these differences can be recognized a prevailing
similarity, the inheritance from the ancestral pioneer group. As
numbers increased, so did tribal competition and tribal selection,
and so the rate of evolutionary change became ever more rapid.

As to the number of separate inbreeding communities in
existence in America when Colombus made his first voyage
(1492), we have only uncertain data. In 1910 Dr. Roland
Dixon [17] enumerated 280 tribes in the United States. Five of
these were large, ranging between 15,000 and 30,000; forty-two
tribes were on the verge of extinction, their representatives
numbering ten or less. In Canada ninety-six separate peoples have
been enumerated; in Alaska, sixty-six. Thus in recent times
there were at least 432 separate breeding units in the six million
square miles which form America north of Mexico. The total
Indian population of that vast area in pre-Columbian times has
been estimated at a little over a million.[18] There would thus
be an area of six square miles for every head of the population.
Almost all of them were hunting people, dependent for food on
the produce of soil, lake, and river. I have found that in most
parts of the earth a primitive food-gathering people, as opposed
to one which is food-producing, needs about two square miles
per head for a comfortable subsistence. Dr. Hinsdale [19] is of
opinion that, so far as concerns the Indians of the central lake
district of the United States, this is a gross under-estimate. From
an examination of the number and size of camps left by former
Indian inhabitants of that area be estimated that there were about
thirty square miles for each member of the community. An
estimate made by Lewis Morgan [20] comes nearer to the estimation
of two square miles per head. He was of opinion that in pre-
Columbian times the State of New York, which contains about
47,000 square miles, never had a population of more than 25,000.

In South America, tribes were smaller and much more numerous. Admiral Markham [21] made a list of the tribes which live,

or which have lived, in the valley of the Amazon, and found they numbered 455. We shall not err greatly if we put the number of separate "evolutionary units" in the New World in pre-Columbian times at 2,000.

At what point the tribes of Mexico, Central America, and of the Andean Plateau began the practice of agriculture and how they came to invent or to acquire this art are matters which lie outside my purview. But the evolutionary effects of such an innovation in the mode of life cannot be left unconsidered. The introduction of a native agriculture made the sparse tribes of the areas just specified, tribes of squat men, darkish brown in complexion, rounded in head, and roughly visaged, into populous communities. It is estimated that before the arrival of the Spaniards, Aztecs, Mayas, and Incas numbered about twenty millions, perhaps five times the population of the rest of the New World. Agriculture made the short, dark, and round-headed breed the prevalent and the most surely rooted type in the continent. The hoe is a more effective evolutionary instrument than the tomahawk.

There are at least two matters in the brief account I have given of the peopling of the New World with its original inhabitants which need amplification. I have written throughout as if there had been only one settlement and no more. There is ample evidence [22] that there have been fresh arrivals from Asia on the north-west coast up to comparatively recent times. The effect produced by such arrivals is of a local nature; the fundamental anthropological unity of the original population remained unchanged. The other point which demands a word of explanation is my use of the term "inbreeding unit." There is a tendency on the part of many to regard exogamy, widely practised in all American Indian tribes, as a form of out-breeding. Exogamy extends only the size of the inbreeding unit. The exogamous tribe is still an inbreeding community.

In this essay we set out to ascertain how the ancestors of man spread from the centre or cradle of their evolution—a centre postulated to have been in Africa—and extended abroad until they became widely disseminated in the Old World. As we have as yet no evidence of the direction nor of the time of the dispersal of pre-hominids, we have been obliged to substitute for them primitive tribes of human beings. The peopling of the New World provided the kind of opportunity of which we were in search. Hence this essay has been devoted to the elucidation of the original settlement of America. In the next essay we are to find that mankind had become a universal species, and we have to consider how and when it became differentiated into so many breeds or races.

/

REFERENCES

[1] See reference No. 8 given on p. 170 *supra*.

[2] See reference No. 7 given on p. 170 *supra*.

[3] Darwin, C., *The Descent of Man*, Murray, 1913, p. 278.

[4] *Ibid.*, p. 909.

[5] Best, Elsdon, *The Maori as He Was*, 1934, p. 28.

[6] Keith, Sir A., *The Antiquity of Man*, 2nd ed., chs. XXIV, XXV; *New Discoveries*, 1931, ch. XIX.

[7] The opinions of those who have devoted special attention to the original settlement of America by Amerinds will be found in *Early Man*, edited by George Grant MacCurdy, Lippincott, 1937.

[8] Torii, R., see work in preceding reference, p. 361.

[9] Shirokogoroff, S. M., *Social Organization of the Northern Tungus*, Shanghai, 1929.

[10] Gates and Darby, *Jour. Roy. Anthrop. Inst.*, 1934, vol. 64, p. 23.

[11] Shanklin, W. M., *Proc. Soc. Experim.*, *Biol. Med.*, 1933, vol. 32, p. 754.

[12] Bijlmer, H. J. T., *Jour. Roy. Anthrop. Inst.*, 1935, vol. 65, p. 123.

[13] Kroeber, A. L., *Anthropology*, 1923, p. 98.

[14] Morant, G., *Biometrika*, 1939, vol. 31, p. 72.

[15] Morant, G., *Man*, 1934, p. 103.

[16] Imbelloni, J., *Anales Museo Argentino, Cien. Nat.*, 1937, vol. 39, p. 70.

[17] Dixon, Roland B., *Indian Population in the United States and Alaska*, Report of Bureau of Census, 1910.

[18] Mooney, J., *Smithsonian Misc. Collections*, 1928, vol. 80, No. 7.

[19] Hinsdale, W. B., *Occasional Contributions from the Museum of Anthropology*, *University of Michigan*, 1932, No. 2.

[20] Morgan, Lewis M., *Ancient Society*, 1877.

[21] Markham, Sir C. R., *Jour. Roy. Anthrop. Inst.*, 1910, vol. 40, p. 73.

[22] Barbeau, M., *The Geographical Review*, 1945, vol. 35, p. 424.

MAN BECOMES A DENIZEN OF ALL PARTS OF THE WORLD

Synopsis.—In this essay it is assumed that Africa was the birthplace of humanity. Zeuner's chronology of the Pleistocene period. Representatives of Early Pleistocene man. In Java. In North China. In Germany. In England. Weidenreich's solution of the Piltdown conundrum. Rhodesian man—the most primitive form discovered so far in Africa. The assumed spread of man's anthropoid ancestors from Africa into Asia and Europe to become the ancestors of Early Pleistocene man. Modification of the African theory to make it applicable to the case of Piltdown man. The evidence of the wide distribution of mankind at the beginning of the Pleistocene period derived from the stone implements preserved in deposits of that period. The Pleistocene may be described as the " human period"; in it mankind underwent its most rapid phase of evolution.

In the two preceding essays reasons have been given for assuming that somewhere in Africa, most probably in the uplands of East Africa, an anthropoid had become human in body, in hands, in feet, and in gait, but in brain and in face still remained anthropoid. Reason was also given for believing that this stage in human evolution was reached at the dawn of the Pliocene period of the earth's history, a period which on the time scale I am following (p. 164) had a duration of some seven million years. It is also assumed that at this juncture of human evolution the human-footed breed of anthropoids, although broken up into a number of groups or communities, were still confined to the area of their evolution.

It should now be my task to follow our anthropoid ancestors into the long Pliocene period, and to note the rise of their brain and their spread into the adjacent continents of the Old World. Alas ! in this year of grace—1947—the anthropologist has to confess that, for him, the Pliocene is his darkest of ages; so far, not a fossil trace of Pliocene man has been found.   Yet that such things did happen during the Pliocene Age we have the most complete assurance, for at the close of that age and at the beginning of the next, or Pleistocene, there is the definite evidence of the existence of primitive humanity in parts of the Old World so far apart as Java in the East, England in the West, China in the North, and the farthest point of Africa in the South.   The evidence provided by the oldest Pleistocene deposits assures me that man had crossed the mental Rubicon which separates him from the ape and had become the maker of tools and an inhabitant of all the continents of the Old World.

In the broad scale of geological time a million of years has been allotted to the last phase of the earth's history, the Pleistocene. Seeing that the events which have determined the form and distribution of humanity as seen in the modern world were enacted during the Pleistocene Age, it is imperative that we have some form of time-scale which will permit us to trace the sequence of these events. Fortunately for us there can be discerned in the geological deposits laid down during the Pleistocene Age four cycles of climatic change, each cycle, so far as Europe is concerned, beginning with a cold or glacial period and ending in a mild or interglacial phase.   In tropical lands each cycle began with a wet or pluvial period passing into a dry or arid phase.   Dr. F. E. Zeuner [1] has made a close study of the evidence relating to the duration of these cycles; the chronology adopted here is based on dates given by him.   We shall work our way backwards into the Pleistocene, beginning from the present.   We are living in the mild period of the fourth cycle, and to this mild space a duration of 18,000 years is assigned.   To the preceding cold or glacial phase of the fourth cycle a duration of 94,000 years has been given, the total length of the fourth cycle being thus 112,000 years.   The term *Würm* is given to the glaciation of this cycle; here we shall use the term " Würmian " to cover the duration of the whole cycle.   We shall speak of the deposits laid down during the Würmian cycle as those of the "Upper Pleistocene."   It was early in the Würmian cycle that the ancient Neanderthal population of Europe was replaced by men of the Caucasian or modern type.

Pushing our way up the stream of time we enter the third

cycle; to this a duration of 114,000 years has been given, taking us to a date some 226,000 years from the present. The glaciation of this cycle is usually named *Riss*, and we shall use the adjective " Rissian " to cover both cold and mild phases of the cycle. The preceding, or second, cycle was of long duration, the sum allowed being 246,000 years. It thus covers a longer period than the third or fourth cycles put together. The cold phase (*Mindel* glaciation) of the second cycle was short, its mild phase being very long. To reach the beginning of the first Pleistocene cycle, which opened with the *Günz* glaciation, we have to go back more than half a million years (586,000 on the Zeuner scale). This cycle had a duration of 114,000 years, being thus of about the same length of time as the third and fourth cycles. Behind and beyond the first, or Günzian, cycle lies a vague hinterland of the Pleistocene period where the Pleistocene fades into the preceding period, that of the Pliocene. To this pre-Günzian hinterland of the Pleistocene must be ascribed a duration of over 400,000 years if we are to give this geological period the round sum of one million years.

When we come to deal with the geological deposits which have yielded the fossil bones of early man, certain terms will crop up which I must touch on now. There is the term " Lower Pleistocene "; this I shall apply to the deposits or strata laid down in the pre-Günzian interval and during the first, or Günzian, cycle. For those laid down during the second and third cycles I shall use the term " Middle Pleistocene," while, as already mentioned, the term " Upper Pleistocene " will be applied to deposits laid down during the cold phase of the fourth cycle.

Having outlined the scale of time we are to apply to the events of the last geological phase of the earth's history, let us take a bird's-eye view of the forms of humanity which were in existence during the first half of the Pleistocene—that is, down to the end of the first cycle (Günzian). Our opening glance takes us to the Far East, to the island of Java, which in Pliocene and early Pleistocene times was joined to the mainland of Asia. Here, during the years 1891–3, at Trinil, near the centre of the island, the first example of early Pleistocene man was uncovered by my friend Eugene Dubois. He was born in Holland in 1858 and was trained as an anatomist, but, believing that the mystery of the " missing link " could be solved in Java, joined the Netherland

East India Army as a surgeon in order that he might have opportunities of exploiting his conviction. As we have seen, he proved that his conviction was justified. Dubois was of opinion that the deposits at Trinil that yielded him a fossil skull-cap, and a thigh bone which was manifestly human, had been laid down late in the Pliocene period, but subsequent investigations have proved that they are later than he thought, being now assigned to the closing phase of the first Pleistocene cycle.[2] Dubois regarded the fossil being he had found at Trinil as neither man nor ape, but as an intermediate creature which shared the characters of both; hence he named it Pithecanthropus—the ape-man.[3] Certainly the skull-cap did look like that of a great ape; it was low-browed, flat roofed, with great projecting eyebrow ridges. But when the cement-like material which filled its cavity was cleared out and a cast taken of the brain chamber, it was found that Pithecanthropus had a brain which was organized on a human pattern and had a volume of 935 c.c., thus falling within the lower limits of the human range. Until 1938 the fossil skull found by Dubois remained a unique specimen, but in that year, from the same geological horizon of Java, von Koenigswald added a second, identical in all points with the original, save that it was more complete and smaller, the brain space measuring only 775 c.c. The second skull is regarded as that of a female; in size of brain she was just across the Rubicon, which it will be remembered was set at 750 c.c. At the time of writing (1946), four skulls and parts of four mandibles have been found, all attributable to the Trinil race of Java.[4] Although this people were ape-browed and small-brained, yet their teeth were human, their canines scarcely rising above the level of neighbouring teeth.

In the eastern extremity of Java, at Modjokerto, there are deposits which are older than those at Trinil, having been laid down at the very beginning of the Pleistocene period. In 1936 von Koenigswald unearthed the fossil skull of an infant with such markings as lead experts to attribute it to the Trinil race. Its brain volume is estimated at 650 c.c.; if the child had lived we expect that its brain would have attained the Trinil level—namely, between 800 and 900 c.c. Thus we have evidence that in Java, at the very beginning of the Pleistocene period, there existed a race of beings who were human in carriage of body, human in dentition, with brains which fell just within the lowest human level, yet in their skulls had many resemblances to African anthropoids. We shall see, in a later part of this essay, that traces of even more primitive beings have been found in the older Pleistocene deposits of Java—beings whose characters are reminiscent of the South African anthropoids.

From Java we are now to proceed to North China, involving a journey of over 3,000 miles; there we are to pass in brief review a community of human beings, the Pleistocene contemporaries of the Trinil breed of Java. The scene of discovery takes us to the village of Choukoutien, situated in hilly country some thirty-seven miles to the south-west of Peking. Near the village is a small limestone hill which has proved to be a Pleistocene mausoleum. During the first half of this period its caves and fissures had become filled up, and, as they filled bones of the men and animals inhabiting the adjacent area became cemented in, and thus preserved. Excavation of the hill began in 1926, and by 1940, when war brought excavations to an end, parts of thirty-eight human individuals had been found and examined.[5] Only five of the skulls were sufficiently complete to provide exact measurements. We turn at once to what these can tell us of the cerebral outfit of this Peking breed or race of Pleistocene humanity. The smallest of the five has a capacity of 915 c.c.; the largest 1,225 c.c.; the mean of the five being 1,070 c.c. They were thus considerably larger brained than the Trinil breed. Because of this increase of brain, the Peking men had skulls with higher vaults, less receding foreheads, but they still retained the supraorbital torus of the African anthropoids; teeth and jaws were robust, but the rudiment of a true human chin had made its appearance. Although the Peking breed had advanced a degree nearer to modern man than the Trinil race, yet, as there are so many points in common between the two, we must infer both had sprung from the same ancestry at no very remote date. The chief point to note is that an early Pleistocene people living in the temperate climate of North China had made an evolutionary advance on their contemporaries living in the tropical climate of Java.

Having noted the evolutionary stage reached by mankind along the eastern lands of the Old World during the earlier phases of the Pleistocene period, we now set out in search of their contemporaries in lands of the extreme West. So far as Europe is concerned only two sites have yielded fossil remains of people who can be regarded as contemporary with the Trinil and Peking breeds. These sites are at Heidelberg in Germany and at Piltdown in the south of England. At Heidelberg [6] a complete lower jaw was found; the gravel deposit in which it lay has been accurately dated; it was deposited towards the end of cycle 1—that is, during the Günz–Mindel interglacial; Zeuner gives it an antiquity of about 500,000 years. The Heidelberg mandible is of a type which, in discoveries made in Europe of a later date, has always been found associated with a skull of the Neanderthal form, implying that Heidelberg man had a prominent supraorbital torus and pent forehead, thus resembling the African anthropoids. There are reasons for believing that the anthropoid-browed type extended right across the Old World from China to Germany during the first half of the Pleistocene period.

The gravel deposit at Piltdown in Sussex, in which the fossil fragments of the skull and mandible of a human being were preserved, is less well dated than that in which the Heidelberg jaw lay. This, however, may be affirmed: that Piltdown man was at least a contemporary of Heidelberg man; more likely he was of greater antiquity. The English representative of ancient man differed altogether from the types we have been examining in Java and China. His forehead was like that of the orang, devoid of a supraorbital torus; in its modelling his frontal bone presented many points of resemblance to that of the orang of Borneo and Sumatra. Indeed, experts have attributed the Piltdown mandible to an extinct form of orang; others to a form of chimpanzee which had made its home in the weald of Sussex during Pleistocene times.[7] It is quite true that the teeth do present a mixture of human and anthropoid features; in degree of development the canine tooth rivalled that of the female chimpanzee. The skull of Piltdown man, although thick-walled and massive, yet in its general structure conforms to the type met with in modern races of mankind;[8] for instance, the mastoid processes, to which the muscles of the neck are attached, were such as are found in the most evolved of modern mankind. In size of brain he had reached a modern level; the cerebral volume was not less than 1,350 c.c.

The discovery of Eoanthropus, or Piltdown, man (1911–13) presented students of human evolution with a conundrum. How are we to account for this unique type of early Pleistocene man in England while the rest of Europe, and apparently the whole of

Asia, were inhabited by variants of the pent-browed type? If we could get rid of the Piltdown fossil fragments, then we should greatly simplify the problem of human evolution. We should have to account for the evolution of the pent-browed type only, and the development of modern races from that type. A leading authority on such problems, Dr. Franz Weidenreich, has recently proposed [9] that the right solution is to deny the authenticity of the Piltdown fossil remains. Here are his exact words : " Eoanthropus should be erased from the list of human fossils. It is the artificial combination of fragments of a modern-human braincase with orang-utang-like mandible and teeth." That is one way of getting rid of facts which do not fit into a preconceived theory; the usual way pursued by men of science is, not to get rid of facts, but frame theory to fit them. That is what I propose to do. It is important to remember, in connection with the Piltdown problem, that in Pliocene and early Pleistocene times England, like Java, was joined to adjacent continental lands, and so might provide a refuge for early, aberrant continental types. If we are convinced that evolution is the true method of creation and that man and anthropoid have been evolved from a common ancestry, what is more probable than that we should find early human forms in which anthropoid and human features are combined?

Having made a running commentary on the early Pleistocene inhabitants of the Old World from Java in the east to England in the west, we return to Africa to see what that continent has to tell us of their contemporaries. So far not a complete bone of an African of the early Pleistocene age has been found; [10] only their stone tools. The oldest of the African races so far discovered is that represented by Rhodesian man.[11] His skull and skeleton were exposed deep in a limestone quarry in North Rhodesia in 1921; the fossil bones of animals found with him represent, for the greater part, living species. Such evidence as there is points to his existence late in Middle Pleistocene times. In several respects the skull of Rhodesian man is the most primitive of human forms known to us. It is provided with the most enormous supraoribital torus ever seen in any skull, anthropoid or human. Like the gorilla, Rhodesian man was long- and heavy-faced; indeed, in several of his facial features he resembled the gorilla. His upper jaw is particularly massive, and no doubt the lower jaw, which is missing, was equally so. The volume of his brain was a little over 1,300 c.c., thus falling short of that of Piltdown, but exceeding that of the largest-headed of the men of Peking.

Let us now return to the theory adumbrated in an opening passage of this essay (p. 223)—viz., that the centre of evolution of our anthropoid ancestry was in Africa, that by the beginning of the Pliocene period a stage had been reached equivalent to that represented by the extinct races of anthropoid apes of South Africa. From this African centre the anthropoid-headed, human-footed ancestors of the human family began to spread outwards into neighbouring regions. They were certainly social animals, divided into many separate groups or communities. Some of these communities, we may assume, prospered and multiplied in numbers, and this led, as virgin territories were entered, to division and re-division of their small societies. We may feel assured that some communities, in their struggle for a living, went to the wall and were replaced by groups with a better outfit for the new form of life. And so groups slowly changed and evolved as they extended their distribution. No doubt there were " stay-at-home " groups who preferred to remain in the territories they knew, while others, more enterprising and adventurous, pushed past in search of new homes. Probably the " advancing front " moved at a snail's pace compared with the rapid expansion which marked, as we have seen (p.219), the settlement of the New World, but our Pliocene time-scale—one which allows seven million years—provides more than a sufficiency of time for our scattering communities to reach the most distant parts of the Old World, before the dawn of the Pleistocene Age.

A time came when these African forerunners of humanity reached the confines of Asia. In Pliocene times there was an easy access to that continent from Africa; there was no Red Sea, no Persian Gulf; Arabia was watered and wooded. As our forerunners moved towards the north, some groups, we may suppose, moved westwards into Asia Minor, where they would find a landbridge leading on to Greece and providing access to Central and Western Europe. Other groups may have passed into Central Asia, but the pioneers which hold our immediate interest are those who turned their faces towards India and ultimately reached Java and North China, where, according to this theory of the African origin of humanity, they became the ancestors of the Pithecanthrops and Sinanthrops of the early Pleistocene of these lands.

To the anatomist, the conversion of a South African type of anthropoid into the primitive forms of humanity found in Java and in China seems a feasible proposition. Such a transformation implies merely an increase in the organization and in the size of the brain, with a reduction in strength of jaw and teeth. There is additional evidence in favour of the theory I have outlined. In 1945 Dr. Weidenreich [12] reported that fragments of excessively large jaws and teeth, stamped with humanoid features, had been found in early Pleistocene deposits of both Java and southern China. These fossil fragments have much in common with the corresponding parts of South African anthropoids.

We now return to Africa to apply our theory to one of its own products—Rhodesian man. Of all forms of extinct anthropoids known to us those of South Africa serve best as his probable ancestor. It does not seem too much to suppose that in the course of some six million years or more the brain of an anthropoid should increase in size from 650 c.c. to 1,300 c.c.—the volume of the Rhodesian brain. Such a rate of evolution could not be described as rapid. In the case of the female Pithecanthropus of Java the rate was even less, for her brain had a volume of only 775 c.c. In his teeth and jaws Rhodesian man may well be the descendant of Paranthropus, a South African anthropoid discovered and described by Dr. Robert Broom. [13]

The African theory, as just outlined, accounts very well for the pent-browed early types of humanity, but leaves unexplained such an aberrant type as that of Piltdown. To account for Piltdown man our theory must be modified in the following respects. So far it has been assumed that the pioneer groups were made up of individuals conforming to one type—namely, that of the South African anthropoids. This may not have been the case—there may have been more than one type. Seeing the close relationship of the orang to the African chimpanzee and gorilla, it is probable that this anthropoid, too, is of African origin. If this were the case, then it is possible that among the early forerunners of mankind in Africa some had inherited the orang form of skull and forehead. This is what I am assuming. This modification of my theory involves two other assumptions:—(1) that it was the orangoid forms that turned westwards into Europe and ultimately reached England, where their further evolution continued; (2) that those characters of the human skull we count modern,

Q

such as the mastoid process and chin, have been evolved independently in several early races of mankind.

There is one important source of evidence bearing on the universality of mankind at the beginning of the Pleistocene period on which I have not touched—namely, the evidence of his tools. The Pleistocene deposits of Africa, of Asia, and of Europe, from the oldest to the most recent, carry the stone tools which man fashioned at the time these deposits were laid down. Indeed, there is good evidence that tool-makers were alive in England long before the dawn of the Pleistocene. My friend the late James Reid Moir (1879–1944) convinced most experts that stone implements of several types, which he found under deposits of late Pliocene date, had been shaped by human hands.[14] At Rabat, in Western Morocco, the Abbé Breuil found stone tools in the very oldest of Pleistocene deposits.[15] In and under the early Pleistocene on the eastern shores of Lake Victoria, at Kanam, were found tools shaped out of pebbles and also a fossil fragment of a human mandible.[16] A map showing the distribution of stone industries in earlier Pleistocene times, such as that prepared by Dr. T. T. Paterson,[17] shows a trail of this pebble culture from South Africa to Java. On many occasions Dr. L. S. B. Leakey has claimed that Africa led the way in the development of stone cultures.[18]

Although man crossed the mental Rubicon which separates ape from man in late Pliocene times, yet his real period of evolution was in the Pleistocene. We may well speak of this period as that of the " human age." It is the age of human evolution. Even when we allow a million years to the " human age," we must count the rate of man's evolution during this age as very rapid.

REFERENCES

[1] Zeuner, F. E., Geolog. Mag., 1935, vol. 72, p. 350; Proc. Prehist. Soc., 1937, No. 8; The Pleistocene Period: Its Climate, Chronology and its Faunal Succession, 1945.

[2] von Koenigswald, G. H. R., Early Man, edited by G. G. MacCurdy, 1937, p. 25.

[3] Dubois, E., Pithecanthropus erectus, Eine Uebergangsform, Batavia, 1894.

[4] Weidenreich, Franz, " Giant Early Man from Java and South China," Anthrop. Papers Amer. Mus. Nat. Hist., 1945, vol. 40. p. 1.

[5] Black, Davidson (1884–1934), Palæontologia Sinica, 1927, vol. 2, p. 1; Weidenreich, F., ibid., 1943, no. 127; 1936, vol. 7, Fasc. 3; ibid., 1937, no. 101.

[6] Keith, Sir A., *The Antiquity of Man*, 1925, vol. 1, p. 319.

[7] Dawson and Woodward, *Quart. Jour. Geolog. Soc.*, 1913, vol. 69, p. 117.

[8] Keith, Sir A., *The Antiquity of Man*, 1925, vol. 1, p. 319.

[9] Weidenreich, F., *Palæontologia Sinica*, 1943, no. 127, p. 273.

[10] In 1933 Dr. Leakey found the symphysial part of a human mandible in early Pleistocene deposits at Kanam, on the Eastern shore of Lake Victoria. The fragment was heavily mineralized, bearing worn incisor, canine, and pre-molar teeth.   In their size and arrangement these teeth agreed with those in modern man, but the fragment is too imperfect to give information as regards the type of man.   (See *Man*, 1933, no. 66.)

[11] For an account of Rhodesian man, see Keith's *The Antiquity of Man*, 1925, vol. 2, p. 377.

[12] Weidenreich, F., see under note 4.

[13] Broom and Schepers, *The South African Fossil Ape-Men: The Australopithecinæ*, Pretoria, 1946.

[14] Moir, J. Reid (1879–1944), *Nature*, 1941, vol. 149, p. 77.

[15] Breuil, L'Abbé H., *Nature*, 1942, vol. 149, p. 77.

[16] Kent, P. E., "The Pleistocene Beds of Kanam and Kanjera," *Geol. Mag.*, 1943, vol. 79, p. 117.

[17] Paterson, T. T., *Nature*, 1940, vol. 146, p. 49.

[18] Leakey, L. S. B., *The Stone-Age Cultures of Kenya Colony*, 1931.

THE FIVE MAJOR DIVISIONS OF MANKIND

Synopsis.—For the sake of brevity the author proposes to name the Australopithecinæ, " Dartians." The application of the " African " Theory to explain the distribution of the races of mankind. For this purpose a survey of their distribution is made in the essay. The population of the Old World is separated by " the great Divide " into a pigmented southern zone and a less-pigmented northern zone. The northern zone is divided into Caucasia and Sinasia ; the southern zone into Africa, Indo-Asia, and Australia—each of these five divisions being inhabited by a distinctive stock of humanity. The racial characters of Caucasia. The Europinoids of Sinasia. Proto-Mongols. The Mongolian facies is of recent evolution. The racial characters of Sinasia. The Ainus. The triple division of the southern, or pigmented, zone. The racial features of Africans. The facial features of the typical Negro are of recent origin. Tribal organization prevails throughout native Africa. The former existence of pigmented peoples in Arabia and in Irania. The racial features of the peoples of India. The Indonesians of Malayasia. The Andamanese. Australasia and the racial characters of its native peoples. The theory of group evolution serves to explain the regional distribution of human races.

IN the preceding essay I felt the lack of a suitable name for the human-footed, ground-living anthropoids which we had reason to believe were evolved in Africa and, spreading into the other continents of the Old World, had given rise to the various known forms of early Pleistocene humanity. Seeing that Professor Raymond Dart [1] was not only the first to describe this form of anthropoid, but boldly recognized it as representative of a stage in human evolution (the role to which I have assigned it in the preceding essay), we may well name all erect, ground-living forms of anthropoids " Dartians " instead of Australopithecinæ, the name he gave them. At least by doing so we shall gain in brevity of expression. In this essay we are to fly at much higher game than in the last; there we applied the African theory to explain the origin of the fossil forms of early man, but here we are to apply this same theory to account for the distribution of the living races of mankind, for I am convinced that it is only when we assume that Africa was the evolutionary cradle of early humanity that we find it possible to give an acceptable explanation of the racial distribution in the modern world.

Before we can apply the African theory we must first make a survey of the population of the Old World. To this purpose the present essay is devoted. Although I shall deal with areas and populations as they now are, it will be necessary, from time to time, to hark back to their condition in the Old World of primal times, when men were separated into small groups and lived off the produce of their untilled territories. Primal times, as we saw in Essay III, came to an end with the discovery of agriculture, an event which is usually ascribed to the eighth millennium B.C.

We are concerned here with the main racial " divides " of the Old World, for, as we saw in Essay XXII, the spread of mankind to the New World is a comparatively late event. The great racial divide of the Old World, beginning on the Atlantic coast, follows the northern fringe of the Sahara and is continued eastwards across Arabia until the western end of the Himalayan chain is reached. The divide then follows the line of the Himalayas, crossing Burma and China, to end at the northern extremity of the Philippine Archipelago. All the peoples to the south of the divide are now, or were in primal times, pigmented to a greater or lesser degree, their skins varying from a light brown to a sooty black. To the north of the great divide peoples have skins of a lighter hue, varying from a yellowish-grey to one which is almost devoid of pigment. The great divide, as I have just drawn it, has been bent southwards both to the east and to the west of the Himalayan range. To the east, people of the Mongolian type have pressed southwards, and now occupy the Malayan Archipelago; to the west, peoples from the north have passed into India, Persia, and Arabia, but there is evidence, to be touched on later in this essay, that Africa and New Guinea in primal times were joined by a continuous pigmented zone which crossed Arabia, India, and the lands of the Far East.

We must now pass in brief review the main varieties or racial subdivisions of mankind, beginning with those which lie to the north of the great divide. A line drawn from the western end of the Himalayan range to the home of the Lapps in Northern Europe divides the northern hemisphere into two great regions. The region to the east and north of this line we shall name Sinasia, Sin being the ancient name of China; Sinasia is inhabited by peoples who conform more or less closely to the Mongolian type. The region lying to the west and south of the dividing line we shall name Caucasia, this region being the home of peoples usually described as "whites," or Caucasians. Europe, measuring 3·8 million square miles, makes up the greater part of this region; Caucasia is completed by the addition of that part of Africa which lies to the north of the Sahara and that part of Asia which lies between the Mediterranean and the Pamir plateau at the western end of the Himalayas, additions which give the homeland of the Caucasians a total area of about six million square miles. The population of the area is estimated to be (1946) about 600 millions, of whom 530 are resident in Europe. The Caucasians resemble one another in their hairiness, the relative paleness of their complexions, and in their facial features, in which the nose plays a characteristic part. Pigmentation decreases as we pass from Africa towards the Baltic; the Caucasians who live farthest from Africa are the fairer in colouring, but even in the pigmented south, among the Berbers of North Africa and among the Kurds of Asia Minor, there are islands of fairness. Heads may be long, round, or of an intermediate form. In Europe the inhabitants are grouped into competitive evolutionary units known as nations, but in large areas of African and Asiatic Caucasia the tribal unit still prevails. For instance, Mark Sykes[2] found the Kurds divided into over three hundred tribes; Prichard[3] enumerates seventy-three tribes of Iliyats in Persia, while in the North-West Frontier zone of India there are more than a score of tribal peoples.

We now turn to a consideration of the eastern ethnic region, Sinasia, the home of peoples with a Mongolic cast of countenance —a cast which is easier of recognition than of measurement. Its area is much larger than that of Caucasia, measuring about eleven million square miles, but is in large part thinly populated—the total number of its inhabitants being about 530 millions. In this total are not included some 120 millions of the Mongoloid stock who have passed south of the great divide and occupied Indo-

China and the islands of the Malayan Archipelago. These will come up for consideration when the southern ethnic hemisphere is dealt with. As to Sinasia proper, China, with its estimated population of 400 millions, provides its chief nucleus. Indeed, we may say that China, which is a huge aggregation of village communities rather than a nation, stands to the rest of Sinasia much as Europe stands to the rest of Caucasia. Outside China the majority of Sinasians are organized in local groups, clans, or tribes. Between the Pamir on the west and southern China on the east Keane [4] collected evidence of the existence of about one thousand separate local communities. Tibet is still tribal for the greater part; at one time the Mongols were divided into 226 clans or " banners "; the Manchus were divided into sixty tribes, the Buriats into forty-six. In the whole of Sinasia there is but one people, the Japanese, organized and moved by the national competitive spirit which animates most of the peoples of Europe.

Before enumerating the points which distinguish Sinasians from Caucasians and the darker peoples of the southern zone, I think it well to make a preliminary assumption. I assume that the fully developed Mongolian countenance is an evolutionary event which, in a geological sense, is of recent date; that down to late Pleistocene times the facial features of the primitive inhabitants of Sinasia had many points of resemblance to those of the Caucasians. This assumption is supported by observations made on peoples living along the 3,000-mile frontier line which separates Sinasia from Caucasia. Along the frontier are many tribes which, although akin to the Mongols in speech, differ from them in having Caucasoid features. The Yakuts of the Lena valley are such a people; so are the pastoral tribesmen of western Tibet; the Turks came into being in this frontier zone. We may speak of people of Sinasia who have the Caucasoid type of countenance as Proto-Mongols. The tribes of N.E. Siberia which effected settlements in the New World were Proto-Mongols; so apparently were the late Pleistocene cavemen of Choukoutien of North China.[5] In Manchuria, in China, and in the upland valleys of Tibet, Burma, Siam, and Tonquin there are sporadic occurrences of individuals described as " Europinoids "—people with Caucasoid features, and of a paler tint than is usual among true Mongols. If we accept the assumption that the earlier inhabitants of Sinasia had Caucasoid facial features, then we may regard " Europinoids " as individuals who have retained ancestral traits and assume that western Turkish tribes have preserved the Proto-Mongol type.   The explanation usually given of the occurrence of Europinoids in Sinasia is that at an early date this ethnical region was " penetrated " by inroads from Caucasia.   Such penetrations on a small scale there may have been, but if during the long Pleistocene period there had been a free intermingling of the peoples of Asia with those of Europe and vice versa, then there should have been, not a solid mass of one type in Caucasia and of another type in Sinasia, but a uniform hybrid type extending from Japan in the east to Ireland in the west.   We must assume, then, that the Caucasian and Mongolian stocks have been evolved in the region where they are now found, but that both have a common ancestry.

The natives of Sinasia are characterized by their facial features and by certain other traits.   The hair of their heads is straight, stiff, long, and black; their bodies are almost hairless; beards, if grown, are sparsely haired.   The people of one area, the Ainus, have retained not only the Proto-Mongolian facial features, but have developed hair to the extent usually found in Europeans. The most feasible explanation of the hairiness of the Ainus is to regard it as a gene mutation, which occurred in people of the true Mongolian stock, or due to the survival of ancestral genes. The skin of the natives of Sinasia, varying in colour from that of brown leather to that of chamois leather, is uniformly more deeply pigmented than that of the Caucasians.   The Chukchi of N.E. Siberia are said to be " of fair complexion " with a " coppery-coloured " skin, and some of the Samoyed tribes of the far north-west are described as " blond," yet it cannot be said of Sinasia as of Caucasia that the farther from Africa the lighter the degree of pigmentation, for the Sinasians of the Arctic north are as dark as those of the extreme south.   But this is true : the farther from Africa the more emphasized does the Mongolian cast of countenance become.   The Sinasians differ from the Caucasians in the relative proportions of their blood groups.   In Western Europe the propor-tion of the " A " group is high, that of the " B " group is low. In Eastern Asia it is the opposite; the proportion of " A " group is relatively low while that of the " B " group is relatively high. There is evidence that the " B " factor or gene has extended its distribution from Asia into Eastern Europe.

Having separated the lesser pigmented peoples of the northern hemisphere into two main divisions, we are now to give our attention to the more deeply pigmented peoples of the southern hemisphere of the Old World. We are to divide the southern zone into three main areas, each of which carries its own variety of humanity. The three main divisions of the South are:— (1) Africa, with its 125 millions of Negroid inhabitants; (2) Indo–Asia, which includes that part of Asia which lies to the south of the Himalayan range and extends from the Red Sea in the west to the Moluccas Passage in the east, thus taking in all the Malayan Islands which were joined to the mainland of Asia in earliest Pleistocene times;. and (3) Australasia, which embraces Australia, New Guinea, and the chain of Melanesian Islands. The Australasians are the aborigines of these lands.

Seeing the important role which I believe Africa to have played in the evolution of early humanity, it is necessary that we consider in some detail the dimensions of this continent and the physical characters of the peoples who now inhabit it. The majority of its peoples are deeply pigmented, their skin being black or of a deep-chocolate brown. While the Dinkas of the Nile Valley may be described as black, the not-distant tribes on the Welle, the Mombuttu and Zandeh, have skins of a ruddy brown. The Bushmen and Hottentots of the extreme south have skins of a light brown or brownish-yellow tint, reminiscent of the degree of pigmentation found among Mongolian peoples. The natives of West Africa are more heavily pigmented than those of East Africa. All natives of the continent south of the Sahara—for that is the part of Africa with which we are dealing—have black " woolly " hair; only in the peoples of the north-east region, the home of the Hamitic Negroes, does it become frizzled and mop-like. The Hamitic Africans have their facial features modelled on Caucasian lines, their noses being relatively narrow and straight and their jaws not unduly prominent. In the population throughout the rest of the continent we meet with peoples who have assumed, in varying degrees, the facial features of the typical Negro. Noses are wide, and flattened on the face; the lips are full and everted. We must regard the facial features of the full Negro, like those of the evolved Mongol, as something new, something which came into being in Pleistocene times. Two fossil, but imperfect, human skulls found by Dr. Leakey in mid-Pleistocene deposits on the eastern shore of

Lake Victoria certainly foreshadow the facial features of the true Negro; so far this is the earliest record of the existence of the primitive Negro. As regards cranial capacity, which may be accepted as an index of brain volume, the measurement which prevails in Africa is about 100 c.c. less than is met with in Caucasia and Sinasia.

The area of Africa is 11.5 million square miles, but for our present purpose we must deduct from this the Mediterranean zone which has been added to Caucasia and also the whole of the Sahara, so that the habitable area that remains for native Africans is only a little over eight million square miles. In a large part of this area the climate is tropical and much of the country is thickly forested. In the 125 million inhabitants of this area we find social units at all stages of evolution, from small local groups, as among the Bushmen, to multi-tribal kingdoms, such as that of the Baganda in East Africa and that of Bushongo in the lower Congo. The majority of the population, however, is grouped, or was so until Africa passed under the control of European Powers, in tribal societies of varying sizes, each society occupying a separate or independent territory. In the Belgian Congo Hambly [6] enumerates 117 tribes, in Uganda sixty-one. The number of tribes given for Tanganyika [7] is 117. Keane [8] enumerates 110 peoples in the Bantu-speaking area; in the Soudan, which crosses Africa from west to east, south of the Sahara, he gives a list of 108 peoples. Many of these Soudanese peoples have borrowed genes, as well as culture, from Arabia. In the seventeenth century B.C. Egyptians found the Berberines living above the first cataract divided into 113 tribes. But nowhere in native Africa has a group of tribes been welded together so closely as to form a national unit. Only in Egypt has this evolutionary stage been revealed, and, after some hesitation, I have assigned Egypt to Caucasia.

We now pass to a consideration of the middle zone or division of the " Pigmented South "—Indo-Asia, of which India with its 400 million inhabitants is the sole intact and surviving part. The lands which lie between N.E. Africa and India are now occupied by peoples of the Caucasian type, but there are reasons for believing that in primal times the pigmented belt swept on unbroken from west to east. Many of the Himyaritic tribes and peoples of South Arabia are deeply pigmented, with a strong resemblance to the Somali of N.E. Africa. The natives of Persian Arabistan are noted for the darkness of their complexion; the Brahuis of Baluchistan speak a language allied to the tongues of Dravidian India. But the chief circumstance which leads an anthropologist to assume a former continuity of the peoples of Africa with those of India is the degree of resemblance he finds between the Hamitic peoples of Africa and the Dravidian inhabitants of southern India. Here is Keane's description of typical Dravidians: " The stature is short, the complexion very dark, almost black, hair plentiful with a tendency to curl, head long, and nose very broad." [9] I would modify this description by saying that although " broad noses " are to be seen among Dravidians, yet the prevailing type is narrow and straight, and the features of the face, like those of the Hamites, are regular and Caucasoid. Among Indian hilltribes we meet individuals with the woolly hair and thick lips of the African, but these are only interesting exceptions; most Dravidians have hair that is wavy or straight, and always black. The Dravidian body, like that of the Hamite, is almost devoid of hair and the face is usually beardless. In India, as in Africa, there are areas occupied by short- or round-headed folk,[10] yet in both countries long-headedness is the type which prevails. As regards volume of brain, Indians and Africans are on an equality; their mean cranial capacity is about 100 c.c. less than holds for Caucasians and Sinasians.[11] In spite of invasions and penetrations from the north-west, India still remains part of the pigmented zone; so far as concerns colour of skin these invasions have served merely to lessen the depth of pigmentation among the more northerly peoples.

The inhabitants of India, like those of Africa, have retained a tribal organization. Within its area of 1·7 million square miles there are over 600 principalities, large and small, but in none of them, either now or in former times, was that degree of cohesion reached which entitled them to be described as national units. Millions of Indians are still grouped in primitive tribal units. The vast majority of Hindus are organized into social units known as castes; there are over 3,000 of them. Castes represent evolutionary units of a peaceful disposition.[12]

Beyond India, on its eastern side, is an area almost equal to that of India itself, which may be named the " submerged region " of the middle pigmented zone. It includes Indo-China, the Malay Peninsula, the Malayan Archipelago, and the Philippines. The inhabitants of all these lands, numbering some 120 millions, have the Mongolian faces developed to a greater or lesser degree, but ethnologists have long recognized that in the present population there are traces of an older one. The Andaman Islands, situated between India and Indo-China, have preserved a sample of this ancient stock. The Andamanese are exceptionally short of stature, with deeply pigmented skins, and woolly black hair, but their nose is not flattened nor are their lips unduly thick. Peoples with similar Negroid features and of short stature are found in the Malay Peninsula and in the Philippines. Besides these aberrant peoples there are found throughout this wide region tribes of ordinary stature, with facial features which may be described as Caucasoid, with skins varying in colour from light to dark brown, with hair which may be wavy or straight. In many parts this older Indonesian stock seems to have been absorbed by the invading Malayan stock. Among the Indo-Asians, as among the true Indians, long-headedness prevailed; the Malays, on the other hand, are mostly round-headed.

There now remains for our consideration the third of the divisions of the pigmented southern hemisphere of humanity and the fifth and last of the human population of the Old World. The Australasians are the aborigines of four separated areas:—(1) the continent of Australia, extending to almost three million square miles; (2) the great island of New Guinea; (3) the chain of islands which stretch southwards from New Guinea into the Pacific and which will be spoken of as Melanesia and their inhabitants as Melanesians; (4) the island of Tasmania. I look upon the aborigines of these four lands as descendants of a common ancestral stock, their racial divergence being the result of long separation (from mid-Pleistocene times or earlier); the evolutionary changes are such as ensue in populations which are long isolated and inbred. The area of Australasia is about 3·5 million square miles; it is probable that its aboriginal population has at no time reached the million mark. Thus the Australasians form by far the smallest of the five great divisions of mankind, but for the student of human evolution they represent the most interesting and instructive of human stocks.

In all members of this stock the skin is pigmented to a varying degree; among Australian aborigines it is of some shade of brown; in the outlying lands—in New Guinea, Melanesia, and Tasmania—

skin pigmentation is deeper, sometimes almost black. The Papuans of New Guinea have hair which is black, frizzled, and long, assuming in the mass the appearance of mops, but individuals with woolly hair and others with wavy hair are also to be met with. In Melanesia hair is usually frizzled, but true woolly hair is much more abundant than in New Guinea. The hair of the extinct Tasmanians was black and woolly. Among the aborigines of Australia wavy hair is the prevalent form, but in certain areas, particularly in the south, individuals with curly, almost frizzled, hair are still not uncommon. Perhaps the most outstanding of the physical characteristics of the Australasian are the lowness of his forehead and the prominence and strength of his supraorbital ridges, particularly in the natives of the mainland and also of Melanesia. The nose is usually low and wide, but among Papuans it may be prominent and hooked. Jaws are strongly fashioned, especially the lower jaw. As is the case in Africa and Indo-Asia, long-headedness prevails throughout, although focuses of round-headedness do occur. The mean volume of brain is a little lower than in the two other divisions of the pigmented zone. Taking him all in all, the Australian aborigine represents better than any other living form the generalized features of primitive humanity. Throughout the whole of Australasia evolutionary units take the form of tribes or of village communities.

In this essay we have seen the reason for dividing the total area of the Old World into five major areas, each of which is inhabited by a particular type of humanity. We may now ask ourselves: "How has such an arrangement come about?" "Why is each distinctive stock of mankind confined to one particular region of the earth?" If we believe, as many authorities do, that man, from his earliest stage of evolution, has been a nomad and a wanderer, that human communities have always been on the move from one part of the earth to another, everywhere meeting and mingling their genes, then we can offer no explanation of regional differentiation of races. But if we accept the theory of group evolution, which implies that from the very beginning human groups were attached to their territories and moved from them only when numbers increased and new homes had to be found, or when compelled to shift because of the aggression of stronger neighbours, then an explanation can be given. Regionalization of race is in conformity with, and gives support to, the theory of group evolution.

In the essay which follows we shall assume that Africa was the original cradle of humanity, and proceed to ascertain how far this assumption is justified by the racial characters to be observed in each of the five primary divisions of mankind.

REFERENCES

[1] Dart, Raymond, vol. 116, *Nature*, Feb. 7th, 1925; *Amer. Jour. Phys. Anthrop.*, 1940, vol. 26, p. 167.

[2] Sykes, Mark, *Jour. Roy. Anthrop. Inst.*, 1908, vol. 32, p. 451.

[3] Prichard, J. C., *Physical History of Mankind*, vol. 4, p. 56, 3rd ed.

[4] Keane, A. H., *Man: Past and Present*, new ed., 1920, p. 183.

[5] Weidenreich, Franz, *Peking Nat. Hist. Bull.*, 1939, vol. 13, p. 161.

[6] Hambly, W. D., *African Anthropology. Field Museum Publications*, 1937, no. 394.

[7] *Handbook of Tanganyika Territory*, 1930.

[8] See under reference 4, ch. III.

[9] See under reference 4, p. 187.

[10] Round-headedness is very uncommon among native peoples of Africa and of India. Lesser degrees of it occur among peoples of the Nile–Congo watershed (Keane, p. 79) and in peoples of the Cameroons. Most of the round-headed peoples of India have been derived from outside sources.

[11] Dr. Gordon Harrower of Singapore found that the mean brain volume of men of South China was 1,496 c.c., while that of Tamils of India was 1,350 c.c.

[12] Hutton, J. H., *Caste in India*, 1946; Keith, Sir A., *Essays on Human Evolution*, 1946, p. 189.

[13] Keane, A. H., *Ethnology*, 1896, p. 264.

THE AFRICAN THEORY APPLIED TO EXPLAIN THE DISTRIBUTION OF THE RACIAL TYPES OF MANKIND

Synopsis.—*The African Theory assumes that the Dartians were dark skinned and carried the genes responsible for melanin production to all parts of the Old World. The evidence on which this assumption is based. Why the inhabitants of the southern zone retained the power to form melanin, and why this power was lost to a greater or less degree by those of the northern zone. The distribution of woolly, frizzled, wavy, and straight hair; difficulties in explaining this distribution. The difficulties are no less if we assume the centre of dispersal to have been, not Africa, but India. To explain the distribution of pygmy forms of mankind within the southern zone it is assumed that the tendency to produce dwarf forms was inherent in the genetic constitution of the early Dartians. This tendency is linked with two other characters, woolly hair and pigmented skin. The Dartians were of short stature, but carried the potentialities of a wide range. Dolichocephaly prevailed among the early Dartians, but the fossil forms found in South Africa, like living anthropoids, ranged from dolichocephaly to brachycephaly. The Dartians had anthropoid features; human facial features have been evolved since the dispersal. The explanation of Mongoloid features in Africa and in Western Europe and of Caucasian features among Mongolian peoples. Certain types of body and of face occur in all races. Evidence as to mental and moral nature of the early Dartians. Their habits of life. The African theory as a working hypothesis.*

IN Essay XXIII it was assumed that human-footed, ground-living anthropoids had been evolved in some part of Africa, and that during the long Pliocene period these primitive forms, which we are to speak of as " Dartians," spread slowly abroad, and so laid the foundation of humanity throughout the Old World. Of what colour were the Dartians, our anthropoid forerunners? Seeing that the African anthropoids, the gorilla and chimpanzee, are heavily pigmented, and that all true natives of Africa are dark-skinned, we may infer that this was so in the case of the extinct anthropoids of South Africa, and also in the case of their cousins, the Dartians, who, spreading abroad, carried the melanin-producing genes into the most distant parts of the earth. The African theory thus postulates that the originals of all races were dark-skinned, an assumption made by John Hunter in the eighteenth century on the evidence then available to him.[1]

The African theory thus explains why the three great racial divisions of the southern hemisphere should be inhabited by dark-skinned peoples, but gives no answer to those who ask the question: " Why have the peoples of the two great regions of the northern hemisphere—Sinasia and Caucasia—lost their original pigmentation, especially the Caucasians? " To answer this question we must return to the evolutionary centre in Africa and imagine what must have happened during the long period of dispersal. The Dartians were organized into a large number of small social groups, each being a separate inbreeding society. Some groups, we may legitimately assume, prospered, multiplied, in numbers, and, because of this, divided, new groups being thus formed. These new groups, to find room, had to move forwards to the growing or advancing edge of the area of dispersal. Thus the growing edge would be formed by groups which had recently undergone separation from older groups. Now, we have seen (Essay XXII, p. 219) that a new group carries with it an assortment of genes somewhat different from that of its parent group; the more frequent the division of a group, the more will its assortment of genes tend to depart from the original outfit. These new groups, as they advance into fresh, virgin territory, are exposed to conditions which are novel to them They thus become further changed by new selective agencies coming into operation. Other influences also produce changes in advancing or pioneering groups. Their advance exposes them to changes of climate, of food, and of surroundings; immigrants are affected by such changes.[2] Thus the groups which had advanced farthest from the original centre of dispersal would have undergone the greatest degree of evolutionary change.

Here I expose myself to a criticism. The Dartians who laid

the foundations of humanity in Java had made a longer evolutionary journey than those who carried their genes to China or to Europe. Why, then, did they retain their pigmentation while the others lost theirs? My answer is that the Dartians were evolved in a tropical climate and that their pigmentation protected them from the evil effect of actinic rays.[3] As long as their progeny remained exposed to tropical conditions, pigmentation had a survival value, and therefore such as tended to lose their pigmentation were weeded out. It was otherwise with the Dartians who succeeded in reaching the more temperate climates of Sinasia and Caucasia; if changes which involved a diminution of pigment-formation were otherwise advantageous to them, then they were free to undergo such changes. Among the changes I have in mind are those described under the heading of " fœtalization " described in Essay XX. Some of man's greatest evolutionary advances seem to have been made by his assuming characters which made their first appearance at a fœtal stage of his existence. The white and glabrous skin of the European is a fœtal inheritance. The Mongol, with his yellow and hairless skin, has inherited this new trait to a lesser degree. We attribute, then, the paler skins of the northern hemisphere to the inheritance of a fœtal condition.

We come now to the problem of the origin and distribution of that short, crisp, woolly form of hair which prevails throughout the greater part of native Africa. Man is the only Primate which has such hair. That of the great anthropoids is straight; for example, in the orang it is long, straight, and harsh to the touch. We must infer, therefore, that woolly hair arose as a mutation. This opinion is justified by the fact that it still does come into existence in families of pure European descent, sometimes in families which have blond hair.[4] I assume that the woolly mutation occurred in certain groups of Dartians while still within their African centre of dispersion; other groups retained the straight or wavy anthropoid type of hair. Even in those groups which had mutated, one may assume that they still retained the genes for straight hair as " recessives," and that, in certain circumstances, these groups could give rise to non-woolly progeny. Thus the African theory assumes that woolly hair made its first appearance in Africa and that its seeds or genes were carried by the Dartians into all parts of the southern hemisphere of humanity.

The theory, then, is that all the peoples of the southern hemi-

R

sphere were originally woolly-haired as well as pigmented. How, then, has it come about that in the extremes of this hemisphere—in Africa in the west, and in Melanesia and Tasmania in the east—woolly hair has been retained, while in intermediate areas, represented by Hamitic Africa in the west and by New Guinea in the east, peoples are now frizzle-haired? How, too, are we to account for the fact that modern India, in the very centre of the pigmented zone, has a population which is predominantly wavy or straight-haired, although among its hill-tribes woolly-haired individuals are still to be found? How, too, did the peoples of Sinasia come by their straight and stiff black hair, and those of Caucasia by hair which is wavy and may be black, brown, or blond? The explanation I offer is that the Dartian groups which emerged from Pliocene Africa still carried in their bodies, but in a recessive state, the genes for straight or wavy hair, and therefore it was always possible for their progeny to become again wavy-haired.

It must be admitted that the African theory, in order to explain the distribution of woolly, frizzled, and wavy hair, makes very large drafts on the bank of genes. Critics may point out to me that all these drafts might be saved by presuming that it was not Africa but India which was the original centre of dispersal, for in the latter all types of hair are represented. If my critics assume that the first wave of people to emerge from India was woolly-haired, then they can account for the distribution of this type of hair in the extremes of west and east. If the second wave which went out from India was frizzle-haired, then that would account for this type of hair occurring in Hamitic Africa and in New Guinea. Lastly, it could be assumed that the last wave of humanity to emerge from India was wavy- or straight-haired; from the third wave was populated Australia, Sinasia, and Caucasia.

Those who favour India as the original centre of dispersal have in mind India as it is to-day; but the India we are concerned with is that of Pliocene times. In those times India was rich in her anthropoid fauna, but so far no evidence has come to light of a ground or Dartian type. Even if this type were to be found in India, we should still have to explain, first, how woolly hair was evolved, then frizzled, and lastly, hair of the wavy or straight type. We should still have to make large drafts on the bank of genes.

As the evidence now stands we must regard Africa as the home of the fundamental Dartian type.

We now turn for a moment to consider another problem—the origin and distribution of pygmy peoples. They are found only within the southern-pigmented hemisphere. In South Africa they are represented by the Bushman; in the Congo basin by at least five separate groups; in India by the Andamanese; in the Malay Peninsula by the Semangs; in the Philippines by the Aetas; in New Guinea by the Tapiro and Aiome dwarfs. Two pertinent facts must be noted in connection with these dwarf peoples:—
(1) they have woolly hair and are more or less deeply pigmented;
(2) that in facial features and in colouring they resemble people of normal stature who live now, or presumably did in former times, in the same neighbourhood. For example, the dwarfs of the Welle Valley have the features and red colouring of the Azandeh and Mombuttu tribes of that valley; the Tapiros of New Guinea are dwarf forms of neighbouring Papuans. We infer, therefore, that these dwarfs do not represent a single race, but that they have arisen in several places, and at diverse times, as sports or mutations; that the tendency to produce such mutations is inherent in the germinal constitution of Negroid peoples; and that this tendency existed in the emigrating Dartian groups, and was carried by them to all parts of the southern zone. Somehow this tendency to give rise to dwarf forms is linked with the genes responsible for the development of woolly hair; at least in those regions of the world where woolly hair is lacking there is an absence of pygmy forms. The African theory helps us to understand why the distribution of pygmies is as we now find it. It is also of interest to note that one of the African anthropoids—the chimpanzee—has a pygmy form or sub-species.[5]

In modern Africa we meet with peoples of all statures, from the Bushmen of the Cape with an average height of 4 ft. 10 ins., to the tall Dinkas of the Nile Valley with an average approaching 6 ft. The extinct anthropoids of South Africa were of small size. From the fragments of their limb-bones one infers that they had the stature of Bushmen, and may therefore be regarded as dwarfs or pygmies. Their African cousin, the gorilla, is of massive size; a male may attain the weight and strength of four ordinary men. Taking all of these circumstances into consideration, it seems quite probable that the Dartians, in their exodus from Africa, carried with them the potentialities of a wide range of statures.

Does the African theory throw any light on the distribution of long-headedness and of round-headedness among human races? Among the modern peoples of the southern hemisphere long-headedness prevails everywhere—in Africa, in India, in New Guinea, in Melanesia, and Australia. In only a few minor areas is there an appreciable degree of brachycephaly. It is otherwise in the northern hemisphere. In Caucasia, while long-headedness prevails among the peoples of the south, west, and north-west, those of the centre, of the east, and of the south-east are mostly short- or round-headed, or, as I would prefer to say, short-brained, for it is brain-growth that is the chief agent in determining the shape of head. When we pass from Caucasia into Sinasia, short-brainedness still holds, but nevertheless the prevailing brain-form among the Tibetans and Chinese is of an intermediate type. Weidenreich [6] is of the opinion that there has been an immense transformation from long-headedness to round-headedness among the central peoples of the northern hemisphere during recent millennia. In this I am in agreement with him, although the manner in which this transformation has been effected still remains obscure.

To explain the distribution of head-forms described in the preceding paragraph we should expect the early emigrants from Africa to be pronouncedly long-brained and long-headed. Let us, then, look into the brain-form of the African anthropoids. We shall call all those brains short if their width is more than 80 per cent of their length, and long if their width percentage is less than 80. Professor H. A. Harris [7] found that in the gorilla the width of the brain-chamber varied from 72 to 86 per cent of its length, the prevailing form falling near the line which separates "long" from "short." In the chimpanzee the index figure varies from 78 to 84, while in the Asiatic orang shortness is dominant, the index varying from 82 to 87. More to our purpose is the shape of the brain in the extinct anthropoids of South Africa. The first of these to be discovered had a long and narrow brain, the width being only 70·5 per cent of its length. Schepers [8] reports that in two other species of South African anthropoids (Dartians) which were discovered by Dr. Broom the brain width varies from 78 to 85 per cent of the length. Thus among the early Dartians there were both long-brained and short-brained forms. We must note, too, the brain porportions in the earliest forms of humanity known to us. Among the fossil men of Java the brain index varied from 76 to 82; among those of China (Sinanthropes), from 74 to 79; in Piltdown man it was about 79; in Rhodesian man, 79; among the Neanderthalians, from 79 to 84. Thus we find the same range of brain proportions among the earlier forms of man as among the earlier forms of African Dartians.

As regards their facial features the African Dartians were true anthropoids. Their noses were wide and flat and sank into the contour of their prognathous, snout-like faces. We must assume, therefore, that the differentiation of the human nose into its several racial types took place after the Dartian dispersal. There is a parallelism between the distribution of forms of hair and of types of nose. Taking the southern-pigmented zone first, we note that in the extremes of this zone—in Africa in the west, in Melanesia and Tasmania in the east—a wide and flat nose accompanies woolly hair. The aborigines of Australia, although they are no longer woolly-haired, retain the wide Negroid form of nose. In India, in the centre of the zone, noses have become narrow and straight and the hair wavy or straight. In nose shape the frizzle-haired Hamites of Africa agree with the natives of India, while the Papuans of New Guinea, on India's eastern flank, have noses of many forms; often they are prominent, sometimes with an arched or " Jewish " outline, and usually of moderate width. In the peoples of Sinasia, in whom Mongolian features have reached a full development, the nose is relatively small and of moderate width. Its bony part, its root and bridge, seem as if they had become submerged in the inter-orbital region of the face. It is among the peoples of Caucasia that the nose has undergone its greatest evolutionary development. It is usually prominent, sharply demarcated from the rest of the face, relatively narrow, and is capable of assuming an endless number of shapes. A consideration of the distribution of the various racial forms of nose, while bringing no support to the African theory, is not out of harmony with that theory.

In favour of the African theory there is evidence which I must now touch upon. I have already remarked (p. 238) that anthropologists have often noted the occurrence of " Europinoids " among the peoples of Sinasia. In Africa, too, they have noted individuals with Mongolian traits. The resemblance of Hottentots to Mongolians in the colouring and in some of their facial features is a matter which has often caused astonishment. If it is remembered, as postulated by the African theory, that Hottentots and Mongols are co-descendants of a common Dartian stock, then we should not be surprised if some of these descendants have undergone a parallel evolutionary development. They are co-heirs of the same ancestral set of genes. Then there is the case of the Ainus of Sinasia, a hairy people with features in which Caucasian and Mongolian features are blended. If we accept the African theory, then we have to regard the peoples of Sinasia and of Caucasia as the collateral descendants of the early Dartian groups who made their way northwards into the central regions of the Old World. Therefore I regard the Ainus, not as immigrants from Europe, but as " isolates " who have retained a high percentage of the characters which were common to the ancestry of Asiatic as well as of European peoples. Likewise in Western Europe individuals are occasionally to be met with who manifest Mongolian features in their faces. To explain such occurrences we make big demands on the bank of genes, but, then, it must be remembered there are many undiscovered vaults in that bank.

Two other potentialities we may ascribe to our Dartian forerunners. We may assume that in their genetic constitution there was a tendency to produce two opposite types of body—the short and thick and the long and slender, for, as Weidenreich [9] has observed, these opposite types occur in all races of mankind. It is true that the short and thick type prevails among Mongolian peoples, and the long and thin type among the aborigines of Australia; in Caucasia both types are equally common. We may presume, too, that there was a wide variety of facial features among the early Dartians. No two had exactly the same combination of parts; each individual had its own distinctive marks. Schultz [10] found among hundreds of American monkeys of the same species, collected in the same area of jungle, that the features of their faces " differed as much as an equal number of city-dwellers." Every Primate, be it ape or man, carries its marks of recognition in its face; hence the infinite variety of facial features within the same race. Yet under a coloured skin and arrayed in a distinctive racial livery one recognizes types of face which are common to all races. When living among a native people of the Malay Peninsula, I met with many faces which recalled those of my friends at home. Bijlmer,[11] I find, had the same experience when he lived among the Papuans of New Guinea.

We come now to the most important of all matters which concern the early Dartians. What were their habits? How did they make their livelihood? What can we say of their mentality? As to the South African anthropoids, their discoverer, Professor Dart,[12] has no manner of doubt; they were " animal-hunting, flesh-eating, skull-cracking, and bone-breaking " apes. If the evidence on which he has relied proves to be well-founded, then we must infer that in their habits and nature ground-living anthropoids differed altogether from the tree-living forms. The latter subsist on shoots, buds, fruit, leaves, and insects, but in no sense can they be described as hunters. The social groups in which they live are devoid of the instincts which animate a " hunting pack." In 1920, five years before the discovery of the South African anthropoids, my friend Carveth Reade [13] published a book in which he maintained that man had inherited his hunting, co-operative, cruel, and warlike proclivities from ground-living anthropoids which had all the instincts of a pack of wolves. The name he proposed for this form of anthropoid was Lyco-pithecus, the wolf-ape. At a still earlier date, another of my friends, Dr. Harry Campbell,[14] gave many reasons for believing that the " pre-human ape was a hunter." Such a life, he claimed, created situations " in which intelligence counted in the life struggle as it had never before counted." Dartians seem to answer to the postulates of these two thinkers: In the caves of South Africa are found the broken skulls of extinct forms of baboons; these Professor Dart regards as the victims of his anthropoids. If this is so, then it is possible to suspect the Dartians of the cannibalistic practices which were certainly indulged in by early forms of mankind.[15] Another of my intimate friends, Mr. Morley Roberts,[16] taught that cannibalism had been " a powerful factor of progress and human advance," a doctrine which was repugnant to my personal outlook on humanity. Yet he may have been right, for we find a sober-minded ethnologist like Keane [17] saying this of cannibalistic peoples of Africa: " Here again the observation has been made that the tribes most addicted to cannibalism also excel in mental qualities and physical energy. Nor are they strangers to the finer feelings of human nature." All these items of evidence bearing on the mental and moral nature of the early Dartians are unsubstantial and highly speculative, yet to me they are far from incredible. When discussing the duality of human nature (p. 121), we noted how easy and natural it is for men and women to frame their behaviour on a dual code of morality; so universal is the practice of this code that we must believe that the mental attributes on which it is based are a common inheritance of mankind. We have seen that the dual code is still in its incipient stage in arboreal anthropoids (p. 41), but in the ground forms, the Dartians, it seems to have become completely established. If we agree that the ground forms of anthropoids were evolved in Africa, and that their mental and physical nature were such as has been outlined in this essay, and that in Pliocene times these anthropoid or Dartians spread abroad and laid the foundations of humanity in the various regions of the Old World, then we have a working hypothesis which explains much that is now obscure in the rise of humanity. Such a hypothesis has one essential merit: it can be proved or disproved by the discoveries which the future will certainly bring to us.

REFERENCES

1 Hunter, John, *Collected Works*, edited by Palmer, 1837, vol. 4, p. 280.

2 For changes in head-form and in stature of the children of immigrants, see Boas, Franz (1858–1942), *Changes in the Bodily Form of Descendants of Immigrants*, 1910; *Kultur and Rasse*, 2nd ed., 1922; Shapiro, H. L., *Migration and Environment*, 1939; Morant and Samson, *Biometrika*, 1936, vol. 28, p. 1 (a criticism of Boas's work).

3 Dr. Rupert Willis informs me that among the people of Australia those with lightly pigmented skins are the most liable to cancer of the skin. In the congenital condition known as *Xeroderma pigmentosa*, the parts of skin exposed to light are those most liable to turn cancerous.

4 Cases of woolly hair occurring in European families have been reported by Anderson, F., *Jour. Hered.*, 1936, vol. 27, p. 444; Mohr, O. L., *ibid.*, 1933, vol. 23, No. 9; van Bemmelen, *Bull. Soc. Morph.*, 1928, No. 1–2; Talko-Hyrncewicz, J., *Bull. Acad. Sc. Cracovie*, 1911, p. 164.

5 A dwarf species of chimpanzee (*A. paniscus*) was discovered in the Congo by C. Schwarz in 1929. A full description of this new species was given by Dr. H. Coolidge in the *Amer. Jour. Phys. Anthrop.*, 1935, vol. 18, p. 1.

6 Weidenreich, Franz, *South-Western Journ. Anthrop.*, 1945, vol. 1, p. 1.

7 Harris, H. A., *Proc. Zool. Soc. Lond.*, 1927, p. 491.

8 Schepers, C. W. H., see note 13, p. 233 *supra* (Essay XXIII).

9 Weidenreich, F., *Rasse and Koerperbau*, 1927.

10 Schultz, A. H., *Science Monthly*, 1932, vol. 34, p. 360.

[11] Bijlmer, Dr. H. J. T., *A Thesis on New Guinea*, 1922.

[12] Dart, Professor Raymond, *S.A. Jour. Sc.*, 1929, vol. 26, p. 648; see also p. 21 of work cited in note 13, p. 233 *supra* (Essay XXIII).

[13] Reade, Carveth, *The Origin of Man*, 1920, pp. 8, 18.

[14] Campbell, Dr. Harry, *Lancet*, 1921, (2), p. 629.

[15] Keith, Sir A., *Essays on Human Evolution*, 1946, p. 178.

[16] Roberts, Morley, *Warfare in the Human Body*, 1920, p. 146.

[17] Keane, A. H., *Man: Past and Present*, 1920, p. 82.

A NEW CONCEPTION OF THE GENESIS OF MODERN RACES *

Synopsis.—*A statement of the problems relating to the origin of modern races of mankind. The theory which was prevalent in the opening decades of the twentieth century. The theory of regional evolution enunciated by the author in 1936. The origin of the native peoples of Australasia traced to the Pithecanthropus type of Java. Evidence pointing to the descent of Bushman and Hottentot races from a Pleistocene type represented by Rhodesian man. The fossil evidence, although incomplete, favours the idea that the Hamitic type was evolved in East Africa and the Chinese type in China. The origin of the Caucasian type. It is held that this type was evolved in Central or S.W. Asia from an ancestor of the Neanderthal type. The bearing of the discovery of an intermediate fossil type at Mount Carmel on this interpretation. The Pleistocene invasion of Europe by Caucasians and the extermination of the Neanderthalians. Evidence that human races have "converged" during the Pleistocene phase of their evolution. The reasons which have led the author to abandon his earlier belief that the "modern type" of man was of ancient origin.*

IN order that you may follow my line of argument, let me put before you samples of the problems I intend to explore in this essay. Take the Mongolian peoples, for example, so different

* The opening passages of this essay are taken almost verbatim from a Presidential Address which I gave to the members of the British Speleological Association at Buxton on July 25th, 1936. This was, so far as I know, the first time the conception had been put forward that modern races of mankind are the direct descendants of early Pleistocene forms of humanity. The address was published in full in *Caves and Cave Hunting*, vol. 1, and in *Nature*, 1936, vol. 138, p. 194. Knowing nothing of my address, Dr. Franz Weidenreich enunciated the same idea in the *Trans. Amer. Philosoph. Soc.*, 1941, vol. 31, p. 32. Professor Ruggles Gates also favours the idea that races have been evolved in the regions where they are now found (*Amer. Jour. Phys. Anthrop.*, 1944, N.S., vol. 12, p. 279).

individually, and yet so alike in the mass that they are unmistakable to the trained eye.   When and how did the eastern lands of Asia become the home of these peoples?   Was the type evolved where we now find it?   Or let us ask—is Africa the home of the Negro?   Was the type evolved in that continent?   Then let us take the Australian type, represented by the aborigines of Australia and by the natives of adjoining islands.   When and where did this type of humanity come into existence?   Was it cradled and evolved in that part of the world where we now find it?   Or was its cradle elsewhere?   Then there is our own type— the European or Caucasian.   Were our bodies and brains evolved in Europe?   If not, where are we to seek for the ancestor of our type?   All these types—Mongolian, Australian, Negro, and Caucasian—we presume to be the progeny of a common or primordial stock.   Has cave exploration thrown any light on the break up of this stock and of its dispersion into all parts of the earth?

Does the evidence which we are now accumulating support the preconceptions we have formed concerning the solution of these problems?   I have to confess that recent discoveries are upsetting our older ideas.   The new facts, such as they are, do not support opinions usually held concerning the origin of the chief racial stocks of humanity.   The most divergent races of modern man are, from an anatomist's point of view, not really far apart. There is no race that is not fertile with another.   All seem to be the progeny of a common stock.   We have been searching caves and river deposits all over the world in the hope of finding the common ancestor of modern types of humanity—black and . brown, white and yellow.   We have expected to find their common ancestor among the fossil types which flourished during the middle part of the Pleistocene period, one which—on the shorter reckoning—carries us back some 250,000 years, or, if we count by generations, then some 10,000 of them.   From a single centre we expected to be able to trace the diffusion of modern man into all parts of the earth where demarcation of colour and of features occurred.   Such was the theory which guided our inquiries and such *were* our expectations.

The theory just outlined is, in reality, little more than a modified version of the account in Genesis of " Shem, Ham, and Japheth."   Instead of accepting Noah as the ancestor of modern

races we substituted for him a " mid-Pleistocene ancestral stock ";
in place of drowning all Noah's contemporaries in a universal
deluge, we supposed that the races of modern man, as they spread
abroad on the earth, exterminated all other and older races. We
supposed that all the earlier Pleistocene types of men had been
destroyed, leaving no issue. Thus after the mid-Pleistocene dispersion the earth became divided among peoples who were
members of the same species of humanity—*Homo sapiens*.

Alas! our advances in knowledge bring no support for such a
theory. Many fossil types of humanity have been discovered,
but not one of them answers to our conception of a common
ancestor for modern races. No evidence has been found of an
outward migration from a common centre in mid-Pleistocene
times. What has been found compels us to recast our ideas
concerning the origin of human races. It does now seem as if
the racial territories which were marked out in Essay XXIV are
of ancient date, that by the beginning of the Pleistocene period the
ancestors of the Mongol, of the Australian, of the Negro were
already in occupation of the continental areas where their descendants are now found. In 1936 this was a new conception,
for the prevailing belief then was, and indeed still is (1946), that
early man was an incorrigible wanderer, and passed from continent
to continent as the mood moved him.

The thesis I put forward to account for all the facts we now
have concerning the origin of modern races has the following
distinctive points :—(1) that their separation is very ancient and is
traceable back to the beginning of the Pleistocene period; (2)
that each of the main racial divisions was evolved in its own continental area; (3) that at the date of separation each race was still
in the " rough "—and that each has undergone similar or
" parallel " changes independently of each other. These parallel
changes are represented by a reduction in size and of strength of
tooth and jaw; a continuing increase in size and in complexity of
the brain, the maximum of cerebral development being reached
by late Pleistocene peoples. There were, too, independent trans-
mutations of simian markings into those of a human character.
I see no possibility of explaining the evidence now at our disposal
unless we admit that " parallel evolution " has been just as potent
in the evolution of human races as it certainly has been in the
evolution of species of horse and of elephant.

As the evidence which connects the aborigines of Australia with Pithecanthropus of early Pleistocene Java is more complete than in the case of other races, I shall begin by tracing the origin of the peoples of Australasia.   At the date just mentioned the Malay Peninsula was continued through Sumatra and Java to Timor, an arm of the sea about twenty-five miles wide separating the latter island from Australia.   Australia was then joined to New Guinea, Melanesia, and Tasmania.[1]   That at some point of the Pleistocene period human beings succeeded in reaching Australia by crossing that arm of the sea is proved by the discovery of Pleistocene man in Australia.   In 1943, at Keilor, near Melbourne, a fossil skull of Australoid type was found at a depth of 18 ft. in a gravel terrace which is contemporary with, or even earlier than, the last glaciation in Europe.[2]   The brain was remarkably large, the cranial capacity approaching 1,600 c.c.   The facial features might well be the ancestral type from which those of the aborigines of Australia and of Tasmania were derived.   At a still earlier date, 1914, the Talgai (Queensland) fossil skull came to light; [3] it, too, was Australoid in all its characters, but its palate far exceeded any modern aboriginal palate, while its cranial capacity, 1,300 c.c., although much below that of the Keilor man, was rather above the mean for aborigines.

In 1896, two years after Dubois had announced the discovery of Pithecanthropus, Keane [4] noted that an extinct tribe of Australian aborigines " had the enormous superciliary arches and some other traits of Pithecanthropus."   Hermann Klaatsch (1864–1916), an anatomist of great originality of mind, visited Australia in 1904 to study the anatomy of the natives.   In his report [5] occurs the following passage : " My recent experiences show so many connections between Pithecanthropus and Australian and Tasmanian skulls that I am more inclined than before to accept a very close approximation of Pithecanthropus to the first tribe of human beings."   Then, in 1920, Dubois published an account [6] of two fossil skulls found at Wadjak in Java ; their characters were pronouncedly Australoid, but their brains were very big, the cranial capacity of the larger being 1,650 c.c. ; their palates, too, were of great size.   In 1932 Dr. Oppenoorth made a discovery which served to link Wadjak man to Pithecanthropus.   In a terrace of the Solo river, of later date than that which yielded the fossil remains of Pithecanthropus and only a little way from the original site, he unearthed parts of eleven individuals; six of their skulls were sufficiently intact to be measurable. These Solo people had brains which varied from 1,035 to 1,255 c.c., their mean capacity being 1,100 c.c., which is more than 200 c.c. above the mean for the Pithecanthropians. They still retained the sloping forehead and prominent supraorbital ridges of the older type. Between 1931 and 1941 von Koenigswald succeeded in adding four more Pithecanthropoid skulls to the original discovered by Dubois, one of them being the infantile (Modjokerto) skull from a deposit of earliest Pleistocene date (see p. 226).

With such a record of intermediate, linking forms it is difficult to doubt that the individuals of at least one modern race of mankind—the aborigines of Australia—is the evolutionary progeny of an early Pleistocene type—namely, that represented by the Pithecanthropians of Java.

But what of the peoples of the other parts of Australasia— the natives of Tasmania, of Melanesia, and of New Guinea? All these must be regarded as insular peoples who have been isolated and inbred since Pleistocene times. The band or bands which first settled in those outlying areas carried with them their own particular assortment of Australoid genes. Those who went to New Guinea were submitted to a climate and a dietary very different from those which met the settlers in Tasmania or in Melanesia. The interaction of these factors—heredity and environment—led to the differentiation of their separate types.

From Australasia we pass to South Africa to inquire into the origin of two other modern races—namely, the Bushman and Hottentot. The stone tools of the early Pleistocene South Africans we know, but of their makers not a fossil trace has been found. The earliest type known is represented by the Rhodesian man; his date is probably towards the end of the mid-Pleistocene era, being thus a contemporary of the earlier forms of Neanderthal man in Europe. His face was gorilline in its characterization; his supraorbital torus was enormous; his jaws were large; his brain of moderate dimensions, had a volume of 1,350 c.c., about the same as a modern Hottentot. The Rhodesian skull [7] was discovered in 1921; eight years previously a fossil skull was found at Boskop in the Transvaal, in circumstances which pointed to a date late in the Pleistocene. The skull found at Boskop differed altogether from that found in Rhodesia; it had a high and long vault, and had contained a brain of great size, one with a volume of 1,630 c.c., nearly 300 c.c. more than fell to the lot of Rhodesian man. Excavation of South African caves by Professor Dart [8] brought to light a number of cranial forms which linked that of Boskop with those of the Bushman and Hottentot, save that the modern representatives of the Boskop type are smaller-brained than the original. The last thing I expected to happen was the discovery of forms which linked the Rhodesian to the big-brained Boskop type. Yet that is what did happen. In 1932 Professor T. F. Dreyer [9] found in the course of the systematic exploration of an Upper Pleistocene site at Florisbad, at a depth of 20 ft., and accompanied by implements of the South African middle stone industry, the greater part of a human skull. The Florisbad skull almost rivalled the Rhodesian in the strength of its frontal torus, but in other features agreed with the Boskop type. In 1945 another fossil skull[10] with the same mixture of Rhodesian and Boskop traits was found at Labomba, on the border between Zululand and Swaziland. The accompanying stone " industry " was that found with the Florisbad skull. Such, then, is the evidence which leads us to the belief that Bushman and Hottentot have been evolved in Africa and that both are descended from a mid-Pleistocene type, such as that preserved for us in the Rhodesian skull.

In East Africa, to which we now turn, the evidence relating to the local evolution of race is less complete than in South Africa. Such evidence as we have is owing to the enterprise of Dr. L. S. B. Leakey, who has succeeded in placing East Africa on the archæological map of the world by the sacrifice of his personal affairs.[11] It was in 1933 that he found the oldest human fragment so far discovered in Africa—the chin region of a human mandible, very heavily mineralized. It came from the early Pleistocene deposits at Kanam on the eastern shore of Lake Victoria. This fossil fragment is remarkable for the fact that the front teeth, both canines and incisors, do not differ from those of modern man. Hence Dr. Leakey believed, and I agree with him, that the Kanam mandible was evidence of the early development of the modern type of man. Both he and I were then ignorant of the fact that small incisors and canines were also characteristic of the South African Dartian anthropoids. It seems to me now to be much more probable that the small front teeth of Kanam man indicate a relationship to Dartian anthropoids rather than to any type of modern man.   As I have mentioned already (p. 239), Dr. Leakey found in a mid-Pleistocene formation at Kanjera, which is near to Kanam, two skulls which provide the earliest indications of Negro features.   All the human skulls he recovered from later Pleistocene deposits indicate the existence in East Africa of men of the Hamitic type.   There remains for mention a fossil skull which Kohl-Larsen discovered in 1935 in the eastern shore of Lake Eyassi, Tanganyika, which Weinert [12] has attributed to a kind of man he has named Anthropodus njarasensis.   The Eyassi skull resembles the Rhodesian in several points; Dr. Leakey gives it a late Pleistocene date. [13]   There are still many blanks in the fossil records of East Africa, but when these are filled in we may hope to have further evidence in support of my thesis that native races have been evolved in the continents they now inhabit.

From Africa we return to Asia to note the evidence relating to the evolution of the Mongolian type in Sinasia.   There is evidence of the existence of man in this region throughout the whole of the Pleistocene period, [14] but at only two points in this long stretch of time have bones of the actual inhabitants been found—namely, at the beginning of the mid-Pleistocene [15] and towards the end of the Upper Pleistocene.   Both these records have been provided by that treasury of fossil remains of man—the hill of Choukoutien in North China (see p. 227).   From its lower caves have come parts of some forty Sinanthrops of the mid-Pleistocene; from an upper cave the remains of a people who may be described as Proto-Mongols. [16]   The Sinanthrops were an advance upon their contemporaries in Java, the mean volume of their brains being 1,075 c.c., 200 c.c. more than the Pithecanthropic mean.   In outward appearance there was nothing Mongolian about the Sinanthrops, but in their teeth Weidenreich [17] detected a foreshadowing of Mongolian characters, and in this I am in agreement with him. Fossil parts of seven individuals were found in the upper cave, but only in the case of one man and two women were these complete enough to supply details.   In the man, with a cranial capacity of 1,500 c.c., Weidenreich noted Mongolian traits.   He threw out the suggestion that these upper cave people might well represent the stock which gave the New World its earliest settlers.   Imperfect as the records from Sinasia are, they support the idea that the Mongolian peoples have been evolved in Sinasia.

Before attempting to unravel the evolution of Caucasian peoples there is a preliminary matter I must deal with. Down to a point in the last period of glaciation Europe was inhabited by Neanderthalians. Then, quite suddenly, some 100,000 years ago, on the Zeuner scale of time, they were replaced by men of the Caucasian type. In the Europe of that remote date a racial transformation of the kind which is now being enacted in the continent of Australia had taken place; a more energetic and better equipped race replaced one which was more backward in these respects. The racial differences between the Neanderthalian and Caucasian types are too great for us to suppose the older and more primitive type had been transformed into the newer and more evolved type. We must explain the event by supposing that the Caucasian invaders had come from a home outside the bounds of Europe and exterminated the older race.

The Caucasian invaders were broken up into many local varieties, the prevailing type being that represented by the Cro-Magnons—tall men with long heads and big brains. Then there were the small, long-headed people of the Mediterranean type, such as still live in the Island of Corsica. There were also the heavy-browed Predmostians of Central Europe.

Where did these early Caucasians come from? What is their evolutionary history? These questions remained unanswered until 1929–34, when an expedition of American and British archæologists, under the leadership of Professor Dorothy Garrod, explored the caves of Mount Carmel in Palestine.[18] From these caves were recovered fossil remains of ten Pleistocene Carmelites who were living in Palestine when Europe was still inhabited by men of the Neanderthal type. The task of examining and describing this people fell on Dr. T. D. McCown and myself.[19] We found in them a strange mixture of Neanderthal and Cro-Magnon characters. The men were tall, robust, and long-headed, big-brained fellows. We concluded that we were dealing with a transitional people—one evolving from a Neanderthal type towards a Caucasian type—and that, after all, Neanderthal man was the ancestor of the proud Caucasian. As the evidence now stands it seems to us that at a period earlier than that represented by the fossil Carmelites, and farther towards the east, a local group of Neanderthalians began to evolve in a Caucasian direction and that the Carmelites represent a later phase

s

of this movement.   At least, if all turns out as we anticipate we may claim that the Caucasians of S.W. Asia still occupy the original area of their evolution.

One enigma remains: What became of the Piltdown race? In mid-Pleistocene deposits, at Swanscombe and in London, human skulls have been found which, so far as can be judged from their characters, are of the Piltdown, not of the Neanderthal type[20] —evidence of the continuation of the Piltdown breed in England. The diagnostic points of the Piltdown species lie in the face, and the facial parts are lacking in the Swanscombe and London fossil skulls, so that their racial nature remains uncertain.   The bones of Neanderthal man have not been found as yet in England, but remains of his stone culture are plentiful; we may well expect that his fossil bones will turn up some day.   This at least is certain— the cave men who lived in England in the closing phase of the Pleistocene period were of the same breed and had the same stone cultures as their contemporaries on the Continent, and therefore were the Caucasian descendants of Neanderthal man.   So were the invaders who came to Britain in post-glacial times.   The sum of the evidence is, then, that the Piltdown breed in England was completely replaced by continental Caucasians.

Must we conclude, then, that human races which seemed so unlike—so far apart—at the beginning of the Pleistocene period converged or approached one another in characterization as time went on, so that ultimately the progeny of races, originally diverse, became moulded into what is spoken of as the " modern type "?   That, I think, is the conclusion to which we must come. The idea of the evolutionary convergence of human races is not new; it was thrown out as a surmise in 1864 by the Swiss anthropologist, Carl Vogt.[21]   Darwin considered the suggestion [22] and thought it was " possible," but not " probable."   Yet that is what does seem to have taken place in the evolution of human races during the Pleistocene period; human races were more alike at the end of that period than they were at the beginning of it.   Let me mention some of these " converging " structural changes—changes which were effected independently in each of the chief races of mankind.   In all of them the brain underwent enlargement; and the jaws and teeth a reduction—two changes which were probably correlated.   The chin was modelled independently, so was the forehead, so was the mastoid process.   The sharp sill of bone which is to be seen at the entrance to the nasal chamber in so many modern Europeans is also met with in the skulls of some ancient Neanderthalians. All races of mankind seem to have inherited an evolutionary "trend" common to every one of them.

As a postscript to this essay let me dwell for a moment on the nemesis which overtook my faith in the antiquity of the "modern type" of man. My first book on fossil man, entitled *Ancient Types of Man*, published in 1911, was written to vindicate the claims of modern man to a high antiquity—claims which were rejected out of hand by the leading authorities of that time. The test case was that of "Galley Hill Man"; his remains were found in 1888 at a depth of 8 ft. in the 100-ft. terrace of the Thames valley; the geological evidence gave him a high antiquity, but, carrying all the modern marks I have just specified, he was placed by the leaders of opinion on the list of rejects. The fossil remains of Piltdown man were found at a depth of only 3 ft., but were immediately accepted because they carried primitive marks and were devoid of the modern ones. This mode of discrimination seemed to me unscientific; I clung to the geological evidence at Galley Hill, but the tide of discovery went dead against me. Even in 1926, when I brought out a new edition of *The Antiquity of Man*, I was still a defender of the antiquity of Galley Hill man and of his many compeers, but a change had overtaken me by 1931, for in a work published in that year I wrote: "Each great region of the world has produced and shelters its own native type."[23] By 1936 the evidence I have touched on in this and preceding essays convinced me that it was easier to believe that there was a flaw in the geological evidence of the antiquity of Galley Hill man than that a race or type of mankind could continue for 100,000 years without undergoing evolutionary change. And so I have had to abandon the claims of the "modern type of man" to a high antiquity, the very thesis which I set out to prove so long ago.

REFERENCES

[1] Cheeseman, L. E., *Nature*, 1943, vol. 152, p. 41.

[2] Mahony, D. J., "The Problem of Antiquity of Man in Australia," *Mem. Nat. Mus. Melbourne*, 1943, No. 12; Wunderly, J., "The Keilor Skull," *ibid*.

[3] For an account of the Talgai Skull, see Keith's *Antiquity of Man*, 1925, p. 449.

[4] Keane, A. H., *Ethnology*, 1896, p. 238.

[5] Klaatsch, Hermann (1864–1916), *Reports from the Lunacy Dept. N.S.W.*, 1908, vol. 1, p. 163.

[6] For an account of the Wadjak skulls, see under reference 3, p. 438.

[7] For an account of the Rhodesian skull see under reference 3, p. 407.

[8] Dart, Raymond, "Fossil Man and Contemporary Faunas in South Africa," *Report of the Sixteenth International Geological Congress*, Washington, 1936. For an account of Boskop and Bushman fossil skulls, see under reference 3, p. 356.

[9] Dreyer, T. F., "A Human Skull from Florisbad," *Proc. Konin. Akad. Wetensch. Amsterdam*, 1935, vol. 38, p. 119; see also Drennan, *Trans. Roy. Soc. S.A.*, 1937, vol. 25, p. 105; Galloway, Alex., *Amer. Jour. Phys. Anthrop.*, 1937, vol. 23, p. 1; Keith, Sir A., *Nature*, 1938, vol. 141, p. 1010.

[10] Cooke, Malan, and Wells, "The Labomba Skull," *Man*, 1945, p. 6.

[11] Leakey, L. S. B., "The Stone-Age Cultures of Kenya Colony," *Man*, 1933, no. 66.

[12] Weinart, Hans, *Enstehung der Menschenrassen*, 1938; *Der Biologie*, 1938, vol. 7, p. 125.

[13] Leakey, L. S. B., *Nature*, 1936, vol. 138, p. 1082.

[14] Pei wen-Chung, *Occasional Papers from the Institute of Archæology*, 1939, No. 2; de Chardin Teilhard, *Nature*, 1939, vol. 144, p. 1054.

[15] The deposits which yielded Pithecanthropus in Java, and those in China which contained Sinanthropus, were formerly regarded as of oldest Pleistocene date, but are now assigned to the middle Pleistocene. See von Koenigswald, *Early Man*, 1937, p. 24; also Weidenreich, F., *Anthropological Papers of the Amer. Mus. Nat. Hist.*, 1945, 40, pt. 1.

[16] Weidenreich, F., *Peking Nat. Hist. Bull.*, 1939, vol. 13, p. 161.

[17] Weidenreich, F., *Palæontologia Sinica*, 1937, no. 101; *ibid.*, 1943, no. 127.

[18] Garrod, Professor Dorothy, *The Stone Age of Mount Carmel*, 1939, vol. 1 (Archæology).

[19] McCown and Keith, *The Stone Age of Mount Carmel*, 1939, vol. 2 (Fossil Remains).

[20] For an account of the anatomical characters of the Swanscombe skull see Keith, *Jour. Anat.*, 1939, vol. 73, pp. 155, 234. For the London skull see Keith's *New Discoveries*, 1931, p. 435.

[21] Vogt, C., *Lectures on Man*, 1864, p. 568.

[22] Darwin, C., *The Descent of Man*, Murray, 1913, p. 274.

[23] Keith, Sir A., *New Discoveries relating to the Antiquity of Man*, 1931, p. 30.

ON THE THRESHOLD OF THE MODERN WORLD OF HUMAN EVOLUTION

Synopsis.—Primal and post-primal periods again defined. The post-primal period brought changes which altered the rate and mode of human evolution. There was a progressive increase in the size of the " evolutionary unit " ; ultimately national units replaced local groups. The mode of increase illustrated. It is estimated that the population of the whole world in mid-Pleistocene times was less than the present population of Scotland. The slow spread of the practice of agriculture. Its effects on the population of Africa. The introduction of pastoralism; its effects on population; attended by certain advantages. The evolutionary advantages of small units. Man attained his full status under the conditions which prevailed in the primal period. Large units are unsuited for the production of definite evolutionary changes. Under the conditions of the post-primal period mankind was subjected to new agencies of selection. Qualities which were favoured and selected. Fertility was given a fresh impetus. Agriculture brought in slavery which is anti-evolutionary in its effects. There is a human factor determining the rate of increase in an agricultural community. Before the end of the primal period tribal units had been evolved.

READERS may recall that in Essay III I divided man's evolutionary history into two very unequal phases—the *primal* and the *post-primal*. The primal phase covers the whole of the Pleistocene period, which, on the accepted scheme of reckoning, is given a duration of a million years, whereas the post-primal phase, in which we now are, began only about 9,000 or, perhaps, 10,000 years ago. In the first or primal phase man was the slave of un-tamed Nature; for a livelihood he was dependent on the natural produce of the territory on which he lived; he was hunter and food-gatherer. In the second or post-primal phase the food-gatherer turned peasant and the hunter became pastoralist; man

discovered how to tame Nature, and thus became a food producer, and with this discovery was ushered in the evolutionary
world in which he now finds himself.

To turn a primal native into a toiling peasant seems a small
matter, yet it was this change, beginning in a limited centre and
spreading slowly from that centre to the ends of the earth, which
transformed the conditions under which humanity lived and
altered radically the means by which its evolutionary change is
effected. In this essay and in those which follow I propose to
examine the nature of the changes which the discovery of agriculture effected in the social life of mankind. The chief change, the
one on which I shall lay the greatest stress, concerns the size of the
" evolutionary unit." In the primal world the evolutionary unit
is represented by the local group—a company of some fifty to
sixty men, women, and children, held together, and at the same
time separated from other surrounding groups, by that complexity
of mental partialities which we shall speak of as " clannishness."
With cultivation, food became more abundant; local groups
increased in size and in number; competition and strife between neighbouring groups ensued, with the result that larger
combinations were formed; several groups became fused to form
one body. When fusion had reached that point where all the
groups involved had lost their spirit of separatism and become
sharers of the same clannish feeling, then a new size of evolutionary unit had come into existence, to which the name tribe is
given. Local group and tribe are dominated by the same
mentality; they differ in size and in fighting strength or power.
Tribes are subject to the same evolutionary conditions as were the
local groups—those of competition and combat, ending in local
tribal fusions. When tribes, caught up in such new combinations,
have lived together for a sufficient number of generations—some
ten or twelve at least—they become conscious not only of a
common fellowship, but also that their fellow-feeling separates
them from all surrounding peoples. When this stage of consciousness has been reached, then a new evolutionary unit has
come into being—the unit which we recognize as a nation. The
same spirit of clannishness which animated and dominated the
local group and the tribe also takes possession of the nation. My
aim, then, will be to prove that the chief difference between the
primal and the post-primal phases of human evolution concerns

the size of the evolutionary or social unit.   We shall also have to inquire how far the machinery of evolution was thrown out of gear by the rise of the monstrous national units of modern times.

To illustrate the effects produced by the discovery of agriculture on the size of a social group, let us take a tribal territory in which the inhabitants are entirely dependent on its natural produce. Let us suppose that this territory measures 20 × 20 miles, thus containing 400 square miles.   If the land is fertile and the winter mild, our territory cannot support from its natural produce more than 400 inhabitants—that is, one for each square mile.   This is Professor Kroeber's [1] estimate, based on what is known of living primal peoples, and it is one with which I agree.   Let us now imagine that our picked primal territory has been ploughed and sown out in wheat : what population could it support with ease? For European countries economists [2] usually allow two acres of wheat for each head of population, and, as there are 640 acres to each square mile, this implies that each square mile, instead of supporting merely one primal man, is now capable of nourishing 320 modern men.   The tribal territory which in primal times could support no more than 400 souls, after the introduction of tillage became capable of carrying a population of 128,000.   The primal tribesmen were divided into local groups,[3] each group leading a nomadic life within its allotted area, whereas the modern inhabitants have no need to roam, but can remain in fixed abodes— towns, villages, and farms.   Such, then, expressed in somewhat crude terms, are some of the changes which took place in the world of humanity when man passed from the primal to the post-primal phase of his evolution.

The picture I have just drawn of a tribal territory gives a too favourable impression of the density of population and of the fertility of the soil in ancient times.   The Wonnarua, an extinct tribe of New South Wales,[4] for example, although it numbered only 500 members, yet occupied a fertile territory of 2,000 square miles along the Hunter river, having thus four square miles for each head of population.   In estimating the population of the primal world one has to remember that very large areas were covered by jungle and forest and were, from the point of view of primal man, inhospitable and almost uninhabitable areas.   Observations made by Dr. W. B. Hinsdale [5] led him to conclude that the thickly forested lands surrounding the central lakes of the

United States never carried a native population of more than one inhabitant to every thirty square miles of territory. In any attempt to estimate the total population of the earth in mid-Pleistocene times a higher allowance than one head for each ten square miles of habitable territory should not be made. If we take the total of habitable land on the earth as forty-two million square miles, and allow ten of them for each head of population, then the total population of the world in mid-Pleistocene times was about 4·2 millions—a total which is less than the present population of Scotland. The 4.2 millions of Pleistocene times has now (1946) become 2,000 millions, and it has been estimated [6] that this number could be increased to 132,000 millions if all lands were properly cultivated. I must own that for me the possibility holds in it more of a nightmare than of a happy dream.

One would expect that agriculture—a discovery so beneficent in its effects—would have spread with hurried feet across the earth. This was not the case: the division of the population into a myriad of small isolated self-sufficient communities greatly hindered the rate of extension. We shall see presently that before the fifth millennium B.C. had begun, people in the south-west region of Asia were tilling the land and keeping cattle; it took over 2,000 years for these practices to reach the peoples of Western Europe. Grain was sown and reaped at a very early date in Egypt,[7] and, although the Egyptians were linked with the tribes of tropical Africa by a continuous series of communities extending along the valley of the Nile, the new mode of gaining an existence seems to have spread very slowly southwards to the tribes in the interior, and to have been adopted by them with much less zeal than was the case in Europe. Even to-day Africa, taken as a whole, has an estimated population which gives only ten people for each square mile of territory: Northern Rhodesia, for example, 3·2 individuals for each square mile; Southern Rhodesia,[8] 5.1; Kenya, 10; Uganda, 30; Nyasaland, which has an all-over average of 34·6, yet in certain areas falls as low as 10, and in others rises as high as 200 inhabitants for each square mile. Nigeria has a mean of 60 per square mile, but in south Nigeria Miss Green [9] found village communities cultivating their tribal land so successfully that it was able to support 450 to the square mile. From which it will be seen that the tribal peoples of Africa have exploited the life-sustaining potentialities of their territories to only a limited extent. It is also worthy of remark that in the whole of this great continent in Egypt alone has tribal synthesis reached the degree that gives the people of that land the status of a nation.

The primitive peasant usually augmented his income from the soil by keeping domesticated animals. There were, however, certain primitive tribes who found it more agreeable to their nature to depend on flocks and herds for their entire sustenance. Pastoral peoples require a much more extensive territory for their maintenance than those who live by tilling the soil. A Tartar family had an allowance of three square miles; the pastoral lands of East Africa carried three members of the Masai tribe to each square mile: the highest estimate I have come across gives seven souls per square mile. Pastoralism, if a pleasant, was an extravagant mode of life: a square mile which could be made to support over 300 agriculturalists could at the utmost carry only seven pastoralists. If pastoralism failed to give man-power, it could claim certain advantages. It was a mode of life suited to the nature of primal man; the primitive hunter took kindly to the tending of herds. Another advantage was mobility; the pastoral tribe had to move every season from its " home " or winter territory in the south to the summer feeding-grounds of the north; the tribe had to be organized for movement as well as for defence. Agriculture tended to favour and to select men of a pacific nature, whereas pastoralism bred warlike qualities. Hence pastoral tribes, in spite of their weakness in man-power, have always been a standing menace to settled agricultural communities.

In the preceding paragraphs I have been seeking to make clear the nature of the changes which came into our world with the discovery of agriculture and the domestication of animals. No doubt the post-primal world is a pleasanter place for man to live in than the primal world, which was his home for a million years. Yet if we are to measure things as a student of evolution should measure them, we must admit that the primal world had a high degree of evolutionary effectiveness. We find man entering that period, upright in body to be sure, but low-browed and meanly brained; before the end of that period, 50,000 years or more before the dawn of modern or post-primal age, he had come by his full complement of brain and by all his modern features of face and of body. The machinery which fashions human evolution has been demonstrably effective. All my essays which precede the present one have been devoted to an exposition of that machinery. Among the cogs or parts of the machinery, I count, as the most important, the division of primal humanity into an exceedingly great number of small isolated groups or units—" parish races," as Bagehot aptly named them. Between these " parish races " there was a spirit of rivalry and of competition, quiescent for long periods, no doubt, but nevertheless relentless and undying. The groups which could not withstand the competition became broken, and disappeared; evolutionary results were speedy and definite. As I have sought to prove, " human nature " had become so constituted as to maintain the isolation and competition of these primal groups. It was this condition of affairs which Herbert Spencer had in mind when he spoke of " the automatic and merciless discipline of the primal world." [10]   Here Spencer overlooked the fact that mercy as well as cruelty prevailed in the primal world. Within each group there was a core of co-operation, mutual sympathy, and responsive mercy. It was the spirit of rivalry, competition, and antipathy which prevailed between groups that made life in the primal world merciless.

As I have said, the division of mankind during the long primal period into a myriad of small, competing groups is the basal part of my theory of human evolution ; it is possible that readers may feel that it is just on this head that my evidence is least convincing. Let me cite Professor Gordon Childe as a witness ; he is an authority on all that pertains to the ways of ancient man. In 1942 he penned the following passage :—

> "A small horde of lower or middle palæolithic hunters would require an enormous territory to support them. . . . Each little group would thus be isolated and virtually condemned to endogamy, and so to inbreeding, which would tend to conserve archaic traits and to prevent that mixing of genes that seems favourable to mutations." [11]

On the other hand, I am of opinion that the rapid evolutionary progress of the primal period was due to the fact that " mixing of genes " was then the exception and not the rule. Professor Childe also finds from archæological evidence [12] that the isolation between groups continued for some time after man had entered the Neolithic Age, that age marking the first stage of man's post-primal world. Although David Hume (1711–76) lived in pre-Darwinian times, he had, as the following passage [13] will show, a clear idea that mankind was divided into small units in the ancient world: " Almost all the nations, which are the scene of early history, were divided into small territories or petty commonwealths. . . . And it must be owned that no institution could be more favourable to the propagation of mankind." Hume was here thinking of the advancement of learning rather than of the progress of the race, yet what is true of learning is also true of race; it is the small unit or nation that produces things which have distinctive qualities. The evidence of Gumplowitz (1838–1909), who lived and wrote in the Darwinian Age, helps to confirm my thesis. " Agglomeration," he wrote, " began in the strife of innumerable petty units." [14]   One other matter I may allude to here. I was under the impression that my division of man's evolutionary history into primal and post-primal was new. I now find that Kant (1724–1804) had made a similar division. What he named the " epoch of natural development " I have called the " primal period," and what he named the " epoch of civil development " I have designated as the " post-primal period." [15]

I am discussing the changes which took place in the process of evolution when mankind entered the post-primal, or modern, period. Perhaps the most important change next to increases in the size of units relates to new modes of " natural selection " to which human communities then became subject. A primal community, dependent on the natural produce of its territory, led an arduous and precarious life, but it was free from the biblical curse, " In the sweat of thy face shalt thou eat bread till thou return unto the ground." To primal man manual labour was repugnant; scores of instances could be cited to prove that pastoral and hunting tribes preferred to reject existence itself rather than submit to the laborious discipline imposed by a life of agriculture. In the early days of the modern period a group or a tribe with even a small proportion of members willing to use spade or hoe had a surer grip of life than the group or tribe which was constitutionally work-shy. As time went on the selection and increase of communities tolerant of labour must have become more and more intense, and the elimination of work-shy peoples more drastic.

And yet I cannot claim that we of Western Europe, after 4,000 years of this selective process, have become true lovers of manual labour. Indeed, rich men seek relaxation by resuming the life of primal man.

Another quality which has been subject to selection in the modern period is that of prudence and foresight. Primal man was not altogether improvident; wild seeds and roots were stored by some of the aborigines of Australia and Tasmania and by the " digger Indians " of California; [16] the Eskimo placed food in " cold storage." Notwithstanding these instances, it may be truly said that the prevailing philosophy of primal man was " sufficient unto the day is the evil thereof." It requires a new philosophy to dig and sow that one may eat some three or four months later. The tribe which had sufficient imagination to learn and to adopt this philosophy stood at an advantage over those which were unable to accept and practice it.

I do not think that intellectual qualities were more strenuously selected in the post-primal world than in the primal one. The group or tribe which included in its number a hunter capable of evolving a new plan for catching game, or of inventing an improved form of trap, or of devising a more effective form of weapon, stood at an advantage over other groups. The same faculty served post-primal man in solving the problems which his new form of life brought him up against. Nor do I think that modern man has gained aught over primal man in the strength of his social habits, nor in the keenness of his sympathy for fellow-members of his community. Throughout the long primal period the groups which felt and acted in concert were the winning groups. Modern man has inherited the unchanged emotional nature of primal man; he has the same store of predispositions and prejudices. " To be born under the law," wrote Bagehot, " blinds us to prehistoric conditions "; [17] it is even more true to say that to be born in the modern period blinds us to the amount we owe to the discipline and selection to which our ancestors were subjected in the prolonged primal period.

Another major change which attended the emergence of humanity from primal to post-primal conditions was this : human lives became of economical advantage. In primal times a tribe lived up to the limits of the natural produce of its territory. By infanticide and other means a primal tribe sought to keep within this limit by maintaining stability of numbers.[18] With the coming of agriculture this ceased to be necessary; additional children still meant additional mouths to feed, but then there were additional hands to wield the hoe and spade, and also, when necessary, to wield weapons of defence. Additional lives thus became advantageous to the tribe. This economic revolution was attended by one disastrous result, due to man's natural aversion to manual labour. Slave labour was of no advantage in primal times; it was then a full day's work for a man to feed himself. It was otherwise in post-primal times; a war captive, reduced to slavery, could produce enough for others as well as for himself. Hence came the introduction of slavery. Now, as I have already pointed out,[19] when a tribe adopts the practice of slavery, its evolutionary machinery becomes clogged. A tribe with one part free and another enslaved is no longer a single unit with a common spirit and a common destiny; it is then a twofold body with a twofold morality, and a doubtful destiny. In due time agriculture became the mother of wealth and of capital; it was capital that turned the local evolutionary units of primal days into the multi-millioned national units of modern times. We may say, then, that capital has clogged the evolutionary wheels which were so effective in primal times.

The numbers which a land can be made to support by cultivation depend on many circumstances—on soil, rainfall, climate, and kind of crop. It has been said, for example, that an acre planted with bananas will afford steady sustenance for fifty natives. A human factor is also involved. For instance, the natives of New Guinea live in village communities and support themselves by clearing areas in the surrounding bush, wherein they grow yams, taro, bananas, sugar-cane, beans, and other garden produce. There are large tracts of unused bush; the number of communities could be multiplied twenty times and still leave room to spare, but the natives prefer to retain their present restricted birth-rates. One may truly say that the natives of New Guinea lack the *ambition* to develop the potentialities of their great island. This is what I mean by the human factor.

There is one other matter I must deal with before bringing this essay to an end; it relates to the size which evolutionary units had attained before the end of the primal period. Our estimates are necessarily based on observations made on primal peoples who have survived into modern times. I quote from data compiled by Professor L. Krzywicki.[20] Among the Fuegians the number of men, women, and children which made up a local group (evolutionary unit) varied from twenty to forty; among the extinct Tasmanians the group never included more than thirty; among the aborigines of Australia units differed very greatly in size; there were isolated self-contained units of forty or fifty individuals, and others of 200 or 250 members; the Arunta tribe of Central Australia included at one time as many as 2,000 individuals. That number was made up of a large number of confederated local groups, which assembled in one place only on special occasions. After a corroboree held by another large tribe as many as 155 fireplaces were counted, indicating an assembly of 1,000 people. Some of these were known to have come from a distance of 300 miles.[21] We may infer that similar tribal confederations had taken place in Europe before the end of the Pleistocene period. This is supported by observations made on the camps occupied by the mammoth-hunters of Moravia. One camp near Predmost covers over 1,000 acres;[22] another camp at Solutre in central France, frequented by men who hunted the wild horse, extends over two acres.[23] These camps, I infer, correspond to the corroboree sites of Australia and indicate meeting-places of confederated local groups. Thus a tribal status had been evolved in Europe before the end of the primal period.

REFERENCES

[1] Kroeber, A. L., *Anthropology*, 1923, p. 414.

[2] Russell, Sir John, *Nature*, April 30, 1927; Carr-Saunders, Sir A. M., *Population*, 1925.

[3] Krzywicki, L., *Primitive Society and its vital Data*, 1935, p. 5.

[4] *Ibid.*, p. 306.

[5] Hinsdale, W. B., see reference 19, Essay XXII.

[6] Knibbs, Sir G., *The Shadow of the World's Future*, 1928.

[7] Caton-Thompson, G., *The Desert Fayum*, 1935; Childe, V. Gordon, *New Light on the Most Ancient East*, 1934.

[8] Dixey, F., *Nature*, 1928, vol. 122, p. 586.

[9] Green, Miss M. M., *Land Tenure in an Ibo Village*, 1941.

[10] Spencer, H., *Principles of Sociology*, vol. 2, p. 231.

[11] Childe, V. Gordon, *Man*, 1942, p. 99.

[12] Childe, V. Gordon, *The Dawn of European Civilization*, 2nd ed., 1939, p. 285.

[13] Hume, David, *Essays and Treatises*, 1772, vol. 2, p. 411.

[14] Gumplowitz, L., *Sociologie et Politique*, Paris, 1898, p. 43.

[15] Hartmann, E. von, *Philosophy of the Unconscious*, trans., 9th ed., London, 1884, vol. 3, p. 32.

[16] Campbell, Harry, *Lancet*, 1905, (2), pp. 781–1667.

[17] Bagehot, W., *Physics and Politics*, 1896, p. 20.

[18] Krzywicki, L., see reference 3, p. 175.

[19] Keith, Sir A., *Essays on Human Evolution*, 1946, p. 33.

[20] Krzywicki, L., see reference 3, p. 5.

[21] *Ibid.*, p. 306.

[22] Keith, Sir A., *New Discoveries*, 1931, p. 371.

[23] Keith, Sir A., *The Antiquity of Man*, 1925, vol. 1, p. 89.

THE ANTIQUITY OF VILLAGE SETTLEMENTS

Synopsis.—*The theme to be discussed is outlined. Evidence of the early practice of agriculture in Egypt and in Palestine. The claims of the Iranian plateau to be considered the cradle of agriculture. Cultivated wheats and domesticated animals occur there in a wild state. The inhabitants of the plateau were members of the Caucasian family. Villages afford evidence of agriculture. The history of villages is preserved in mounds or Tells. Evidence from the excavation of Tell Halaf, Nineveh, Arpachiya, and Gawra. Evidence from ancient village sites on the plateau, at Tepe Giyan and at Tepe Siyalk. From the mound at Persepolis. The author seeks to trace village communities of post-primal times back to local groups of the primal period. The village replaces the local group as an evolutionary unit. The author attributes the discovery of agriculture to a local group and outlines a probable mode of discovery. Evidence that the early Iranian villagers were of a pacific nature. Strife developed as the period of town-building was reached.*

THE thesis I am to put forward in this essay is made up of the following parts : (1) that tillage of the soil and the domestication of animals were first practised, somewhere in the uplands between Anatolia in the west and India in the east, most likely on that part of the plateau which is now included in the kingdom of Iran or Persia; (2) these arts were discovered and put into practice by local communities belonging to the Caucasian division of humanity; (3) village settlements are traceable back to the sixth millennium in Iran, but as the villagers of that early date had already reached a high point in the development of their arts it now seems probable we shall have to go back to the eighth millennium to find their beginnings. Underlying my thesis is the assumption that the existence of village communities in a land, be it ancient or modern, is a sure sign that the people of that land have entered the post-primal phase of human evolution dealt with in the preceding essay.

Before entering on my main theme there are two preliminary matters I want to dispose of. In 1930, while searching for evidence to link cave life to that of settlement on the land,[1] I came to the conclusion that a wide interval of time separated the latest cave dwellers of Palestine—the Natufians [2]—from the earliest grain growers of Lower Egypt. Grain was sown, reaped, and stored in the Fayum [3] and in the western delta of the Nile [4] in the latter part of the sixth millennium B.C. I was then of opinion that the Natufians, who sheltered in the caves of the western slopes of Mt. Carmel and in other caves of Palestine, had preceded the grain-growers of Egypt by several thousand years. The Natufians, a people of Mediterranean stock, knew nothing of pottery; their implements and weapons were shaped out of stone and bone. But they armed shafts of bone with flint blades, and used them as sickles to reap wild grain, as it was then thought, but seeing they had stone querns, mortars, and pestles, it becomes now probable that they grew the grain they reaped.[5] And seeing that the Natufians ornamented the handles of their sickles in a manner very similar to that of the villagers who lived in Iran towards the end of the sixth millennium, it now seems possible that the Natufians may have been contemporary with the early grain-growers of Eygpt.[6]

Turning to the claims of S.W. Asia as the cradle not only of agriculture, but also of the ways of civilized man, one first notes the vastness of the area with which we are concerned. Its combined lands are about equal in size to half of Europe: Iran alone is twelve times the size of England. To travel from ancient Troy in the west to the buried cities of India in the east involves a journey of 2,500 miles; it is also a wide territory extending from the Caspian Sea in the north to the Arabian Sea in the south. It is the land which the Persians conquered in the sixth century B.C., and which the Greeks under Alexander invaded in the fourth century. Much of it is now desert or arid steppe, but in the closing phases of the Ice Age most of it was rolling grassland, well watered, and providing, in the words of Professor Haddon,[7] " a very desirable land and well fitted for human habitation." More to the point is the fact that all forms of wheat, which man has succeeded in cultivating and improving,

T

grew here in their wild and native state.   The animals which he domesticated—the sheep, ox, horse, and pig—were constituents of the wild fauna.   Most of our fruit trees and garden vegetables had their original home in this great Iranian Garden of Eden.   No other part of the earth can make such claims as these.

As to the racial characters of the peoples who inhabited the Iranian plateau in the closing phases of the Ice Age, one has to depend on inference, for their fossil remains are so far unknown. In Essay XXVI I have given my reasons for inferring that S.W. Asia was the region where men of the Neanderthal type became transformed into the Caucasian type, and that, towards the end of the Pleistocene period, this transformed type spread westwards to occupy Europe and Africa north of the Sahara.   The population of the plateau in the closing phases of the Ice Age would thus represent the stock from which the early emigrants to Europe and to Africa emerged.   Our actual records begin at the close of the fourth millennium B.C.   In the arid steppe country which extends into Iran beyond the south-east corner of the Caspian Sea there is a mound, Tepe Hissar, which held the entombed history of a local people who settled there about the middle of the fourth millennium B.C. and lived a continued existence for well over 2,000 years.[9]   They buried their dead under their dwellings; of the several hundred graves found, 184 yielded skulls sufficiently intact for examination.   My friend Dr. W. M. Krogman [10] has reported on the kind of people represented by the skeletons from Tepe Hissar.   He found them to be true Caucasians.   The prevailing type had features of skull we find in Mediterranean peoples; others, forming a smaller proportion, had those characters which are found most frequently in the inhabitants of Northern Europe.   They were a people of rather low stature, the average height of the men being 5 ft. 5·5 ins. (1,662 mm.), that of the women, 5 ft. 2 ins. (1,580 mm.).   They were people with long and narrow heads of good size, quite equal in this respect to modern Europeans; their facial features were those met with in Europeans.   The nose was prominent and relatively narrow.   Herzfeld [11] speaks of these early inhabitants of the Iranian plateau as " Caspians "—a convenient name.   The Caspian type still abounds on the plateau; one finds it among the Kurdish tribes, among the Tajiks of Persia, and among the Afghans. The special Persian type, with prominent hooked nose and long and narrow head, recently described by Dr. Henry Field,[12] occurred also among the ancient Caspians. We shall find that the native Caucasians of S.W. Asia are distinguished by the form of nose rather than by shape of head.

All over the Caucasian region of Asia, from the site of Troy in the west to the buried cities of the Indus valley in the east, there occur mounds or " Tells," which, when excavated, yield the history of villages and towns of past ages. It is the archæological history of these village sites which is to give a clue to the antiquity of agriculture, for it was agriculture which made village life possible. The mound at Troy for example, was made up of seven superimposed towns; the oldest, covering about two acres, began about the end of the fourth millennium B.C., the last, covering about four acres, was sacked by the Homerian Greeks at the beginning of the twelfth century B.C. Thus Troy was a site of human habitation for about two thousand years. From Troy we move eastwards to inland Syria to the upper waters of the Kabur, a tributary of the Euphrates. Here, on the banks of the Kabur, is a mound—Tell Halaf—much older and more extensive than that of Troy; it covers an area of about twenty-five acres. In the basal and oldest settlement of Tell Halaf Baron von Oppen-heim [13] found the remains of town-dwellers who made and used a distinctive form of painted pottery, and had a culture marked by several peculiar traits. It is now generally agreed that the Hala-fian culture must be assigned to an early date in the fifth millennium B.C., and, as it was widely spread in the Ancient East, its occurrence at any particular site provides archæologists with a clue to the date of the strata they expose. For instance, the Halaf culture appears in the foundations of Nineveh, which is in the valley of the upper Tigris, 120 miles to the east of Tell Halaf. Yet at Nineveh the Halafian is the third cultural stratum above the virgin soil; Mallowan [14] had to dig through ninety feet of city deposits to reach the virgin soil. There he found remnants of the mud-walled Neolithic village from which the city of Nineveh had sprung. If we assign the Halafian culture to an early date in the fifth millennium, then we must give the Neolithic beginnings of Nineveh a date well within the sixth millennium.

On the plain, near the ruins of Nineveh, is a mound, thirty-four feet high, known as Tell Arpachiya. This was also excavated under the direction of Mallowan.[16] He found in it the foundations of ten superimposed villages. The earliest villagers were exponents of the Halafian culture; the later were of another culture—the al' Ubaidian—which prevailed in Mesopotamia in the latter part of the fifth millennium. Thus village life in Arpachiya began about 5000 B.C., and lasted for about 1,000 years, when the site was abandoned. Mallowan was struck by the architectural resemblance of the Arpachiyan villages to those built by the modern inhabitants of Iraq. Some fourteen miles to the north-east of the village site just described, at the foothills on the frontiers of Persia, there is a famous mound known as Tepe Gawra. It was excavated by Dr. E. A. Speiser, who issued his report in 1937.[16] He found that in the seventy-seven feet of deposits twenty cultural horizons were preserved. The horizon or stratum which marked the Halafian period came in the fifth stratum above the virgin soil. The first or oldest stratum contained the foundations of several village communities, out of which the township or city-State of Gawra had developed. What age, then, are we to give to these ancient peasant communities? Seeing that three strata, each representing a cultural period, are interposed between them and the overlying Halafian stratum, we must assign them to about the middle of the sixth millennium B.C., or even towards its beginning.

From Gawra to Nihavend, on the western end of the Iranian plateau, involves a journey of 240 miles. Near Nihavend is Tepe Giyan, excavated in 1931-2 by an expedition from France.[17] It was found that the two deepest strata were formed when the site was occupied by villagers of the " buff-ware culture," a culture which is widely spread in the ancient sites of the Western plateau, and served archæologists as a time-marker. The two deepest strata at Tepe Giyan are pre-Halafian,[18] for it is in the stratum overlying these two that Halafian influences become evident. Leaving Tape Giyan the French expedition moved eastwards for a distance of 200 miles to explore a still older mound—that of Tepe Siyalk. This mound is near Kashan, and some 200 miles to the south of the Caspian Sea. In the basal and oldest stratum, under ninety-two feet of deposits which had accumulated during an occupation period of over 2,000 years, they found the habitations and outfit of the earliest Iranian villages so far brought to light.[19] Now, the deepest stratum at Tepe Siyalk is older than the deepest layer at Tepe Giyan, and that, in turn, is older than Tell

Halaf; we must therefore give the original peasant villagers of Siyalk a very early date, one well within the sixth millennium.

On the strength of the archæological evidence the village settlement discovered at Siyalk has claims to be considered as the earliest known to us so far. When we consider the culture of these ancient peasants it is clear they are far beyond the first stage in the development of agriculture. "These people," wrote Dr. D. McCown,[20] "formed a self-contained unit. . . . They made the walls of their settled dwellings with beaten mud; they cut grain (wheat and barley) with flint blades set in bone holders, grinding it on saddle-shaped querns and in mortars; they had at least one variety of domesticated sheep." Copper was native to their district, and they made some use of it. They were potters and weavers; they made beads and bracelets, stone hoes and axes, vessels and mace-heads of stone. They buried their dead under their habitations, just as did the cave-dwellers of Mt. Carmel. One other remarkable feature links the Siyalk villagers with the Palestinians; both peoples decorated the bone handles of their flint sickles with carvings of a similar kind. That fact impresses me very deeply, for between these two peoples there intervened 1000 miles of country occupied by a great number of small isolated communities. To explain the wide diffusion of a feature so peculiar in its nature in the sixth millennium, it is clear we must seek for the beginning of agriculture as early as the eighth millennium.

In order to gain more light on the wide distribution of village life throughout the Iranian plateau in the early part of the fifth millennium, and the high stage of culture attained by the villagers, we are now to move to the site of Persepolis, 300 miles to the south of Tepe Siyalk. There we are to find a culture contemporary with, or perhaps earlier than, that of Tell Halaf. On the plain of Persepolis there is a mound which was excavated by Herzfeld.[21] Here are some of the more important points from his description :—

"The Persepolis mound is situated in the middle of the fertile plain at quite a distance from the present beds of the two large rivers that irrigate it, but near to a rich spring, whence a little rivulet emanates which in ancient times probably passed the site. . . . The village is an agglomeration of rooms and courtyards, not of separate houses. In fact it is a kind of bee-hive, one continuous house. . . . Although the potter's wheel was still unknown, the pottery surpasses almost all other wares of a later period. . . . The vessels were made for its household by its own members; hence the large number of small kilns among the rooms of the village. All pottery, except a rough ware for cooking, is painted, and it is amazingly rich in types as well as in decoration. Side by side with naturalistic representations there are the most abstract drawings, shapes reduced to geometric units. Sheep, goats, swine, cows, and dogs were certainly domesticated. . . ."

From this description it is clear that early in the fifth millennium the Iranian peasantry had developed a high artistic ability, and had so intensified their social aptitudes that their community formed a large integrated household. They were already the product of a long Neolithic civilization.

The aim I had in view in writing this essay must not be lost sight of; it was to trace the passage of local groups, of primal food-gathering times, into the village communities of the food-producing post-primal period. The search for the intermediate stages which link the one period to the other has eluded us so far. But seeing that we have obtained evidence that tillage was practised at an earlier date on the Iranian plateau than elsewhere, it seems to me that we are justified in assuming that it was on the pleateau that man made his exodus from a primal mode of existence, and so initiated a revolutionary change in life, which, slowly spreading abroad, ultimately involved almost the whole of mankind. I imagine that the mode by which he made his exodus was somewhat as follows: It was made most probably towards the beginning of the eighth millennium. Until then every group living on the plateau occupied its own territory and lived on the natural produce of that territory. One of these group territories, we may presume, had a fertile area where a wild form of wheat grew, and in the autumn, when the grain was ripe, the local group repaired to this area and, as is still the habit in some parts of native Australia, not only reaped the grain, but also stored it against the coming winter. We may also assume, from what is known of the mentality of the Australian aborigine, that the primitive Iranian regarded the wheat-plant as a gift of their local god—the god of the soil and of fertility—and he had to be propitiated when they robbed him of his harvest. The natural way of appeasement would be a return of some of the ripe grain to the soil. The response of the soil by the production of new plants would convince the sower that this mode of sacrifice was accepted, and so encourage him or her—most likely her—to continue and extend the practice. When a sacrifice is made by primitive men, it has to be of the best. So it is probable that the best grains were returned to the soil, and thus the first stage in the improvement of wheat by cultivation was instituted. As this field of natural wheat increased in size and productivity, the local group would begin to depend on it more and more for its chief source of food. Ultimately they would anchor themselves by it, build settled abodes, and so bring into existence a village settlement. The group, of course, would still maintain its rights over its hunting territory as an additional source of food-supply. Possibly it added to this supply by the domestication of local animals.

Thus, if my theory is well founded, the local group which was the evolutionary unit of the primal period became in the passage to the post-primal period a village settlement, but this settlement retained all the isolating attributes of the old evolutionary unit. The evolutionary machinery remained the same; only the form, size, and potentialities of the unit were changed. The territory which could provide sustenance for one local group became capable of supporting ten, or even twenty, such groups. The groups increased in size and number. The village communities we have noted at Siyalk and at Persepolis I regard as descendant of the original local groups, modified by the discoveries and accumulated experience of two millennia, but still retaining the essential features of "evolutionary units."

Herzfeld and other students of the village settlements of ancient Iran have been impressed by the absence from them of warlike equipment. The villages were open and unwalled; stone mace-heads and axes were found in them; there were sling-stones, but no arrow-heads or spearheads. The villagers were pacific in nature; they were not big-boned, big-bodied, warlike folk. There seems to have been little rivalry or competition between neighbouring settlements. To me this pacific disposition seems to be one which ought to be expected in a land where discovery had made it possible for twenty families or more to live contentedly where there was previously room for only one family. The discovery of agriculture gave room and room to spare during the earlier millennia of the post-primal period. Such was the condition of the earlier peasantry of the plateau. But in time conditions changed. All the desirable arable areas became occupied; competition set in between neighbouring groups. Village settlements increased in size and in number. It was as towns began to appear that the paraphernalia of war came into existence. These, and other matters, will come up for consideration in the essay which follows.

REFERENCES

[1] Keith, Sir A., *New Discoveries relating to the Antiquity of Man*, 1931, ch. XIII.

[2] Garrod, Dorothy, *The Stone Age of Mount Carmel*, 1939, vol. 1.

[3] Caton-Thompson, G., *The Desert Fayum*, 1935.

[4] Childe, V. Gordon, *New Light on the Most Ancient East*, 1934, p. 51.

[5] Childe, V. Gordon, *Man*, 1942, p. 130.

[6] Professor Garrod expressed the opinion that the Natufian culture may have continued to the sixth millennium or even to the fifth. See under reference 2, p. 118.

[7] Haddon, A. C., *The Races of Man*, 1924, p. 143.

[8] Vavilov, N. I., *Studies in the Origin of Cultivated Plants*, Leningrad, 1926; *Nature*, Jan. 23, 1937; Haldane, J. B. S., *Proc. Royal Institute*, 1931, p. 356.

[9] Schmidt, E. F., *Excavations at Tepe Hissar, Damghan*, Univ. Pennsylvan., 1937.

[10] Krogman, W. M., *Verhand, Kon Nedarld. Akad. Wetensch.*, 1940, vol. 39, no. 2.

[11] Herzfeld, Ernst, *Archæological History of Iran*, 1935; *A Survey of Persian Art*, edited by A. Upham Pope, 1938, vol. 1, p. 42.

[12] Field, Dr. Henry, *The Asiatic Review*, July, 1939.

[13] Oppenheim, Baron Max von, *Tell Halaf*, 1933.

[14] See p. 251 of work referred to under note 4.

[15] Mallowan, M. E. L., *The Excavations at Tell Arpachiya*, 1935.

[16] Speiser, E. A., *Bull. Amer. Instit. Iran. Art*, 1937, vol. 5, p. 3.

[17] Contenau and Ghirshman, *Musée de Louvre : Série archæolog.*, vol. 3, 1935.

[18] McCown, Donald E., *Jour. Near Eastern Studies*, 1942, vol. 1, p. 424; *The Comparative Stratigraphy of Early Iran*, no. 23, Univ. Chicago Press, 1942.

[19] Ghirshman, R., Sialk, vol. 1, p. 11, *Musée du Louvre : Série Archæolog.*, vols. 4, 5, 1938–9.

[20] McCown, Donald E., see reference 18, p. 425.

[21] Herzfeld, Ernst, *A Survey of Persian Art*, edited by A. Upham Pope, 1938, vol. 1, p. 47.

THE TRANSFORMATION OF VILLAGE UNITS INTO CITY UNITS

Synopsis.—Subject of essay outlined. Chronology of cultural periods. The coming of towns and cities in ancient Iran. Iran and Greater Mesopotamia compared. Assyria, Mesopotamia, Babylonia defined. The chronology of the cultural periods at Nineveh. Fate of Nineveh. The author assumes that Babylonia was " settled " by Assyrian peasantry before the end of the sixth millennium. Coming of Sumerians. The Sumerian settlement at al'Ubaid, and at Ur. The archæological history of Erech. Development of theocratic government. The evolution of marsh villages into independent city-States. Estimates of the population of Babylonia; the size of its cities. In the course of 2,000 years the numerous, small, scattered village units of Babylonia were transformed into a score of independent city-States. The racial characters of the Sumerians. Their absorption by people of the Semitic stock. Contention and strife between the cities. Reduced to dependent status by Sargon of Agade. The ultimate fate of the cities. The evolutionary weakness of city-States.

In the preceding essay my theme was the transformation of local communities of primal times into peasant village settlements ; my thesis in this essay is the evolution of village settlements into city-States such as dominated life in early Babylonia. The change from a village stage of existence to the full city stage seems to imply the passage of a long period of time, yet as evidence now stands we must believe that such a transformation began to take place before the end of the fifth millennium. It must be apparent to my readers that the process of human evolution, as carried on between great city-States, and within them, must be a very different affair from that which prevailed in and between small local groups of primitive humanity.

To begin our search for evidence it will be convenient to

return again to the site of the ancient village of Siyalk on the Iranian plateau. Tepe Siyalk, it will be remembered, lies 200 miles south of the Caspian, and is now situated on the edge of the great central desert of Persia. Our first business at Siyalk is to formulate a time-scale which will permit us to compare the village strata and periods with those of the cities of Babylonia. We have seen that the deepest and oldest stratum at Siyalk (Siyalk I) is deemed to be of older date than the Mesopotamian culture of Tell Halaf, and is provisionally assigned to the end of the sixth millennium. The second cultural stratum at Siyalk (Siyalk II) is at present judged to be contemporaneous with the Halafian culture of Mesopotamia, and in the meantime is assigned to the first half of the fifth millennium. Then comes the third stratum at Siyalk (Siyalk III); this is judged to be contemporaneous with a culture which was widely spread in southern Iran in the latter half of the fifth century, and which has been named the Ubaid culture. The Ubaid culture, we shall find, became widely spread in Babylonia, and there supplies archæologists with a datum line.

My second reason for returning to Siyalk is to note the rise of ancient townships on the plateau. When Siyalk III was being laid down, and when the Ubaidian culture reigned in South Iran, a new township came into being at Tepe Hissar, which lay to the east of Damghan. Now, Tepe Hissar, which supplied us with information concerning the Iranian population (p. 280), lies nearly 250 miles to the north-east of Siyalk and fifty miles to the south of the Caspian. Between Hissar and the Caspian rise up the Elburz mountains. Streams rising in these mountains flow southwards until their waters are lost in the desert. Near one of these lost streams the township of Hissar was founded in the period of the Ubaid culture, and therefore in the latter half of the fifth millennium. The deepest stratum at Hissar (Hissar I) was contemporaneous with the Ubaid culture of the south. The cultural stratum which follows (Hissar II) is inferred to be of the same date as a culture which was widely distributed in Babylonia, and is known by the name of Uruk. This culture, at present, is attributed to the first half of the fourth millennium. Over Hissar II come two other cultural deposits which correspond to the Babylonian cultures known as Jemdet Nasr—attributed to the latter half of the fourth millennium—and that of the early Babylonian Dynasties (placed in the first half of the third mil-

lennium).   After an existence of some 2,000 years the township
of Hissar came to an end in the Early Dynastic period.[1]   It was
during the two last periods of culture that Hissar expanded and
began to show traces of contact with the outer world; war
chariots made an appearance and copper was more freely used for
tools and for weapons.   Thus villages were expanding into towns
on the Iranian plateau during the fourth millennium.

When the township of Hissar was being established in the north
during the latter half of the fifth millennium, people of the south,
carrying with them the Ubaid culture, descended from the plateau
and began to build the city of Susa on the eastern threshold of the
Babylonian delta.   The first city of Susa is said to have covered
an area of 300 acres; [2] if it was built in the compact, warren-like
way of Eastern cities, then we may reckon that each acre had
about 500 inhabitants, giving a total population of 150,000.   We
may attribute the rapid growth of Susa to the fact that large
areas of the central plateau were drying up into tracts of desert
during the fifth millennium, while the delta lands were well
watered and fertile.   However this may have been, and whatever
the exact population of early Susa was, the important fact for us
is that city-States were coming into existence by the end of the
fifth millennium.   Thus I am assuming that in the course of
4,000 years the natives of the Iranian plateau passed from membership of small local units of food-gatherers to one which bound
them in massed city units.   Susa had a chequered life of 4,000
years; it was there, towards the end of the sixth century B.C.,
that Mordecai, the Jew, had the satisfaction of seeing his oppressor,
Haman the Proud, hanged on a gallows " fifty cubits high,"
which he (Haman) had prepared for the Jew.

I now come to the major object of this essay—the rise of city-
States in lands which, in later times, became known as Babylonia,
Mesopotamia, and Assyria.   It is necessary to carry with us a
broad idea of the position and size of these three lands.   Assyria,
which was nearly equal in size to England (50,000 square miles),
was situated between the Tigris and the Zagros mountains and
extended from the mountains of Khurdistan in the north to
Susiana in the south.   Mesopotamia, somewhat larger in area,
lay between the Euphrates and Tigris and stretched from Khurdistan southwards to within forty miles of the city of Babylon.
The area of Babylonia was only about 25,000 square miles, being

thus about twice the size of Holland. It extended from Mesopotamia to the Persian Gulf.

In the preceding essay we had occasion to visit the site of
Nineveh in northern Assyria. We must now return to that site
to obtain a date which will link the history of Nineveh with the
city-States of Babylonia. Such a date is supplied by a temple
built in Nineveh by a grandson of Sargon of Agade. This temple
is usually dated 2450 B.C., but it may be a century later. Between
the foundation of this temple and the virgin soil there are seventy
feet of deposits, in which a succession of five cultural periods can
be recognized. The deepest or first stratum is that formed by the
peasant villagers, whose manner of life was very similar to that
we noted in the village settlements on the Iranian plateau at
Siyalk some 500 miles distant from Nineveh. The second stratum at Nineveh (Nineveh II) was also laid down by villagers;
they had become influenced by the Samarra culture, which
appears to have been native to western Iran and is regarded as
older than that of Ubaid. It is at the end of the second period
that Halafian influences reached the Ninevite villagers. If we
attribute the culture of Tell Halaf, which lies 120 miles to the west
of Nineveh, to the first half of the fifth millennium, then we must
allow Nineveh I and II a date well within the sixth millennium,
giving them an antiquity as great, if not greater than, that of
Siyalk I. The important point for us is that by the end of the
sixth millennium the inhabitants of northern Assyria had long
ceased to be members of local groups of food-gatherers; they had
become peasants and lived together in village units.

The three cultural deposits which are interposed between the
village strata and the overlying temple, covering a period of
1,500 years, mark the expansion of Nineveh into a city-State.
No doubt it had its government, its laws, and its demarcated
territory. It had become an evolutionary unit of a new kind.
It began to rise into power in the latter part of the second millennium, became imperialistic and aggressive, a policy which led
to its destruction before the end of the seventh century B.C.,
Assyria then becoming a Median province. At its zenith Nineveh
is said to have covered an area of 1,800 acres. If we allow only
100 inhabitants to the acre, that means a population of 180,000;
it may well have been twice this estimate. In the course of 5,000
years Nineveh passed from its beginning to its untimely end;

during that time some 200 generations had been born and died within its habitations. Nineveh, as a student of evolution measures values, was a failure; it failed because it lacked an essential quality—that which secures endurance.

Having thus obtained reliable evidence that peasant communities had been established in northern Assyria and in the adjacent region of northern Mesopotamia long before the end of the sixth millennium, we bend our steps southwards to the flat, reedy, marshy lowlands which in later times became known as Babylonia. Here we shall find no trace of peasant settlements as old as those of the north. Nay, all the evidence points to the conclusion that long after the art of agriculture had been developed in the north the marshes of Babylonia remained the home of local groups of primal fowlers and fishers. In the absence of direct evidence we have to infer what really happened. We infer, then, that the peasant villagers of the north slowly invaded the hunting-grounds of the primal groups of the south, establishing new settlements on the rich soil of the higher grounds or " islands " of the marshy country. Judging from modern instances, we may be sure that the native hunters retired sullenly before the peasant invaders, fighting many a rear-guard action, but were ultimately driven out. Thus I assume that by the end of the sixth millennium the whole of the marshlands of Babylonia had been settled by small colonies of the northern peasantry.

What was the racial nature of these northern Assyrian peasants? Here, too, the evidence is largely circumstantial, and yet very definite. At many ancient sites along the Tigris and along the Euphrates, sites which are reliably dated in the earlier half of the fourth millennium, representations of human features have been preserved, and among these the prevailing type is that to which I would give the term Assyrian. The arresting features of the Assyrian face are a prominent hooked form of nose, eyes widely open, lips full and somewhat everted, hairy people, thickly bearded in the unshaven; the head usually long, but may be rounded. The Assyrian features are still reproduced in a percentage of the Jewish and Armenian peoples. I do not suppose that, in even the purest and most inbred of communities, every one was of the Assyrian type; the genes needed to reproduce the Assyrian features were so distributed in the community that they came together only in a proportion of conceptions. Nevertheless the reproduction of the Assyrian features is a racial character of the people we are now dealing with. The Assyrian features, I presume, were evolved among the Caucasian natives of the Anatolian area, which extends northwards from Mesopotamia and Assyria; and I also assume that the early peasants of Assyria were of this race and that it was this race which provided the first settlers in Babylonia.

Some time before the middle of the fifth millennium rumours seem to have reached the drought-stricken Iranians of the peace and plenty which crowned the lives of the peasant pioneers of Babylonia. We have seen that they descended to the lowlands to settle at Susa; another branch of Iranians is assumed to have passed into the lower delta areas of Babylonia and to have effected settlements on sites already occupied by the Assyrian pioneers. These Iranian invaders, whom we shall speak of henceforth as Sumerians, brought with them a form of "culture," which was first detected at al'Ubaid, and hence has been named Ubaidian. al'Ubaid, which lies in the desert four miles to the west of the city of Ur, was excavated by Dr. H. R. Hall and Sir Leonard Woolley after the first world war.[3] The excavators found that, tempted by ground which rose high above the surrounding marshes, the Sumerians had made a settlement there. They sowed and reaped; they kept cattle; they were a dairying people. This culture which Woolley found on the surface at al'Ubaid he again encountered in the foundations of Ur; he had to dig to a depth of sixty feet to reach it. The founders of Ur building on the level marsh were bearers of the Ubaidian culture.

Of the various Sumerian cities that have been excavated down to the virgin soil, Erech has yielded the clearest information of the manner in which a marsh village became transformed into a great city. Erech—Uruk and Warka, are its other names—was separated from neighbouring cities by thirty to forty miles of intervening territory—the usual distance between Sumerian cities—although Ur, which lay down-stream from Erech, was only twelve miles distant from the most southern city, Eridu. Erech was excavated (1930-32) by a team of German archæologists;[4] they had to pass through seventy feet of stratified deposit, representing five long cultural periods, to reach the original marsh surface. The six deepest strata (I-VI) represented developments of the Ubaid culture of the Sumerian villagers—

developments usually assigned to the latter half of the fifth millennium, being thus post-Halafian in date. The next seven strata
(VII–XIII) carry objects of another cultural period—that of Uruk.
This culture is regarded as a gradual development from the preceding Ubaidian culture, and is attributed to the first half of the
fourth millennium. In this period at Erech we meet with ziggurats,
with the foundations of superimposed temples of magnificent
style and dimensions, with pictures of arm-tied captives, and of
war chariots. The ziggurat and temple are signs that a theocratic government had been established; the priest-king had
become recognized as the intermediary between the people of
Erech and the God of Erech; the God owned the land and the
people; to him all rents and revenues were paid.

After the Uruk period followed that of Jemdet Nasr (strata
XIV–XV). In this cultural period, attributed to the latter half
of the fourth millennium, temple-building continues and an
early form of writing comes into use. Then follow strata attributed to the first half of the third millennium, the period of the
" Early Dynasties," the period which saw Babylonian cities at
the zenith of their development and with their hounds of war
straining on the leash.

Looking at the surface of things with the eye of a student of
human evolution, I try to discern the nature of the forces
which, in 2,000 years, transformed marsh villages into great
cities. This is how I imagine the transformation to have been
effected. At the beginning we have village communities spread
over the marshlands of Babylonia, each community being an
independent unit, owning its territory and capable of its own
defence. As tillage improved villages would increase in number
and also in size of population. With these increases came the
struggle between adjoining village communities, weaker villages
combining against the stronger neighbour, until, finally, some
one village, because of the courage and enterprise of its chief or
of the natural fertility of its territory, or because of its favourable
situation for trade, or of a combination of all three factors, became
a central power, and the foundation of a city-State. Thus it
happened that the 25,000 square miles of Babylonia became
divided into the territories of some twenty independent city-States.
What was the population of Babylonia when the city-States were
at the height of their development? I can find no previous esti-

mate, but seeing the high state of irrigation and tillage then reached, it does not seem too much to allow 320 inhabitants for each square mile of territory, an allowance which gives Babylonia a maximum population of eight millions. The population of an average city with its surrounding territory would thus be about 400,000. This estimate may be checked in several ways. There are areas of city sites. The old, walled city of Ur covered 250 acres; if we allow 500 inhabitants to the acre, this gives a population for the city of 125,000; if we allow an equal number for the rural area, the total number of Urites would be 250,000. The later Ur is said to have had an area of over 5,000 acres, but much of this remained as open space. The city of Erech is given an area of 1,280 acres; at 500 inhabitants to the acre, this indicates a population of 640,000. The ruins of the city of Kish cover 120 acres, indicating a population of about 60,000; the walls included an area of over 6,000 acres. The township of Jemdet Nasr (3400 B.C.) covered an area of only seven acres, indicating a population of 3,500. Even if we halve these estimates, it is clear that the independent or evolutionary units in Babylonia had undergone a transformation in the course of 2,000 years. Many hundreds of small competing village communities had become changed into about a score of powerful, competing city-States.

In a racial sense, what sort of people were the Sumerians? Sir Leonard Woolley gave me an opportunity of examining and reporting on a sample of skulls from an Early Dynastic cemetery of Ur, presumably Sumerians.[5]   They had the same long, narrow, high heads as the early people of Siyalk and of Hissar (see p. 280); in size of brain they were quite the equal of modern Europeans. Their facial features were regular, the chin ample, and in a proportion of the men the nose was quite Assyrian in size and in shape. From this circumstance it does seem probable that the original peasant population had assimilated the Sumerians of Irania. Cultural and political influence spread from Sumer (the southern half of Babylonia) up the Tigris and Euphrates, but the Sumerian tongue remained confined to their own cities. By the beginning of the second millennium B.C. their tongue also had been conquered by that of the peasant pioneers; from which we may infer that the Semitic speech and the Semitic features have qualities which are at once stable, dominant, and persistent.

In the first half of the third millennium (Early Dynastic period) we find the city-States of Babylonia in a state of contention and strife, each competing against the other. Lagash goes to war with its neighbour Uumma to settle disputes about frontier and irrigation rights ; Kish, Erech, and Ur, in turn, attempt to dominate the whole of Babylonia; after temporary successes the old spirit of local independence asserts itself. After the middle of the third millennium Sargon appears; he is a sprout from the old peasant (Assyrian) stock ; he establishes his capital at Agade in northern Babylonia; becomes master of a standing army of 54,000 men; fights thirty-four battles, reduces all the other cities to dependencies, and so establishes an empire from " sea to sea." For 200 years the Sargonic dynasty had often to repress the spirit of local independence. When the dynasty of Sargon fell, Erech, Ur, and Larsa succeeded in turn to universal but temporary rule. And so we reach the beginning of the second millennium B.C., when Hammurabi of Babylon, like Sargon, a Semite, again reduced all the other cities to a dependent status and established a single law and god throughout the land. In 1740 B.C. the government of Babylon was interrupted by another Iranian invasion (Kassite), which survived until the rise of Assyrian power towards the end of the fourteenth century; then the brief resuscitation of Babylonian power (635–539 B.C.); this was brought to an end by another Iranian invasion—the arrival of the Persians under Cyrus. Local government broke down; irrigation channels became clogged; food failed, and life in the cities of Babylonia flickered out. Some inhabitants, I suspect, sought homes in other cities, but most probably joined local tribal communities. Thus some 4,000 years after emerging from a tribal state most of the inhabitants of Babylonia returned to that state.

It was my intention to follow the rise of city-States in Asia Minor, in Crete, in Greece (both in Mycenæan and Athenian times), in northern Italy (A.D. 1000–1500), and in Germany (Frankfort and the cities of the Hanseatic League). This seems to me now unnecessary; the lesson they have to teach us is that which we have already learned from Babylonia—namely, that from a evolutionary point of view, city-States carry a weakness which sooner or later proves mortal. All go the way of Nineveh. What the nature of that weakness is may come to light by the survey of a people which has maintained a continuity of at least 8,000 years. Hence my next essay is devoted to Egypt.

U

REFERENCES

[1] The estimated ages of the cultural strata of ancient Iran are based on those given by Dr. Donald McCown.   See preceding essay, reference 18.   See also Dr. Henri Frankfort's *Archæology and the Sumerian Problem*, Study No. 4 in " Ancient Oriental Civilization," Univ. Chicago, 1932.

[2] Morgan, J. De, *Mission archæologique de Perse; Mémoires Tomes* 16–24, 1921–34.

[3] Woolley, Sir Leonard, *Ur of the Chaldees*, 1929.

[4] For an account of the cultural strata found at Erech, see Professor Gordon Childe's *New Light on the Most Ancient East*, 1934, ch. VI.

[5] Woolley and Keith, " Excavations at al'Ubaid," *Publications of the British Museum*, 1927.

EGYPT AS THE OLDEST HOME OF NATION-BUILDING

Synopsis.—*Egypt the oldest of historical nations. Definition of Nation. How formed. The national rise of Egypt compared with that of Babylonia. Conditions favouring the formation of a nation in Egypt. The Egyptians were and are a peasant people. Their mentality; Egyptian dough and Babylonian leaven. Egypt has been claimed to have been the cradle of the world's civilization. The prior claims of Asia. Evidence of the early arrival of Asiatics in Egypt. Estimates of the population of Egypt in primal and in post-primal times. The Egyptians as a national or evolutionary unit. National life was interrupted from time to time by reversion to a multi-tribal state. Egypt under foreign domination. Sovereignty not essential to give a people a national status. The Arabization of Egypt. The physical history of the Egyptians is more complete than that of any other people. A nation has the power to assimilate foreign types to its own. Anthropological inquiries favour the conclusion that modern Egyptians have reverted to the pre-dynastic type. The origin of the Egyptians; their nearest relatives. How the Semitic and Hamitic tongues may have sprung from a common root. The possibility of an early settlement in the delta of a people of the Caucasian stock.*

ABOUT the middle of the fourth millennium B.C. the tribal communities of Lower Egypt, each living on its own territory, began to be amalgamated under a dominant chief who succeeded in establishing a kingdom. A parallel process took place in Upper Egypt; the score or more of tribal groups or nomes, strung like beads along the banks of the Nile from Aswan downwards for a stretch of over 300 miles, were brought under a single government by the chief of the Falcon Nome or clan, who thus became king of Upper Egypt. His home territory was on the east bank of the river some forty miles below the site which Aswan now occupies.[1]

A century or two before the end of the fourth millennium—the date usually accepted is 3300 B.C.—war broke out between the two kings, victory going to the Falcon King of Upper Egypt. Of the vanquished 6,000 are said to have been slain and 12,000 taken prisoner. Thus was brought into existence the first nation (in the modern sense) of which we have record. The first nation was brought into existence by war; war has proved to be the midwife of nations ever since. It is also worthy of note that when the first pharaoh established rule in Egypt the separatist cities of Babylon were in the Jemdet stage of their cultural evolution.

What do I mean by a nation—in the modern sense? Let me base my definition by taking Ancient Egypt as an illustration: (a) A single central government was established; (b) the people so ruled occupied an extensive continuous country, one which extended from the Mediterranean to the first cataract—a distance of 550 miles as a plane flies. (c) The tribal communities, or nomes, gradually forgot their local differences and became conscious of membership of a larger or national unit; or to state the same thing in other words—the men of the nomes transferred, to the central pharaoh, wholly or in part, the allegiance formerly given to their local chiefs. (d) The love of an Egyptian for his home-territory—his patriotism—extended to all parts inhabited by his fellow subjects. (e) The Egyptians became conscious that they and their nation were separate from, and different from, all other nations and peoples. (f) They became speakers of the same tongue, heirs of the same customs and of the same tradition, subjects of the same laws, and believers in the same gods; all of these attributes served as national bonds. (g) They became aware that their personal security and safety were bound up with that of their country and learned that national security can be bought only at the price of personal sacrifice.

To make all these national feelings glow with a steady ardour required the passage, not of one, but of many generations. Fate smiled on the early dynasties of Egypt; from the first Dynasty to the sixth, covering a period of over 800 years, central government remained strong and the nation united. During that time more than thirty generations came and went; one would have thought that a unity, after prevailing over this long period, would have become consolidated as a permanent element in the national tradition.   The event proved that this was not the case ; in times when central government became weak local chiefs again rose to power.

Why was it that the local village communities of Babylonia developed into a number of independent single States while those of Egypt became merged, at a stride, into one great national unit? There were several reasons, the chief being the distribution of arable and inhabitable land in Egypt.   The desert encroached so closely to both banks of the Nile that only narrow green verges remained for habitation.   Nowhere could rebellious minorities retreat to mountainous fastnesses; all were exposed on the river-banks; a central government using the Nile as a highway could bring a superior force to bear on any recalcitrant nome.   That, I think, was the main factor in the early nationalization of the Egyptians.   Another factor was the passion of the Egyptian peasant for his soil.   To be stable a population must be based on the land.   In Babylonia peasant villagers freely left the land to live in towns and share in trade.   To these factors there is one more to be added—namely, the mentality of the ancient Egyptians. They were more apt to obey and follow than to lead and command.   They were deficient in the ability needed to invent and to initiate, but were clever at copying and modifying.   Theirs was not a jealous competitive mentality.   In those mental qualities where the Egyptian fell short the Babylonian abounded. Plainly an addition of a little Babylonian leaven to the Egyptian dough should be attended by happy results.   It was something of this kind which actually happened at the dawn of civilization.

It will repay us to look at the ancient Egyptians through the eyes of my friend and fellow-anatomist, Grafton Elliot Smith (1871–1937).   He was born in Australia,[2] educated for medicine in the Universities of Sydney and of Cambridge, and was called to fill the chair of anatomy in the Government Medical College, Cairo, in 1900, and there he remained until 1909.   During his stay in Egypt discovery after discovery was throwing a new light on the early history of Egypt, not only on that of the first Dynasty of Kings (3300–3200 B.C.), but also on that of the preceding or pre-dynastic period, carrying the prehistory of Egypt back to the middle of the fifth millennium B.C.   After making a thorough study of the pre-dynastic inhabitants of Egypt,[3] Elliot Smith became more and more impressed with the importance of their culture. So completely had Egypt preserved every stage in the evolution of its culture that he became convinced that civilization had been born and cradled on the banks of the lower Nile and nowhere else. He had great courage as well as conviction; there was no rest for him until he had tried to bring the world to his way of thinking. Long before Elliot Smith commenced his advocacy many experts regarded Egypt as the mother of civilization. If this were really the case, then all the early cultures we have encountered in Iran and Babylonia should be traceable to Egypt.

Between the two world wars our knowledge of the ancient cultures of S.W. Asia went forwards at an amazing pace; the Indus Valley proved to be at one extremity of the area of culture, Egypt at the other. The central position of the Iranian plateau and the early cultures already discovered there make it probable that it was the inhabitants of this part of Asia who initiated the cultural movement which has revolutionized the grouping of mankind. The Egyptians and Indians were copyists rather than creators. In the case of Egypt there is evidence that she received immigrants at an early date. In 1895 five small ancient burying-places on the west bank of the Nile near Abydos were opened by the celebrated French archæologist, J. de Morgan; these early graves are now dateable to about the middle of the fifth millennium, the time at which the Sumerians are supposed to have brought the Ubaidian culture to Babylonia. The people buried in these early graves were described by Dr. Fouquet.[5] They differed altogether from the pre-dynastic Egyptians, and were of a type found by Sir Leonard Woolley at Ur. They had big heads and brains (the latter being in point of size equal to those of modern Europeans), whereas the pre-dynastic brain fell about 100 c.c. below the European average. A still older culture, the Tasian, was discovered (1927-9) by Mr. Guy Brunton in Middle Egypt on the east bank of the Nile;[6] it is usually assigned to the earlier part of the fifth millennium, and would be thus contemporary with the Halafian culture of Mesopotamia; it may even be late sixth millennium. The Tasians were agriculturalists; their cranial characters indicate an Asiatic rather than an Egyptian origin. Whether or not the earliest traces of the art of agriculture in Egypt are older than any found so far in Asia is debatable,[7] but when all the evidence is taken into account I am of opinion that Asia has the better claim.

I am assuming, then, that down to the end of the seventh millennium the inhabitants of Egypt were in a primal state of existence, obtaining a living by hunting and by food-gathering. I am assuming, too, that by this time desert conditions had set in and that only the narrow valley, some 550 miles in length when all its bends are allowed for, afforded the inhabitants subsistence. What was the population of Egypt then? And how was it organized? We have seen (p. 269) that it needs one square mile of fertile land to support a single individual in primal times ; the fertile arable land of modern Egypt is reckoned to be 12,000 square miles. If we take this as a measure of the country available to the food-gatherers, then the total population of primal Egypt was 12,000 souls. More than half of the arable land is in the delta, less than half along the 550 miles of valley. As the valley was the better hunting country we shall assign half of the population to the valley area and half to the delta. Six thousand people spread in groups along 550 miles of valley gives nine to each mile of the river. A local group is likely to have occupied a territory extending about ten miles along the valley, and would thus be made up of about ninety members—men, women, and children. The population of the valley would thus be divided into about fifty-five separate local communities. We may assume that the primal population of the delta was also separated into local communities similar in size to those of the valley, giving a total of over one hundred independent evolutionary units in primal Egypt. As agriculture prospered the local groups became swollen in size ; they also became fewer in number owing to fusion of local groups. In the pre-dynastic period these local territorial groups became known as nomes.

We are now in a position to appreciate what the union of the Crowns (3300 B.C.) means to the student of human evolution. The population of Egypt which, in primal times, was arranged in a myriad of independent small communities, became, in dynastic times, fused into one huge unit. With this union the struggle between local groups was eased, but the dangers of a struggle with peoples outside the bounds of Egypt were heightened. Against outside enemies Egypt was most fortunately situated. Everywhere she was protected by desert save at her southern end (where she bordered on the valley tribes of Nubia) and at her northern or Mediterranean frontier, where a land bridge gave Asiatics access to the fertile marshlands of the delta. From pre-dynastic times onwards it was by this Asiatic bridge that her immigrants and invaders made their approach.

Thanks to the progress of irrigation and tillage the population of Egypt, which we have estimated at 12,000 in primal times, numbered, in the more flourishing dynastic eras, about seven millions.[8] The square mile which supported only a single being became capable of nourishing over 580 lives. At the present time (1946) the population of Egypt is estimated at seventeen millions, which implies that for each arable square mile there are 1,400 inhabitants—double the number met with in the most densely populated countries of Europe. When we consider such changes as these, we are compelled to admit that the spade and hoe have revolutionized the conditions of human evolution.

I am regarding the Egyptian nation as an evolutionary unit— the first of its kind to come into existence. It has now a history of more than 5,000 years; no other nation has retained its individuality over such a lengthy period. It provides the evolutionist with an opportunity of discovering wherein lies the strength and also the weakness of the national unit. The weakness which interrupted national life was the reversion to a multitribal state when the central government declined in power. The first "interruption," which marks the end of the Old Kingdom and the beginning of the Middle Kingdom, began in the weakness of the sixth Dynasty and was ended by the local Theban chief who established the eleventh Dynasty and so restored unity. The second interruption, which, like the first, lasted for about two centuries, separated the Middle Kingdom from the New Kingdom; again unity was restored by a Theban chief—the founder of the eighteenth Dynasty. The New Kingdom began strongly, but time after time the former weakness reappeared; disruption was succeeded by restoration until the Assyrian conquest of 665 B.C. Egypt then entered on her long period of foreign domination; what the Assyrians began was continued by one Power after another—Persian, Greek, Roman, Arab, Turk, and finally British. At this present moment (August, 1946) negotiations are on foot for a complete withdrawal of British armed forces from Egyptian soil. Thus after a lapse of twenty-five centuries Egypt resumes her absolute sovereignty—in so far as a nation can be sovereign in the modern world.

Readers may have noted that in my definition of a nation at the beginning of this essay there was one qualification I did not mention—that of sovereignty. Viscount Bryce,[9] for example, denied that Wales and Scotland were nations, because they were no longer sovereign Powers. Has that fact deprived these peoples of their national spirit or even damped it? The opposite is the case ; it has tended to strengthen their feeling of difference and their determination to nurse their separate national traditions. It was so in the case of the Egyptians; foreign domination never destroyed their sense of apartness; the fellaheen which form the body of the nation to-day are the lineal descendants of the fellaheen of 3300 B.C. It is true that the peasants of Egypt have always been passive rather than active nationalists ; they have been content to follow those in command; they have never been democrats. But these limitations do not take away from the nationhood of the Egyptians. They are an inbreeding isolated people; they have been so from pre-dynastic times ; they are determined to remain so. Every such people is a nation.

In only one period of the later history of Egypt was there a large influx of new blood (or genes). This was in the centuries which followed the eviction of the Byzantine and the installation of Arab power (A.D. 639–41). An Arab force of less than 15,000 men succeeded in doing this at a time when the Egyptians numbered several millions.[10] The Egyptians were conquered, not by the sword, but by the Koran. As the Egyptians learned to read that book they also learned to speak a new tongue—that of the Arabs. The Bedouin desert tribes which hovered on the verge of the sown lands sometimes gave up their nomadic life, settled on the soil and inter-married with the fellaheen. In this way a half-million of Arabs were added to the native population.[11] The process still goes on. So completely have the Egyptians become Arabized in mind that they claim (at least their leaders claim for them) a place among the Arab peoples. If the mind of the Egyptian has been affected, his body seems to have escaped, for, as we shall see presently, extensive examinations made by anthropologists have detected no measurable change in the body. This may be due to the fact that the Bedouin, in a physical sense, is not unlike the Egyptian. Or it may be that the change effected has escaped detection by the anthropological technique employed.

Records of the dead have been preserved far more perfectly in

Egypt than in any other land. Skulls and skeletons have been recovered and measured from graves which range in date from earliest pre-dynastic times down to the Egyptians buried in the period of the Roman occupation. We thus know the physical history of the Egyptian nation far more completely than that of any other people. Our knowledge of the bodily characters of the pre-dynastic Egyptians was first made known to us by Elliot Smith; [12] he found them to have been a slim people of short stature (5 ft. 5 in.), with elongated but relatively small skulls. In more recent times Dr. G. M. Morant [13] has instituted an elaborate comparison of skulls recovered from cemeteries of all parts of Egypt and of all dates down to that of the Roman occupation. His two main conclusions are these. Down to the Early Dynastic period the Lower Egyptians differed from the Upper Egyptians by having wider and larger skulls and also bigger faces. He found evidence that, as time went on, the type of Lower Egypt spread up the Nile and gradually replaced the Upper type. He also found that, in a racial sense, the historic Egyptians became a homogenous people.

How do the Egyptians of to-day compare with those of ancient times? I shall cite only three authorities. First, the late Dr. Charles S. Myers,[14] who collected data among living Egyptians at the beginning of the twentieth century. He found the same form and size of head prevailing from the delta to the first cataract as prevailed in ancient times ; he observed that the skin tended to darken and the nose to widen as he passed from Lower to Upper Egypt. He compared measurements taken on the living with measurements taken on the long-past dead of the same province and found the degree of variability to be the same in both. Then there are the calculations made by Mr. J. I. Craig [15] on many thousands of prisoners drawn from all the provinces of modern Egypt. Everywhere the mean breadth of the head varied from 74 to 75 per cent of the length. One of his observations I regard as of particular importance—there is a tendency for each province to produce its own particular physical type. That I infer to be the result of local inter-marriage. My third witness is Professor Sydney Smith,[16] who during his professional residence in Cairo had many opportunities of comparing the skulls of modern Egyptians with those of pre-dynastic times. His data forced him to the conclusion that in spite of minor cranial changes, the modern Egyptian had, in a physical sense, reverted to the pre-dynastic type—this had happened in spite of all the disturbance and the influx of strange blood which had occurred in the long period of 7,000 years. At the end of that period the pre-dynastic type, like Pharaoh's " ill-favoured and lean-fleshed kine," had swallowed up and made all of its own kind. Flinders Petrie counted the power to assimilate other types to its own as a mark of a nation or race. Certainly the Egyptians had this power. The matter which arrests our attention, however, is Professor Smith's main conclusion. What does a nation profit if it endure for 5,000 years and find that at the end of that period it has, in an evolutionary sense, gone backwards rather than forwards? Is the reversion a result of the fusion of a myriad of small competing groups into one massive national unit? To this problem I shall return in a future essay.

What is the relationship of the Egyptians to other peoples of North Africa and to those of S.W. Asia? To obtain an answer we have to go back to the later part of the Pleistocene period, when climatic conditions were very different from what they are to-day. The upland sandy wastes on each side of the Nile were then habitable; so were large areas of Arabia. We have seen (Essay XXIV) that in late Pleistocene times the Hamitic peoples of Africa were linked, by a series of transitional forms, with the Dravidians of India. Thus the Egyptians would be distantly related to the peoples of India. Their relationship to the dark-skinned, fuzzy-haired Hamitic peoples was nearer and more direct. Even to-day they are united to the peoples in the heart of Africa by a chain of transitional types lying along the valley of the Nile. Perhaps their closest relationship is to the Libyans occupying the upland country to the west of the Delta and extending along the shores of the Mediterranean. When the uplands turned to desert, their inhabitants had to seek homes elsewhere—in the valley of the Nile, on the shores of the Red Sea, and along those of the Mediterranean. Thus the ancestors of the pre-dynastic Egyptians were cut off from other members of their race, from the Libyans on the west and the Red Sea peoples on the east. But the link with tropical Africa continued.

In all our speculations concerning the origin of the ancient Egyptians there is one circumstance we must not lose sight of. This is the relationship of their Hamitic speech to that of the Arabs.

Scholars seem to be agreed that the Hamitic and Semitic languages have been evolved from a common root and that the speakers of these tongues must have lived beside each other at one time.   To obtain a satisfactory explanation we must give our attention for a moment to the origin of the Arabs.   The solution I offer is this. Long before the discovery of agriculture, even before Egypt was separated from Arabia by the Red Sea, when the dark-skinned aborigines of Arabia were leading the lives of primitive food-gatherers, they were invaded by a Caucasian people from the north.   The invaders interbred with the natives and learned the native speech, which I suppose to have been an early form of the Semitic tongue near akin to the Hamitic.   Thus I regard the Arabs as a cross between the original natives of Arabia and a branch of the Caucasian stock.   Such an explanation has the twofold advantage in giving a reasonable explanation of the physical characters of the peoples of Arabia, as well as the relationship of the Hamitic to the Semitic tongues.

One other circumstance must be considered before coming to a final decision concerning the origin of the Egyptians.   In Essay XXVI I developed the idea that the transformation of Neanderthal man into the Caucasian type had taken place in S.W. Asia, and that from a centre in Asia the Caucasian stock spread westwards, not only into Europe, but also into Africa north of the Sahara.   If such had been the case—and the evidence in favour is strong [17]—then Caucasians may have settled in Lower Egypt at a date long prior to the pre-dynastic period.   The larger-headed type found in Lower Egypt may thus be of Caucasian origin.

REFERENCES

[1] Hornblower, G. D., *Man*, 1941, p. 97.

[2] Dawson, Warren H., *Sir Grafton Elliot Smith*, 1938.

[3] Smith, Sir G. Elliot, *The Ancient Egyptians*, 1911.

[4] Morgan, J. De, *Recherches sur les Origines de l'Egypt*, 1897.

[5] Fouquet, Dr. D., see preceding reference.   Also Dr. G. M. Morant's important article in *Biometrika*, 1925, vol. 17, p. 1.

[6] Brunton, Guy, *Mostagedda and the Tasian Culture*, 1937.

[7] Childe, V. Gordon, *New Light on the Most Ancient East*, 1934.

[8] Clelland, Wendell, *The Population Problem in Egypt*, 1937.

[9] Bryce, Viscount, "The Rise of Nations" in *South America*, 1912, p. 424.

[10] Thomas, Bertram, *The Arabs*, 1937.

[11] Murray, G. W., *Jour. Roy. Anthrop. Inst.*, 1937, vol. 57, p. 39; Sons of Ishmael, *A Study of the Egyptian Beduin*, 1935; Lane, E. W., *The Manners and Customs of the Modern Egyptians*, 1836, Everyman ed., 1908.

[12] See reference 3.

[13] Morant, G. M., see under reference 5.

[14] Myers, C. S. (1873–1946), *Jour. Roy. Anthrop. Inst.*, 1905, vol. 55, p. 80; 1908, vol. 58, p. 99.

[15] Craig, J. I., *Biometrika*, 1911, vol. 8, p. 66.

[16] Smith, Sydney, *Jour. Anat.*, 1926, vol. 60, p. 121.

[17] Vallois, Henri, *Archives de l'Institut de Paleontologie Humaine*, Mémoire 13, pt. 2, 1934.

EVOLUTION OF NATIONALITIES IN EUROPE ILLUSTRATED BY THAT OF SCOTLAND

Synopsis.—Why Scotland was chosen to illustrate the process of nation-building. Agricola's invasion of Scotland. A national spirit manifested by the Caledonians. The tribal territories of Scotland. The origin of the tribal peoples encountered by Agricola. First settlers. The "harpoon people." Settlers on the east coast and on the west coast during the second millennium B.C. The Celts. The coming of the Irish and the Anglo-Saxons. In the sixth century Scotland was divided into four kingdoms. By the thirteenth century these four kingdoms had become fused into one and the basis of a single nation was thus laid. The nationalization of the people was completed in the eighteenth century. The racial elements which went to the making of the Scottish nation. Nation-building in Egypt was 4,500 years ahead of that in Scotland. Manifestations of patriotism in the thirteenth century. The urge for independence. The author holds that independence is not an essential factor in nationality. The assimilation of one nation by another rarely takes place. There is a confederation of British nations, but there is no British nation. The nature of nationality. Definition of a nation. In Scotland the clan or tribal spirit was transformed into a national spirit.

FROM nation-building in Egypt we turn to nation-building in Europe. Up to the autumn of 1939 the wide expanse of Europe was partitioned into twenty-six national territories, the inhabitants of each of these territories regarding themselves as not only separated from, but also different from, the occupants of all other territories. Each nation claimed to be independent of the others ; all sought to control their own evolutionary destiny. In a previous series of essays [1] I have given brief accounts of the rise of three European nationalities—namely, those of England, France, and Germany. In the present essay I propose to trace the origin of the Scottish nation, my choice being determined by two considerations; first, because what is true of nation-building in Scotland is true of nation-building on the Continent; second, because, having been born and bred in Scotland, I am familiar with the strength and nature of the national spirit of that land, at first hand, whereas my experience of nationalism of other lands has been gained later in my life and at second hand.

In the year 80 of our era Agricola led a Roman army northwards across the Tweed and thus brought that part of Britain now known as Scotland into the page of history.[2] Having overrun the homelands of five separate peoples or tribes, he reached the Forth–Clyde isthmus, where he erected a line of forts. North of this line Scotland was inhabited by Caledonian tribes some thirteen or fifteen in number, each having its own territory. In the autumn of the year 85 Agricola led his army into the heart of the Caledonian country until the Grampians came into full view.

There, on rising ground, he found the tribal forces of the Caledonians drawn up in battle array. He estimated the hostile army at 30,000 men and found it was commanded by Galgacus, a Caledonian chief. At this stage Tacitus makes Galgacus address his troops in a speech which breathes the fierce spirit of nationalism, a fact which ought to astonish those historians who are of the opinion that the national spirit appeared in Europe for the first time in the fifteenth century A.D. Galgacus in his appeal to the Caledonians said:—

" We are the men who never crouched in bondage. Beyond this spot there is no land where liberty can find a refuge . . . children and relatives are dear to us all. It is an affection planted in our breast by the hand of nature. Are our wives, our sisters, and our daughters, safe from brutal lust and open violation? . . . The Romans by a strange singularity of nature are the only people who invade with equal ardour the wealth and the poverty of nations. To rob, to ravage, and to murder, in their imposing language, are the arts of civil policy. When they have made the world a solitude they call it peace. . . . And shall not we, unconquered, and undebased by slavery, a nation ever free, and struggling now, not to recover but to ensure our liberties, shall we not go forth the champions of our country? "

On the other hand, the speech which Tacitus put into the mouth of his father-in-law, Agricola, is a vigorous exposition of the Roman policy of conquest, a policy which involves the destruction of local nationalities. In this speech Agricola said:—

> "It is now, my fellow soldiers, the eighth year of our service in Britain. During that time, the genius and good auspices of the Roman Empire, with your assistance and unwearied labours, have made the islands our own. . . . We have carried the terror of our arms beyond the limits of any former general; we have penetrated the extremity of the land. . . . Britain is discovered, and by the discovery conquered. . . . One victory more makes this new world our own."

The extracts, quoted above, from the two speeches bring us in touch with the forces which are ever at work in building a people into a nation. The appeal by Galgacus proved of no avail; the morning after the battle saw the Caledonian tribesmen in disorderly retreat, each to his own territory, leaving 10,000 dead on the fatal field. This signal victory proved to be a barren one for Rome, for ultimately she found it expedient to leave Scotland outside the limits of her empire.

Scotland, then, in the first century of our era was divided into about a score of separate and independent tribal States. We have now to inquire into the origin of these tribal inhabitants of Scotland. Where did the ancestors of these peoples come from? When and how did they reach the country now named Scotland? In seeking to answer these questions we have to remember that Scotland—and the same is true of Scandinavia—became fit for human habitation with the final retreat of the ice-sheet, an event usually assigned to the tenth or twelfth millennium before our era began. At that time, and for long after, the Rhine flowed northwards along a plane now submerged in the bed of the North Sea; Britain was thus connected with the Continent by a wide land bridge. Along the continental as well as along the British shores of the North Sea are found many traces of the " harpoon people," so named because of the harpoon heads they fashioned out of bone. They were people of the Caucasian stock, very similar, so far as our limited knowledge of them permits us to go, to the late cave men of Western Europe. The stone and bone culture of the harpoon people has been traced across northern England and into southern and western Scotland; it has also been traced into Norway and Sweden. These rude, savage, food-gathering, harpoon people seem to have provided both Scotland and Scandinavia with their first inhabitants. Their arrival in Scotland is usually assigned to the eighth millennium B.C.[3] This, too, is the date we have assigned to beginnings of agriculture on the Iranian plateau.

Before the dawn of the second millennium B.C., land and sea had taken on their present form. The practice of agriculture was appearing on the Continent and its inhabitants were increasing in numbers; new homes were in demand. Sea power had become a factor in the spread of peoples. Early in this millennium galleys were crossing the North Sea, and landing fresh settlers along the east coast of Scotland from John O' Groats to Berwick.[4] These new arrivals, usually spoken of as the " beaker people," brought with them their domesticated animals, and a knowledge of agriculture; they were round-headed, being of central European derivation. While the eastern lands of Scotland were being thus colonized, its western lands were receiving new inhabitants from a totally different source. These new settlers in the west came from Brittany, from France, and from Spain.[5] Late in the third millennium, and all through the centuries of the second millennium, the Irish Sea had become part of a shipping lane which continued up the west coast of Scotland to Baltic lands. Along this route came the " long-barrow " peoples, dark-haired and narrow-headed pastoralists, who effected settlements at various points, many of them being on the western shores of Scotland. Thus eastern Scotland received its new settlers from lands lying on the opposite side of the North Sea, while western Scotland became the home of peoples from the south-western parts of Europe. For long these eastern and western colonists remained apart because the central parts of Scotland were covered by thick forests.

From 800 B.C. onwards the enterprising Celtic-speaking peoples of the Continent increased rapidly in numbers and spread as rulers into France, Spain, and ultimately to the British Isles. Some four or five centuries before the coming of the Romans, Celtic tribes invaded southern Scotland, and gradually spread throughout the land, giving its inhabitants new rulers, a new speech, new arts, both of peace and of war.[6]   Such, then, is a brief account of the origins of the tribal peoples of Scotland who fought the Roman invaders in the first century of our era.

After the departure of the Romans from Britain at the beginning of the fifth century, two additions of the highest importance were made to the population of Scotland—one on the west coast, the other on the east. We shall take the Irish settlement on the west coast first. A long tongue of land extends from the south-western part of Scotland (Argyll) towards N.E. Ireland. It was at the base of this tongue of land on which three tribes from N.E. Ireland settled at the end of the fifth century of our era.   There is ample evidence of intercommunication between Ulster and Argyll for 2,000 years before this date, but historians are agreed that it was the settlement of the Irish Scots at Dalriada at the end of the fifth century that brought the Gaelic tongue and Gaelic dominion to Scotland.[7]   The Scots extended their dominion over the western tribes very slowly.   The arrival of missionaries from Ireland in the sixth century (St. Columba, 521–98) taught the inhabitants of Scotland to read the Bible in the Gaelic tongue, and thus prepared the way for the extension of the rule of the chief or king of the Dalriad Scots. The Koran made the Egyptians speakers of Arabic; the Bible made the inhabitants of Scotland speakers of Gaelic.

So much for the Irish settlement on the west coast; we now turn to the Anglo-Saxon conquest and colonization on the east coast. By the middle of the sixth century the kingdom of Bernicia extended from the Tees to the Forth.   Thus at this date there were four kingdoms in what is now Scotland; south of the Forth-Clyde line there was that of Bernicia on the east, and that of the Welsh-speaking kingdom of Strathclyde on the west; north of the Forth-Clyde line was the kingdom of the Celtic Picts on the east and the kingdom of the Scots in the west. The hammers which beat these four kingdoms into one were provided by the royal dynasty of the kings of the Scots. In 1057 Malcolm III was crowned at Scone as king of Scotland. But even then the Scottish people can hardly be called a nation. A common tradition had not then been established.

There are two important omissions in my list of peoples which went to the making of the Scottish nation—namely, the Norse and the Danes.   Early in the second millennium the migration stream off the west coast of Scotland was directed towards Norway and the Baltic, but before the end of the ninth century A.D. the tide had turned; the Norse began to colonize Caithness, the Orkneys, the Hebrides, and lands along the west coast.   The threat of a Norwegian domination of Scotland was removed by the battle of Largs in the reign of Alexander III (1259–83).   The victory at Largs was not the only contribution that this king made to the unification of Scotland.   Under him the English speech of southern Scotland became the national tongue, save in the Highlands, where heart and tongue remained loyal to ancient tradition. He planted feudal lords in tribal territories, hoping thus to break up the clannish spirit of the Highlanders, but in vain.   Even at the end of the sixteenth century there were still thirty-four clans, each loyal to its chief.   It required the cruel and brutal practices which followed the Jacobite rebellion of 1745 to root out the tribal spirit of the Highlanders and to establish a unity of government in Scotland.   Even now the Highland spirit is not dead.

We see, then, from the example of Scotland, how tedious, prolonged, precarious, and cruel the business is of welding a diversity of peoples into a single evolutionary unit—that is, into a nation. The processes employed to bring about amalgamation have been those of statecraft, education, social ostracism, and war.   The peoples incorporated came from all the countries of Western Europe—Norwegians, Danes, Germans, Flemings, Dutch, French, and Spaniards in varying proportions, to say nothing of the harpoon people, the beaker folk, and the men of the long-barrow type.   Ireland, too, had made her contribution, and still continues to add to it.   It is true that all these peoples had undergone a local differentiation in the lands from whence they came, and it is customary to speak of them as races, a usage which I shall justify in my next essay.   But it has to be remembered that all these races or peoples are the progeny of one stock—the Caucasian —and were so alike in their physical characters that the most expert anthropologist cannot distinguish the skull and skeleton of one race from those of another.   When mingled, as they have been in the Scottish nation, it is impossible to say of any given man whether he is of Celtic or of Saxon origin.   It has taken about 10,000 years to build the Scottish nation.   It is worthy of note that the stage of national evolution attained in Egypt thirty-three centuries before the birth of Christ was reached in Scotland twelve centuries after that event. Nation-building in Egypt was forty-five centuries ahead of the same process in Scotland. What is true of Scotland is also true of all the nationalities of Europe; indeed, in several of the countries of Europe nation-building is still at the stage reached by Scotland in the thirteenth century.

There can be no nation-building unless all the people of a country are imbued with patriotic feelings—feelings which give their native land and their fellow-subjects a special place in their affections. One other passion, one which seems so irrational to the uninitiated, is also essential—a passion which drives them to seek the freedom or independence of their country. Earlier in this essay I quoted from the patriotic speech attributed to Galgacus, the Caledonian chief. Let me now quote from a speech which George Buchanan (1506–84) imputes to Wallace, the heroic leader of Scottish Independence. After the battle of Falkirk (1297) Wallace is supposed to have met Bruce, then fighting on the side of the English invaders, and chides him in the following terms:—

> When I saw my countrymen, by your slothfulness, destitute of governors and exposed not to slavery only, but even to the butchery of a cruel enemy, I had pity on them, and undertook the cause which you deserted; neither will I forsake the liberty, good, and safety of my countrymen till life forsake me. . . . I will die free in my country which I have often defended; and my love to it shall remain as long as my life continues." [9]

Here we see in Wallace a contest between two of the strongest of man's inborn instincts or passions—the passion for life and the passion for country and nation; he preferred to die for his country rather than to live at ease in England. Strange and strong passions are needed for the task of nation-building. Dr. Agnes Mure Mackenzie [10] cites an earlier instance of Scottish patriotism, this time manifested by the common people. It is recorded that when Henry III of England invaded Scotland in 1242 "the people came out not fearing death for their own country." No matter what size an " evolutionary unit " may be—whether it be only a small local group, a large tribe, or a great nation—it is always animated by the urge of independence, of separation from all surrounding units. Only if a nation is independent, is it free to work out its untrammelled evolutionary destiny.

Must a people, then, possess complete independence—free exercise of sovereign powers—before it can be regarded as a nation? Such was the opinion of Viscount Bryce, who defined a nation thus: "Whenever a community has both political independence and a distinctive character, recognizable in its members as well as in the whole body, we call it a nation. . . . It must feel and act as a whole." [11] He therefore denied that the peoples of Scotland and of Wales were nations. This is also the opinion of the group of experts who reported on " Nationalism " in 1939; [12] they regard a nation as a " political unit " and speak of " the Scots and Welsh as having been assimilated in Great Britain."

Now, the power of assimilation is a character of a nation. Let us take England as an example; she takes into her midst natives of Scotland, of Wales, and of Ireland, and in two generations makes them indistinguishable from true natives. But the assimilation of one whole nation by another is a very different matter. When James VI of Scotland crossed the Tweed to become James I of England he united in his person the loyalty and allegiance of both the English and the Scots, but the boundary between the two nations remained as firmly fixed at the Tweed as in former times. The Act of Union (1707), which merged the parliament of Scotland in that of England, was a union of " heads," not of " hearts "; the national heart of Scotland continued to beat with as steady and strong a pulse as before. Under the shelter of England national life in Scotland was more secure than it would have been had she continued to face a warring world independent and alone. The union of Scotland to England is a federation, not a fusion. I hold, then, that a nation is much more than a " political unit "; the forces and mental qualities which go to the making of a nation are parts of the evolutionary machinery which no independent people can by-pass.

When I say that the sense of nationality is deeply rooted in the Scot, I am speaking of the mass, not of the individual. To make my meaning clear I shall use a simile. Every babe is born with the desire and power to suck and is fed on milk; as it grows up its mind, like its body, develops an appetite; that, too, has to be fed; it is fed on the lore contained in the national tradition. Thus the creation of a national spirit requires two factors, a mental factor and a material factor, the material factor being the national tradition. The outlook and reactions of a whole people could be changed only by rooting out the old national tradition and putting in its place a new one—a Herculean undertaking. But what is so difficult in the case of the mass is easy in the case of the individual. Scotsmen emigrate to the United States, to Canada, to South Africa, to Australia and New Zealand, and in the countries of their adoption feed on a new national tradition which, in time, replaces the old. This is made possible because the emigrant carries in him or her an inborn social appetite.

British passports are issued daily, but is there a British nation? Certainly not within the United Kingdom; here there are only English, Welsh, Irish, and Scottish. We are a confederation of nations, each wedded to its own national tradition. The only peoples which could legitimately claim to be British are the nations now developing in Australia, New Zealand, and Canada; the major part of their populations have been derived from all parts of the British Isles.

What, then, are the essential characteristics of a nation? It would be too wearisome to enumerate the scores of definitions I have gathered from standard authorities. I shall therefore confine my discussion to points which, in my opinion, give the inhabitants of Scotland the right to consider themselves a nation. The Scots are a nation because they are conscious of being " members one of another " and of being different from the peoples of other lands. They are, and always have been, an inbreeding people. They have a particular affection for their native land. They are proud of their country, of themselves, of their name and fame, and of their national emblems. They speak dialects of the same tongue, all save a remnant of the Gaels. If their country or its people are in jeopardy, or have been made the butt of foreign insult, they rally to its defence; they would give their lives freely to preserve the integrity of the land and the liberty of its people. They are the heirs and executors of a firmly implanted national tradition. They are sharers in a common interest and in a common destiny; they hope and believe that their stock will never die out. They inhabit a sharply delimited territory and claim to own it. They have national heroes, national songs, national dances, and national music. They have their own courts of justice, their own system of laws, their own churches, their own universities, and their own schoolmasters. They are emulative and keenly competitive; they are also co-operative. They have the power of assimilating strangers into their community and of making those assimilated sharers in all their hopes and fears, traditions, customs, and modes of speech. They formulate their own public opinion and are sensitive and subservient to that opinion. The genes or germinal units which circulate within the frontiers of their land differ in their potentialities from those which circulate in all other countries. The Scottish people form, in a physical sense, a homogeneous community, but only a small proportion of them have features which are peculiar to their nation. Such, then, is a list of the qualities which give the Scottish people a right to claim the status of a nation. Any people possessing these traits is a nation not only in a political sense but also in a biological or evolutionary sense. "The earlier nations," wrote Ramsay Muir,[13] "achieved nationhood, not by theory, but by their own instincts and traditions." I am of opinion that nationhood can never be achieved by theory; nationgenic qualities lie in the unconscious region of human mentality.

It was my intention to trace the transformation of the clan or tribal spirit into the national spirit. The late persistence of a clan or tribal organization in the Highlands of Scotland provides material for such a study. It will be sufficient for my present purpose to point out that the map prepared by Dr. James Browne[14] shows forty delimited small territories, each a statelet, each occupied and owned by a clan and ruled by a chief. Every one of the characters I have attributed to the Scottish nation was exhibited in miniature by each of these local self-governing communities. Each was a separate, independent evolutionary unit. With the forceful detribalization of the clans, the inborn predispositions and instinctive urges of the clansmen, which gave allegiance to their chief and nursed the preferential interests of the clan, became transferred to the wider circle of the nation. Group spirit, tribal spirit or tribalism, national spirit or nationalism are one and the same thing, with this limiting circumstance—the larger the group the more is the spirit spread out and attenuated.

REFERENCES

[1] Keith, Sir A., *Essays on Human Evolution*, 1946, p. 77.

[2] *The Historical Works of Tacitus*, Everyman ed., vol. 2, p. 347.

[3] Keith, Sir A., *New Discoveries relating to the Antiquity of Man*, 1931, p. 422.

[4] Keith, Sir A., "The Origin of the Scottish People," *Nineteenth Century and After*, 1922, vol. 91, p. 819; Turner, Sir William, *Trans. Roy. Soc. Edin.*, 1903, vol. 40, p. 547; *ibid.*, 1915, vol. 51, p. 171; Mitchell, Margaret E. C., *Proc. Soc. Antiq. Scot.*, 1934, vol. 68, p. 132; Reid and Morant, *Biometrika*, 1928, vol. 20, p. 378.

[5] Bryce, T. H., *Scottish Historical Rev.*, 1905, p. 275.

[6] Childe, V. Gordon, *The Prehistory of Scotland*, 1935; *Scotland before the Scots*, 1946.

[7] Skene, W. F., *Celtic Scotland*, 1876, 3 vols.; Browne, James, *A History of the Highlands and of the Highland Clans*, 1852, vol. 4, p. 385; Mackenzie, Agnes Mure, *The Kingdom of Scotland*, 1940; *The Foundations of Scotland*, 1938.

[8] Johnston and Robertson, *Historical Geography of the Clans of Scotland*, 1899, 3rd ed.

[9] Buchanan, George, *The History of Scotland*, 5th ed., 1762, vol. 1, bk. VIII, p. 346.

[10] Mackenzie, Agnes Mure, *Times Lit. Suppl.*, June 2, 1945, p. 271.

[11] Bryce, Viscount, *South America*, 1912, p. 424.

[12] *Nationalism: Report of a Study-Group*, 1939, p. 293.

[13] Muir, Ramsay, *Nationalism and Internationalism*, 1916, p. 86.

[14] Browne, James, see under reference given in note 7.

THE MAKING OF HUMAN RACES

*Synopsis.—The confusion resulting from the use of the term " race "
in two senses. The term was originally given to a lineage group.
Later it was restricted to distinctive varieties of mankind. " Nation " is
the term used to designate the lineal descendants of a local group. For
an Australian aborigine his tribe is his race. The discovery of agriculture
brought nations into existence. Nations, although not physically differentiated from one another, remain apart. "Nation" is defined. The
sense in which a nation is a race. The translators of the Bible used the
term " nation " as equivalent to race. Popular usage of the term " race."
The restriction of the term "race" to a differentiated people began in 1839.
Huxley's advocacy led to the change in usage being adopted. The
taxonomic methods of zoology are unsuitable for mankind. The claims
of the South Irish to be a separate race. The former usage of the term
" race " should be restored. The twofold meaning of the term " race "
exemplified. The degree to which nations may be regarded as of
mixed origin. The homogeneity of the inhabitants of Great Britain.
Bagehot was of opinion that nation-making had replaced race-making.
The Egyptians are a race in both senses of that term. The degree
to which the population of Scotland and of Sweden are physically
differentiated. A nation is a variety in course of formation.*

IN the year 1919 Mr. John Oakesmith wrote a well-reasoned
book [1] to show that race and nation had nothing to do with each
other—race being one thing and nation quite another. In the
same year I also published a book [2] which sought to prove that
race and nation were near akin—that a nation was in reality an
incipient race. When he wrote, Mr. Oakesmith knew nothing of
my book; nor did I know of his. Now, when two men have
the same facts before them and are in search of the truth and come
to diametrically opposite conclusions, it will usually be found that,
although they have used the same terms, they have attached a

quite different meaning to these terms.   He used the term " race " in one sense; I in quite another, yet each of us could justify our usage by an appeal to authority.   This twofold use of the word " race "—an " incendiary term " Professor Fleure [3] has called it— has been, and still is, the source of infinite misunderstanding and quarrel.   Before I can go into the process of race-making, I must first clear up this confusion in the use of the term " race."

To illustrate this twofold usage let us turn back for a moment to a large area of the primal world and note the manner in which its primitive inhabitants were broken up into isolated local groups, each representing an " evolutionary unit " or, as Bagehot [4] named it, " a parish race."   Each local group was an inbreeding, isolated, closed society, with its own assortment of genes, tracing its origin back to a common ancestry.   Each group had been winnowed and selected in its competition with other groups and in its struggle with surrounding conditions.   Now, any group, tribe, or nation which represents the progeny of a common ancestry is a race in the strict meaning of that term.[5]   We may, then, legitimately apply the term " race " to each local group;   each group was a potential race-maker.   This is one use of the term " race ";   now for its other use.   All these local groups, working collectively, pro- duced a population with a certain assortment of physical char- acters which distinguished it from the populations of surrounding countries.   Now, a people which can be distinguished by its physical features is also called a race, but this is a late use of the term.[7]   Thus the term " race " came to be applied in two senses : first, to a local or race-making group—being as it were the loom on which the genetic threads were woven—and secondly, to the product of evolution—the differentiated people, the woven web. In one sense the term refers to an evolutionary process ;   in the other to an evolutionary product.   The difference between Mr. Oakesmith and myself was due to his using the term " race " to mean a people differentiated in a physical sense—the finished pro- duct—while I used it to designate a group or a people involved in the process of differentiation.   A race, as I see it, is a thing which is consciously and vitally alive;   race as viewed by Mr. Oakesmith and by physical anthropologists is inert, unconscious, and passive.   My race is passionate;   his is devoid of passion.

As we trace the evolution of mankind towards the present, the evolutionary unit grows in size;   the local group is replaced by the tribe, and then the tribe by the nation. The tribal stage was preserved in the continent of Australia up to the latter part of the eighteenth century. The native population was divided into more than a thousand separate territorial units or tribes. Each tribe was a self-reproducing, inbreeding lineage—a " race " in the original meaning of that term. Each tribe was a race-making unit, but the physical type or types produced by one tribe differed in only a slight degree from those of neighbouring tribes. Yet the collective action of all the tribes was to fill the continent with a population which was physically distinguishable from all other peoples of the world. The collective result of the evolutionary process has given the Australian natives a distinctive appearance and won for them the name of " Australoid race." Of the existence of such a race the native was ignorant; his living interests were centred on his local clan or tribe; for him his tribe was his " race."

In preceding essays I have traced the effects which the discovery of agriculture produced in the size of evolutionary units; tribes were replaced by nations. We best realize the effects of that momentous discovery if we compare the continent of Europe as it is to-day with the continent of Australia as it was at the beginning of the eighteenth century. The myriad of tribal territories of Australia are represented in Europe by twenty-six national territories. Some of these territories, such as Great Britain, the Soviet Republics, Yugo-Slavia, Czecho-Slovakia, Switzerland, and Belgium, are occupied by a confederation of nations, so that the total number of nations in Europe may be nearer forty than twenty-six. No nation claims to be physically differentiated from its neighbours, yet all remain apart and are very conscious of their frontiers. They are conscious, too, of being different from each other. All are inbreeding, self-reproducing units; each and all are animated by that complex of emotions, feelings, sentiments, and convictions known as " national spirit."

A nation, then, is a separated community reproducing its own local types, and in the original meaning of the term is a race. Collectively the nations of Europe produce variants of that distinctive division of mankind known as the Caucasian race. Here, again, we return to the confusion which results from using the term " race " as a name for the local national race-making unit and the collective evolutionary result produced by these units—namely, the Caucasian race. Europeans are indifferent as to their Caucasianhood, but they are very much alive to their nationhood. For most Europeans, their nation is also their race.

If we use the term " race " to indicate a people that is sharply differentiated by its physical characters from all other peoples, then there are very few nations to which the term may be applied legitimately. But if we use it, as I think it should be used, to indicate a delimited, inbreeding, self-reproducing community, then we rightly, and with advantage, speak of a nation as a race. The English translators of the Bible, not having the term " race " at their disposal, used the term " nation " as a substitute. In the tenth chapter of Genesis the Hebrew scribe, after enumerating the eleven nations of Palestine who traced their lineage to Canaan, son of Ham, ends his account in a verse which was translated in the following words: " These are the sons of Ham, after their families, after their tongues, in their countries, and in their nations." In the strict dictionary meaning of the term these nations were " races."

In current English " race " is still used as a term for nation both by the educated and the uneducated. Mr. Winston Churchill, who is careful in his use of words, has spoken of the " Irish race " and of the " Scottish race "; the learned historian of Europe, the late Mr. H. A. L. Fisher, used the term German " race "; so did J. H. Green. The latter historian also wrote of the English and of the Welsh race. Lloyd George, at the zenith of his career, claimed a racial status for his own people—the people of Wales. Even the great Huxley, who was so strict about limiting the term " race " to fully differentiated peoples, relapsed occasionally to its original meaning. In 1871 he wrote of " the great faculty for physical and metaphysical inquiry, with which the people of *our race* are naturally endowed." [7] " Our race " in this instance was the English race. Leslie Stephen, Francis Galton, and Karl Pearson speak of the English as a race. Such examples could be greatly multiplied, but enough has been cited to prove that the Englishman, when he uses the term " race," has in mind, not a people that is marked off by physical traits, but a people that is differentiated by its feelings, its modes of thought, its speech, its habits and customs, and by its tradition—in brief, by its culture.

I have been stating the case for those who maintain that " race " should be used in its original meaning—namely, as the designation of a separated community which is concerned in reproducing itself, and so taking part, quite unconsciously, in the great evolutionary process of race-building. Let me now put up the case, as fairly as I can, of those—and they form the majority of anthropologists—who maintain that the term should be restricted to peoples who are so completely differentiated in a physical sense that they can be instantly distinguished from each other at sight. Linneus (1707-78) did not use the term " race "; he divided mankind into four " varieties " or sub-species, each occupying a continental area. His four sub-species were: Americanus, Europaeus, Asiaticus, and Afer (Blacks). Blumenbach (1752-1840) did not use the term " race "; he amended the classification of Linneus by substituting the name Caucasian for European and added a fifth variety or sub-species to include the Australasian peoples. Buffon did not use the term " race "; he added a sixth sub-species. Lawrence,[8] as late as 1834, did not use the term " race "; he was a devout and discriminating follower of Blumenbach. The application of physical characters to the definition of races is traceable to the year 1839. My authority for this statement is the eminent French anthropologist, Paul Topinard;[9] up to that date the term " race " had been given to any separate people; it was then resolved that no people could be deemed a " race " unless it was distinguishable by its physical markings. Prichard (1786-1848), in his learned and still useful five-volumed treatise,[10] notes this change in the definition of race,[11] and, like Topinard, was greatly disturbed by it. It was due to Huxley, more than to any other man, that physical differentiation was made the mark of race.[12] So clear and vigorous was his argument and so great was his influence that from 1865 onwards the physical definition of race was accepted throughout the anthropological world.

Huxley's main contention seemed to be undeniable; man, being a member of the animal kingdom, must be classified by the same rules as are applied to animals. Huxley and those who followed him forgot that man is a unique animal. In defining man Linneus gave as man's chief character—nosce te ipsum—the self-conscious animal. Man differs from all other animals in his use of names; he has a name for his individual self and names for all those with whom he mixes. He is a conscious animal—conscious first of the family in which he is born, then conscious of the local group of which he is a member, and finally conscious of his nation and of the name given to it. All other animals except man are passive in the hands of the classifier; but man is a self-namer and a self-classifier. For him the accepted name of his race is that of his local group, of his tribe, or of his nation. For over a century anthropologists have been seeking to impose their concept of race on political opinion, but with no result ; the old opinion prevails—namely, that a folk or a nation, no matter what its physical characters may be, if animated by a sense of difference, is a race. It so happened in the late sixties of the nineteenth century, when Huxley was devoting his attention to anthropological problems, that the people of Ireland were demanding separation from England on the ground of a difference in race ; they were a Celtic people, whereas the English were Saxons. Huxley, having noted that both peoples were mixtures of the same physical types, came to the conclusion that the Irish claim was without foundation. " If what I have to say in a matter of science," he declared, " weighs with any man who has political power, I ask him to believe that the arguments about the difference between Anglo-Saxons and Celts are a mere sham and delusion." [13] It never occurred to Huxley that he was using the term " race " in one sense, the Irish in quite another.

Such was the case. The Irish based their claims for separation, not on any physical difference, but on a difference of tradition and outlook. They were animated by what one may call the " race-making " instinct, which ultimately led (1922) the greater part of the people of Ireland to secede from the fraternity of British nations and to set out alone to work out an evolutionary destiny.

From what I have written my readers may have received the impression that I undervalue the labours of the physical anthropologist. That is very far from being the case ; I prize the vast treasuries of anthropological fact they have gleaned from the peoples of all the world. But I do think it a matter of urgency that they should give up the use of the term " race " to designate a people that is marked off from all others by colour, hair, features of face, and head-form, and revert to the term used by the founders of physical anthropology—namely, sub-species or variety.

When I took up the study of anthropology in the nineties of last century, I was an ardent follower of Huxley and was convinced that the right meaning to attach to race was the one he attached. My doubts were awakened about 1914 when I began my inquiries into the origin of the chief varieties—or, to use Huxley's words, "the easily distinguishable persistent modifications"—of mankind. No matter which of these great divisions I chose to study, when I went to their homeland I found them broken up into competing units. These units may be only a local group, or a tribe of varying size, or a nation, but all of them are separate breeding units, actively engaged in the production of that particular variety of mankind of which they form part. To these elements of evolving humanity Shirokogoroff[14] gave the name of "ethnic unit"; my name for them is "evolutionary unit"; the name given to such a unit, according to English usage, is "race." It was then that I realized that a race was a real live thing and that we should never come by an understanding of the problems of human evolution until we had restored the term "race" to its original meaning. It is the rivalry, competition, and conflict between these evolutionary units or races which keep the world in a continual state of turmoil.

In my youth we had in Aberdeenshire a celebrated breed or variety of shorthorn cattle; it was distinguishable at sight, and might, therefore, be called a "race" in the Huxleyan sense of that term. Where, then, were the representatives of "race" in my sense of the term? They were the score of pedigreed herds, each sheltered, tended, and segregated in farms scattered over a wide area of country. Although all the herds were of one breed, yet they differed in being composed of varying strains or lines. Each owner or farmer sought to improve his herd by emphasizing this point or that; or he might introduce fresh blood to secure this end; he aimed at making his herd superior to those of his fellow-breeders. In this sense we may say there was rivalry and competition between the herds. The collective result of all these efforts at race-making in the various farms was the production of a distinctive variety of ox—the Aberdeenshire shorthorn. Now, the essential and vital element in bringing about this result was the herd; it is the evolutionary unit and corresponds to "race" in the breeding machinery of mankind.

For many a year, and never more than at the present time, geneticists and historians have proclaimed aloud that "pure" races no longer exist in the world and that all peoples are of mongrel origin. Let us look into this problem. Karl Pearson was in the right when he claimed that " the purest race is the one which has been longest isolated, inbred, and selected for the longest period." The local groups—the lineages—into which mankind was divided in the springtime of the world may be regarded as " pure " races, but even in their case lines were broken when a local group flourished, divided into new groups, which as they spread abroad absorbed members of neighbouring groups. The strangers so absorbed were of the same local breed as the host group; the genes which the host group added to its circulation were of a similar coinage to its own. From the very beginning the local group or race had this power of incorporating and assimilating fresh genes. As evolutionary units increased in size, passing from a tribal to a national stage, this power of assimilation was practised in ever-widening circles, but the fresh genes incorporated were always those of the same wide area and of nearly the same genetic origin. It is true that there exist in the world true mongrel or hybrid peoples—that is to say, peoples compounded out of two diverse *varieties* of mankind. The progeny of such unions differs physically from both paternal and maternal stocks and is recognizably different. But the degree of mongrelization met with in Europe is of a more limited kind. Celt cannot be distinguished from Saxon by physical marks; when they interbreed the mongrel progeny cannot be distinguished from that which claims to be pure Celt or pure Saxon. In dealing with the origin of the Scottish nation, I touched on all the " racial " elements which went to its composition. With the exception of the beaker people all were of the same physical type; all were of the West European breed. In my own estimation the inhabitants of the British Isles are, in their physical appearance, the most homogeneous and least mongrel-like of all the peoples or nationalities of Europe. In this opinion I have the support of an expert and impartial witness—Professor Hooton of Harvard. He has expressed his opinion thus: " Within the British Isles, for example, several different white races and subraces have inbred since the Norman conquest without any vast increment of foreign blood. The result is a comparative physical homogeneity that almost justifies the statement that a British ' race ' or sub-race is in process of formation." [15]

I have been discussing the twofold use of the term " race," first

as meaning a " variety " of mankind, and, secondly, as the designation of a " race-making " community, or, in the original meaning
of the word, a race, in order that I might answer the question:
" Is a nation a race in the latter meaning of the word? " I
answer most definitely that it is.   A nation is the lineal successor of
the original evolutionary unit—the local group.   But is a nation
a race-making or *raciogenic* unit?   Here I again cite Professor
Hooton as a witness.   According to him, isolation and inbreeding
" constitute the most potent race-making complex." [16]   Both of
these factors are operative in a nation.

Walter Bagehot [17] was greatly puzzled about the relation of
" nation-making " to " race-making "; he used race as a name
for a distinctive variety of mankind.   Everywhere he found
nation-making at work, but nowhere could he find evidence of
a people assuming a new and distinctive appearance.   That was
because he had not looked at a nation long enough to mark the
physical changes which do ultimately come into existence.   So
far I have dealt with the origin of only two nations, those of
Eygpt and of Scotland.   Egypt is the oldest of nations; Scotland
one of the more recent.   Are the Egyptians more sharply differentiated from neighbouring peoples than the Scottish are from
neighbouring nations?   Undoubtedly they are.   While spending
the winter 1930–1 in Egypt I devoted myself to the study of the
external markings of the natives, for I was then, and still am, of
opinion that as an instrument for " racial " discrimination the
expert eye is a far more trustworthy guide than any form of
measuring callipers.   I also took every opportunity of examining
all neighbouring peoples—Arabs, Syrians, Libyans, Turks, and
Greeks.   Before leaving Egypt a particularly favourable opportunity gave me a chance of putting my experience to a test.   Just
before the arrival of the Queen of the Belgians in Cairo, regiments
in a uniform not unlike that of British soldiers and drawn mostly
from Lower Egypt were stationed along the lines of approach.
I passed along the lines of standing men, noting mentally those
who were not distinctively Egyptians in appearance, but might
be confused with other Mediterranean peoples.   I found that
ninety per cent of the soldiers were distinctively of Egyptian
appearance.   The Egyptian nation, then, could claim to be a race
in both senses of that term ; race-making had nearly succeeded in
transforming it into a distinctive *variety* of mankind.

Y

I am familiar with the Scottish physiognomy and have had many opportunities of testing my ability to recognize it in mixed regiments and in mixed assemblies. My experience has taught me that not more than five per cent of the Scots can be discriminated by their features of face and traits of body. The Scottish nation is only a little above zero in the process of physical differentiation. Those who know Sweden hold that fully fifteen per cent of the population is recognizably different from any to be found in other populations of Europe. The people of Sweden are thus on the way to becoming a distinctive variety of mankind; they can claim to be a race in both senses of that term.

" Varieties," wrote Darwin,[18] " are species in the course of formation." The same may be said of nations in a lower degree; they are varieties in the process of formation.

REFERENCES

[1] Oakesmith, John, *Race and Nationality*, 1919.

[2] Keith, Sir A., *Race and Nationality from an Anthropologist's Point of View*, 1919.

[3] Fleure, H. J., *Bull. John Rylands's Library*, 1940, vol. 24, p. 234.

[4] Bagehot, Walter, *Physics and Politics*, ed., 1896, p. 70.

[5] *The Shorter Oxford English Dictionary* gives " race " (1581) as meaning " A tribe, nation or people regarded as of common stock." *Webster's Dictionary* as " A family, tribe, people or nation believed, or presumed, to belong to the same stock; a lineage; a breed."

[6] For the restriction of " race " to a group structurally differentiated, see: Topinard, Paul, *L'Homme dans la Nature*, 1891, p. 24; Prichard, J. C., *Researches into the Physical History of Mankind*, 4th ed., 1851, vol. 1, pp. 105–9.

[7] Huxley, T. H., *Collected Essays*, vol. 6, p. 245.

[8] Lawrence, William, *Lectures on Physiology, Zoology and the Natural History of Man*, 6th ed., 1834.

[9] Topinard, P., see under reference 6.

[10] Prichard, J. C., see under reference 6.

[11] See under reference 6.

[12] Huxley, T. H., " On the Methods and Results of Ethnology " (1865), included in his *Collected Essays*, vol. 7, p. 209.

[13] Huxley, T. H., " Forefathers and Forerunners of the British People," *Anthrop. Rev.*, 1870, vol. 8, p. 197.

[14] Shirokogoroff, S. M., *Social Organization of the Northern Tungus*, Shanghai, 1929, p. 7.

[15] Hooton, E. A., *Twilight of Man*, 1939, p. 188.

[16] *Ibid.*, p. 67.

[17] Bagehot, W., *Physics and Politics*, 1896, pp. 106, 112, 136.

[18] Darwin, Charles, *Origin of Species*, 6th ed., 1885, p. 105.

THE PEOPLES AND RACES OF EUROPE

Synopsis.—Latham's classification of the peoples of Europe. The taxinomic value of speech. Ripley's Races of Europe. The merits and demerits of Ripley's system. Latham saw uniformity in the population of Europe; Ripley, diversity. Diversity is of two kinds. The face as an index of race. Dr. Coon's classification of Europeans. The author's conception of the racial composition of the population of Europe. The nations of Europe represent its races. The first or Palæolithic colonization of Europe by Caucasians. The population of Europe in late Palæolithic times; its organization. The second or Neolithic settlement of Europe by Caucasians. The number of separate communities in Neolithic Europe. The Palæolithic settlers may have been absorbed by the Neolithic peoples. The size of communities in the last century of the pre-Christian era in Gaul and other lands of Western Europe. The rise of national units. Nations have all the attributes of "evolutionary units" and are the lineal representatives of such units. Nations are races in the original meaning of that term. The merits and demerits of large evolutionary units. The relationship of evolutionary units to fully differentiated varieties or races of mankind.

NEARLY a century ago an observant and erudite Englishman, Robert Gordon Latham (1812–88), published a short treatise [1] on the peoples of Europe and said this of them: " In no part of the world do the differences between the varieties of the human species lie within narrower limits than in Europe." In his survey he passes from people to people, classifying them into " stocks " according to their speech. His " Slavonic stock," for example, included the Great Russians, Little Russians (Ukranians), White Russians, Bulgarians, Serbians, Bosnians, Croatians, Carinthians, Poles, Czechs, and Slovaks. He noted that the Slavs occupied more than half the continent of Europe, and in his census [2] gives their collective number as 78·6 millions. If Latham had been

alive now (1946), he would have found that his Slav stock had
expanded and consolidated its territories and increased its numbers from 78·6 millions to over 200 millions, thus forming almost
forty per cent of the total population of Europe.   Another of
Latham's main divisions of Europeans was the "Great Gothic or
Germanic Stock," which included the various peoples of Germany,
the Scandinavians, the Danes, the Dutch, Frisians, and Anglo-
Saxons.   "As a general rule," he wrote, "the Germanic or
Gothic stock has not only held its own area but has encroached
on that of others . . . the converse rarely, if ever, can be shown
to have taken place."   I cite this passage because it reveals
Latham's interest in the rise and fall of peoples—a matter of the
highest importance to students of human evolution.   His two
other main stocks were the "Keltic" and the Greco-Latin of Italy.
Thus Latham's classification of the peoples of Europe was based
on language—a system which is now rejected by all modern
anthropologists.   This will seem strange to all who are familiar
with the fact that the chief bond of every living community is its
speech;   a people who live together, marry together, and speak
the same tongue become a single people, however diverse their
ancestry may be.   It is by their tongue that we trace the diverse
Slavonic peoples back to a common origin;   new peoples and
tongues evolve hand in hand.   Those who refuse to consider
language as a factor in the classification of peoples point to the
absurd position which would arise if an African tribe were to
adopt a European speech;   it might then be mistaken for a tribe
of Europeans !   The danger of such a mistake, I am sure, is more
imaginary than real.

In 1900 the American anthropologist W. Z. Ripley published a
work [3] which introduced a new era in the discrimination of race
in Europe.   He held that human beings must be classified by the
methods applied to all living animals.   Europeans, therefore,
must be grouped according to their physical characteristics, such
as head-form, colouring, stature, etc.   He spoke of "the fusing
heat of nationality," but held it had nothing to do with "race."
He therefore rejected from his scheme of classification nationality,
language, culture, and custom.   For him there are but three races
in Europe;   there is a blond, long-headed race in the lands round
the Baltic, which he named the Teutonic;   another, long-headed
and dark-haired, occupies the lands round the Mediterranean,

forming the " Mediterranean " race; separating these northern and southern races is a third to which he gave the name " Alpine," this race being mainly centred on the Alps. The Alpines are distinguished by the roundness of their heads—their brachycephaly; in colouring they are, in the main, intermediate to the two other races.

Ripley's scheme has the great merit of simplicity; it is also in accordance with fact, for there can be no question that there is a great blond area of population in the north-west of Europe, and an even more extensive area of deeply pigmented peoples in the south, with an intermediate zone separating these two extremes. There is, however, one fatal objection to his system—it does not work. A perfect classification is one which provides a niche for everybody; this is what Ripley's scheme fails to do. For example, Ammon [4] measured 1,000 Alpine individuals, but failed to find a " pure " specimen; Matiegka [5] examined 102 gymnasts drawn from various quarters of Europe and could assign only eighteen of them to Ripley's categories; in the blondest part of Sweden Retzius [6] found only eighteen per cent of individuals who gave a full display of Nordic or Teutonic characters. Of the many thousands of Europeans measured by Professor Hooton [7] in the United States of America, only one man in ten was assignable to one or other of Ripley's three races. This difficulty in assignation has been attributed to a mixing of the three primary races in recent times. But the idea that in a past age Ripley's three races existed in a separate and pure state is unsupported by evidence. Indeed, as I construe the evidence, Ripley's three areas of differentiation are only now coming into existence and are more distinct to-day than they have been in any previous age.

It is of interest to contrast the general impression which Ripley carried away from his study of the peoples of Europe with that of Latham. Latham, as we have seen, was struck by their physical homogeneity; Ripley, on the other hand, was impressed by their diversity. Here is his statement: " No continental group of human beings, with greater diversities or extremes of physical type exists." How did two men come to such opposite conclusions regarding the racial characters of Europeans? My own experience throws some light on the matter. When I first lived among Chinese I was struck by their similarity; as I studied them I became aware of their individual diversity. Latham was impressed by the racial similarity of Europeans; if met with in Africa, in Eastern Asia, or in Australasia, the European is recognized as different at sight; the only peoples with which he may be confused are his Caucasian cousins of Western Asia. Ripley, on the contrary, was struck by the individual differences. He seemed to forget that every birth produces a unique individual— one which has no exact counterpart among the 2,000 millions that make up the world's population; one which is different from the millions who have gone before or who will come after. The face is our chief means of identification: the human face lends itself to this purpose because of its variability. Yet, with all its variability the face retains what may be called its "racial mask." In identifying the races of Europe Ripley attached the highest importance to the form of head but rejected the evidence of the face. I, on the other hand, regard the characters of the face as the safest guide in the discrimination of one race or variety of mankind from another.

Both before Ripley and after him many racial classifications have been proposed for Europe, but it is not necessary for me to discuss them as they have been summarized in a standard treatise recently published by Dr. Coon. [8] From a close study of this treatise one is made to realize what a complex business the discrimination of race in Europe has become in the hands of modern anthropologists. In the racial map of Europe compiled by Dr. Coon, Ripley's simple conception of three main races is replaced by one which involves the recognition of twelve chief racial types and of six subsidiary ones besides three others, making twenty-one forms in all. Some of these are local; some are spread over wide areas where they are mixed with other types. Practically all these types are regarded as of hybrid origin, resulting from the union of two or more races which had previously existed in a separate state. A European race, according to Dr. Coon, is "a compositie amalgamation of peoples thrown together by the accident of geography and blended into some semblance of homogeneity." [9] Our author has one great merit; although, like Ripley, he does not permit nationality or language to enter into his scheme of classification, he recognizes to the full that in deciding the racial composition of any given nation or people the history of that people and the archæological evidence of their land must be given a position of the highest importance. Here we have a welcome return to the method of Prichard and of Latham.

Having given a brief account of what may be described as the orthodox conception of the racial divisions of the peoples of Europe, I now propose to give a concise exposition of my own conception—heterodox, I admit in the meantime, but which I am persuaded will yet be accepted as orthodox. In the preceding essay I have drawn attention to the confusion which has arisen from the application of the term " race," first, to a race-making group, and second, to a people distinguishable from all other peoples because of their physical characters. The authors whom I have just cited use the term in the second sense—that of a differentiated people—whereas, in the remaining part of this essay I shall speak of differentiated groups as " varieties " and use the term " race " for the smaller groups in which differentiation is being effected. Using the term " race " in the sense just defined, my object will be to prove that the only live races in Europe now are its nationalities and that these are the lineal successors of the evolutionary units of ancient times—of the local group and of the tribe.

The colonization of Europe by groups representing the Caucasian variety of mankind began in a phase of the last Ice Age, between 60,000 and 70,000 years ago. As outlined in a previous essay (XXVI), the Caucasians were probably evolved in Western Asia and entered Europe as separate bands over a long period of time. These intruding bands found Europe sparsely occupied by a distinctive variety of mankind, the Neanderthalians, a type which perished soon after the arrival of the colonists. The physical differences between the native Neanderthalians and the intruding Caucasians were greater than those which separate the European colonists of to-day in Australia from the aborigines of that continent. They were differences instantly recognizable at sight. Hybridization between the natives and colonists of ancient Europe may have occurred, but so far not a fossil trace of it has been found; the fossil skulls found in the Palæolithic deposits of Europe prove to be unmistakably Neanderthalian or decidedly Caucasian. Long before the end of the Pleistocene period the Caucasian vanguard had reached Western Europe. Their fossil remains have been found in the caves of England, of Belgium, of France, of Spain, and of Central and South Germany.

They also lived in the open country, as did the horse-hunters of Solutré in France and the mammoth-hunters in Moravia. All were dependent on the natural produce of the lands they entered and occupied; they knew nothing of agriculture. Seeing that the Caucasians of Palæolithic times occupied the greater part of Europe for many thousands of years, it is surprising that we have found the fossil remains of so few of them; not more than one hundred have come to light. All are cast in the Caucasian mould, but there were distinctive local varieties, or—in my sense of the term—races. The physical type which prevailed among the hunters of Moravia differed from that which characterized the Cro-Magnon people of France.[10] It is worthy of note that the Causcasian pioneers were a big-brained folk.

In Essay III I have stated the grounds on which we assume that primal mankind everywhere and at all times was divided into small, isolated, inbreeding groups, each local group or " evolutionary unit " living on a demarcated territory which it claimed as its own. We assume, then, that the Caucasian pioneers of Europe were so divided and that each group as it advanced westwards and northwards into new lands marked out its territory. A group which prospered and increased in numbers would in due time throw off a new group to continue the westward drive. The westward movement must have been attended by competition between groups, certain of them being favoured and selected; the groups which ultimately reached the limits of occupation in the west and in the north would have been subjected to the greatest degree of selection. I shall assume that saturation point in density of population had been reached towards the end of the Palæolithic period. What would the total population of Europe have been at this point? Seeing that so much of Europe was closely forested and that there were wide areas of barren heathland, we dare not hazard a higher estimate than that of one person to each ten square miles of territory. For the purpose of our calculation we may take the total area of Europe as four million square miles, which, allowing ten square miles for each man, woman, or child, gives a total population of only 400,000. If we make the further assumption that each local group, taking one with another, had fifty members, then the total number of " evolutionary units " in Europe would have been of the order of 8000, each occupying a territory which, on an average, would amount to

500 square miles. However problematical these estimates may be, they do compel us to realize the conditions under which evolution was carried on in Europe of Palæolithic times.

The colonization of Europe just dealt with was the first or Palæolithic settlement of Europe by people of the Caucasian stock. The movement we have now to consider is the second or Neolithic settlement of Europe by Caucasians, infinitely more important than the first, for it gave Europe the basis of its present population. We have seen (p. 283) that early in the fourth millennium the Caucasian natives of the Iranian plateau were practising agriculture, building villages, and rapidly multiplying in numbers. It was this Iranian advance in the mode of living which sent the second or Neolithic colonists moving westwards in search of new lands to till. The new emigrant bands were grouped in tribal village-building communities. By the beginning of the third millennium they were on the fertile lands of south Russia, in the lower valley of the Danube, in the Balkans, and in Crete. Their new settlements were effected on the hunting territories of their Palæolithic predecessors. No doubt they had to fight their way westwards. Following diverse routes the Neolithic colonists succeeded in the course of five centuries in carrying their mode of life to the western and northern shores of the continent The picture of life among the early Slav peoples, drawn by Gibbon,[11] may be applied to the Neolithic colonists of Europe, as well as to their successors of later periods. " Four thousand six hundred villages," wrote Gibbon, " were scattered over the provinces of Russia and Poland. . . . Their huts were hastily built of rough timber in the depths of forest or on river bank. Each tribe or village existed as a separate republic." Thus there were, on the authority of a record quoted by Gibbon, 4,600 " evolutionary units " in the eastern half of Europe, and there was probably an equal number in the western half of the continent. Europe was then a moving mosaic of " parish races." By the middle of the first millennium B.C. the population of Europe had so increased that the movements of peoples which, in the preceding millennia had been towards the north and west, now turned in a southerly and easterly direction.

How far the Neolithic colonists absorbed their Palæolithic predecessors is a moot point. Hunting and pastoral peoples are difficult to convert to an agricultural way of life. Native peoples perished before the advancing colonists of Australia and of the United States. In these cases colonists and natives were members of contrasted varieties of mankind, but in Europe they were of the same great stock; if there were intermarriages, the progeny would be indistinguishable from either parent stock.

When the light of history breaks upon Europe in the last century of the pre-Christian era, enormous changes are found to have taken place in the number and size of its evolutionary units. Let us consider first the state of matters in France—in ancient Gaul. In this area of Europe some 400 tribes or sub-tribes had become grouped so as to form about sixty independent States [12] —each representing an evolutionary unit. The size of such units varied from fifty thousand to two hundred thousand individuals. The same process of fusion of local groups into tribes and tribes into " independent States " or nations was taking place all over Western and Central Europe. Gibbon gives the number of independent peoples in Britain as thirty: in Ireland tribal fusion had given that island about sixteen separate peoples ; the numerous tribes of ancient Germany had become united so as to form about forty units, many of them large and composite. When the Romans entered on the conquest of Spain (133 B.C.), they found the population of that country divided into thirty-five independent tribes. Even as late as the twelfth century A.D. sixty-four " sovereignties " were recognized in ancient Russia. By the dawn of the Christian era the population of Europe, estimated to have been less than half a million in Palæolithic times and divided into many thousands of small units, had increased in numbers to some sixty millions, but the number of independent territorial units had become reduced from thousands to a few hundreds.

We come now to the consideration of the latest type of evolutionary unit—that known in modern times as a nation. With the collapse of Roman rule in the west and the vain attempts of Charlemagne and of the Austrian crown to establish a permanent form of imperial rule, the old process of fusion of local populations to form larger units reasserted itself. In France, for example, a congeries of dukedoms, princedoms, and kingdoms came into existence. These became united under one crown; and with the addition of Burgundy the territorial limits of France were completed. It is one thing to establish a frontier; it is quite a different and more protracted thing to break down the old local allegiances and to bring about their fusion so that all the people within a territory become imbued with a common national spirit. The democratic spirit which swept through France in the closing decade of the eighteenth century speeded up the process of nationalization in that country. The union of Spain may be dated to 1474, when Ferdinand of Aragon married Isabella of Castile, but even to-day the Catalonians and the Asturians (Basques) are still dominated by a separatist spirit. England was put on the way to unity in the eleventh century by William of Normandy; she was the first modern country in Europe to attain nationhood. Holland arose early in the seventeenth century by the union of seven provinces. Early in the nineteenth century Germany was still divided into thirty-eight independent States; in 1933 Hitler, by means of force and flattery, brought all under a single government. When Italy was given unity in the nineteenth century, her statesman Cavour said " We have made Italy . . . now make Italians."

It is a noteworthy fact that the peoples who led the way in nation-building were those of Western Europe; the peoples of Eastern Europe lagged behind. Indeed, in two countries, in Albania and in Montenegro, a tribal organization still continues. The Balkan Peninsula was settled by Slav peoples by a species of tribal permeation which led, in a country like Macedonia, to an intermingling of Serb, Bulgar, and Greek communities, the particularist spirit of each frustrating all attempts at a national union.

To-day the whole of Europe is sharply demarcated into twenty-six national territories, some of them small, others very large. Each territory is inhabited by a population which claims to be separate and different from all neighbouring populations; all claim to be independent sovereign States and responsible for their own evolutionary destiny. All are prepared to sacrifice life to secure their sovereignty. Some of these twenty-six national territories are occupied, not by a single nation, as are those of Sweden, Norway, Denmark, and Holland, but by a confederation of nations. Such is the case in the British Isles where there are five nations; in Belgium there are two, in Switzerland four, in Czecho-Slovakia two, in European Russia three, in Jugo-Slavia six. Thus the population of Europe, now estimated at 530 millions, is divided into some fifty nationalities.

Do these nationalities represent race-making units? Are they races in the original sense of that term? Before giving my reasons for answering both the questions in the affirmative, let me recall the manner in which human evolution has been carried on in the past and is being carried on in the present. All advances have been made by the process of race-building. In primal times the race-building or evolutionary unit was represented by a small local group; each group was in active or passive competition with neighbouring groups. As time went on the competing groups grew ever larger; with the introduction of agriculture they became large communities; with the coming of industries they became national in size. Thus the nation of to-day is the lineal representative of the local group of Palæolithic times; nations are now the race-making units of Europe. They are not only the lineal descendants of ancient evolutionary units; they have retained all the mental dispositions of these units. They live in separate territories to which they have a particular affection. They are animated by the same group or national consciousness ; they have an aversion to neighbouring national units; threats to their welfare or to their security evoke a passionate reaction; they are inbreeding communities. For all those reasons I hold that the nations of Europe are race-making units or races in the original sense of that term. Evolution in Europe is being carried on by co-operation within national groups, and by competition between them; thus Europe is in a continuous state of turmoil.

Is the division of a population into large nations an effective way of bringing about profitable evolutionary changes? Large units have certain evolutionary advantages and also several grave disadvantages. The ancient small inbreeding units gave quick and effective results. If the group was blessed with an ample number of good genes, these were frequently mated, and a strongly differentiated community was speedily produced. If, on the other hand, it was cursed by evil or recessive genes, these, too, were soon mated, and the strength of the group undone. In large freely intermarrying communities local communities, with their good or their bad genes, tend to be broken up and to become scattered in the general population, so that there is less chance of the good genes meeting with the good or of the bad with the bad.[13] The rate of evolution in large units is thus slowed down and made less determinate in its results. Nevertheless, in spite of free intermarriage in large nations, local race production still goes on. In all the countries of Europe which have been fully investigated highly differentiated local groups or populations have been found. Professor Fleure found them in his survey of Wales,[14] Bryn in his elaborate anthropological census of Norway;[15] they have been observed in Germany and in Sweden; even in the great new American nation of the United States.[16]

One important matter still remains for consideration. What is the relationship of race-making units to the partially differentiated varieties of Europeans? If we except those of Mongolian affinities there is no European people in which every individual is so characterized as to be recognizable at sight. Let us take first the southern Europeans which make up the Mediterranean variety or race of Ripley. In Neolithic times the population of South Europe was broken up into scores of local units or tribes, each of which included men and women who had the Mediterranean characters developed to a greater or lesser degree. These tribes were the race-making units; their collective result was the production of a regional variety or type—the Mediterranean type. That type is now being fostered and its potentialities exploited by the nationalities of Spain, of Southern France, of Italy, of Greece, and in the Balkans. In a similar manner Ripley's Alpine and Nordic varieties or races were brought into being by the collective working of numerous small, local groups and tribes. With the rise of nations these local groups were absorbed into national units and, as members of these units, continue their race-making tendencies. Nations are the racio-genic units of Europe.

REFERENCES

[1] Latham, R. G., *The Ethnology of Europe*, 1852.
[2] Latham, R. G., *Descriptive Ethnology*, 1859, vol. 2, p. 18.
[3] Ripley, W. Z., *The Races of Europe*, 1900.
[4] Ammon, O., quoted by F. H. Hankins in *The Racial Basis of Civilization*, 1926, p. 269.
[5] Matiegka, J., *Die Gleichwertigkeit der Europaeschen Rassen*, 1939, p. 59.
[6] Retzius, G., *Jour. Roy. Anthrop. Inst.*, 1909, vol. 39, p. 377.
[7] Hooton, E. A., *Twilight of Man*, 1939, p. 202.
[8] Coon, C. S., *The Races of Europe*, 1939.
[9] *Ibid.*, p. 279.
[10] Keith, Sir A., *The Antiquity of Man*, 1925, vol. 1.
[11] Gibbon, E., *Decline and Fall*, ch. XLII.

[12] Hume, D., *Essays and Treatises*, 1772, vol. I, p. 391; Hubert, H., *The Greatness and Decline of the Celts*, 1934.

[13] Dahlberg, G., *Race, Reason, and Rubbish*, 1942, p. 186.

[14] Fleure, H. J., and James, T. C., *Jour. Roy. Anthrop. Inst.*, 1916, vol. 46, p. 35.

[15] Bryn, H., and Schreiner, A. E., *Die Somatologie der Norweger*, 1929.

[16] Hooton, E. A., *Twilight of Man*, 1939, p. 211.

NATIONALISM AS A FACTOR IN HUMAN EVOLUTION

Synopsis.—The subjects to be dealt with are outlined. Nationalism is an emotional manifestation. A nation is more than a mere political or cultural unit. Nationalism exemplified by the case of Wales. The Welsh Nationalist Party. Welsh nationalism is more than political. The Welsh nation was brought into existence by a long chain of events. Nationalism is not dependent on sovereignty. Politics as the handmaid of evolution. Nationalism is a manifestation of the ancient group-spirit. The Welsh nation is more than a cultural unit. Evidence of race-building in Wales. Assimilation as a factor in the building of nations and races. Nationalism has a greater persuasive force than economics. Underlying nationalism is the fear of absorption. Nationalists are unconscious of the ultimate effects of their policies. Adam Smith's account of the origin and purpose of nation-formation. Race-formation is the essential factor in human evolution. Creation and evolution homologated. Nationalism may remain dormant. The cosmopolitan mind. The power of nationalism. Its area of activities must be circumscribed. The exaggerated forms of nationalism and the hatred which attends them. National sovereignty.

THE contention put forward in the two preceding essays—namely, that a nation is a race in the original meaning of that term—has met with a hostile reception from the vast majority of my anthropological colleagues. Some of them object on the ground that a nation is a man-made community or political unit,[1] whereas a race is a natural creation. Others hold that a nation is merely a large social group or community which has been separated from other groups or nations by a difference of language, a difference of tradition, of custom and of education, and has therefore no biological or evolutionary significance.[2] These objections I shall consider now. I shall also raise and discuss certain pregnant matters which were merely glanced at in the preceding essays.

If nations are simply " political units " or " cultural units," why is national life attended by manifestations of that great galaxy of emotions, feelings, and modes of behaviour which make up collectively the potent force known as nationalism? Why are all the crises in national life attended by displays of fervour and of passion? " Nationalism," said the historian A. J. Toynbee,[3] " is concerned with the life and death affairs of nations." All the processes concerned in human evolution are attended by highly charged emotions and often bellicose behaviour. A political or cultural interpretation of a nation leaves nationalism unexplained, but if my contention is accepted and a nation is regarded as an " evolutionary unit " or race, then national mentality and national behaviour fall into place in my scheme of evolution.

It so happened that on the day this essay was begun (October 28th, 1946) there was a lively exhibition of nationalism in the House of Commons. The Welsh members of Parliament were given a special opportunity to discuss the affairs of Wales. Instead, therefore, of considering in the abstract the matters specified in the preceding paragraph, let us examine them in the concrete, illustrating them by examples provided by the national consciousness of the people of Wales. In the change-over from a war-time to a peace-time economy, unemployment had become rife in Wales. The Welsh party criticized the generous plans for the restoration of prosperity put forward by the spokesman of the Government. He was told that "Wales was united in favour of a direct executive control of her own affairs." " English legislation," he was informed, " was unsuitable for peculiar Welsh conditions." " They were a people with a living language of their own, with a long history and with their own way of life." " The Welsh Nationalist Party," said the representative of the University of Wales, " is growing from day to day and is drawing in the cream of the Welsh intellectuals." Lady Megan Lloyd George complained that " economic necessity was driving young men and women from Wales and seriously weakening the stamina of the nation."

The debate left the House of Commons in no doubt as to the strength of a national spirit in Wales. The people of Wales are keenly conscious of their separateness and of their difference from other peoples; they are eager to maintain their integrity, and brood over their future as well as over their past.

The following incident will serve to illustrate the nature, and also the strength of the spirit of nationalism in Wales. In 1937 three educated Welshmen, one a clergyman, fired and destroyed an aerodrome which the British Government had established in Carnarvonshire, their plea of justification being that it " endangered the culture and tradition of one of the chief districts of Wales "; its presence was " an immoral violation of the rights of the Welsh nation." When a preliminary inquiry was held in Wales, the crowd outside the court sang " Land of my Fathers." The prisoners were guilty of the crime of arson, but so blinding is the passion of nationalism that no Welsh jury could be trusted to bring in a verdict of guilty against men who had committed crime in a cause with which they themselves were in sympathy. The prisoners were moved to London, tried by an English judge, convicted, and sentenced. The case I have cited is not an isolated instance of the partiality of Welsh juries; Judge MacKinnon,[5] who had a life-long experience of the assize courts of England and Wales, said that: " Only in Wales have I come upon juries who returned perverse judgments." I do not suggest for a moment that the people of Wales deliberately cultivate " crooked justice," but simply that they are the victims or subjects of old-time instinctive urges which, arising below the threshold of consciousness, bias their judgments and actions in favour of their own people and of their own country. A people in the throes of nationalism unconsciously adopts two standards of right and wrong, one for their fellow-nationals and another for all who are outside the field of their activities.

Such, then, are some of the aspects of the national spirit which animates the people of Wales. Can we say that the Welsh nation is merely a political unit—a community held together by force of government? The answer is plainly—No. There has been no deliberate planning in its formation ; the nation has come into existence as a result of a long chain of accidents. Cave man found his way to Wales in Palæolithic times ; Caucasians from the south-west of Europe effected numerous settlements on its coasts in Neolithic and Bronze-Age days ; the Brythonic Celts of England imposed their tongue and customs on its inhabitants in the fourth century B.C. The frontier that marks Wales off from England came into being where Welsh resisters were able to keep Saxon invaders at bay. Edward I (1272–1307) carried the Eng-

z

lish sword, the English tongue, and English barons into Wales. It was King Edward who unified the numerous,[6] discordant, and inter-warring tribes of Wales into a nation ; he gave them a common enemy and a common hatred, and thus a bond of union. At the time of the invasion several large tribal confederacies had already come into existence, that in the north being under the leadership of Llewelyn " openly at the head of their race." [7] John Richard Green records the death of Llewelyn in these words : " With him died the independence of his race." [8] Certainly independence, sovereignty, and freedom to plan are the dearest of all national desires, but Wales is a proof that a national spirit may survive and flourish without being technically a sovereign power. There are no fortifications mantling the frontier which separates Wales from England ; nevertheless it is a real frontier along which the pulsating perfervid spirit of the Welsh meets the unostentatious but resolute nationalism of the English.

The national spirit of Wales is based on something deeper than mere politics, and yet the Welsh nation has been fashioned by politics, and, as we have seen, its representatives in parliament still use political means to secure its national welfare and advancement. Most of my colleagues rigorously exclude politics from the purview of anthropology, but in an earlier essay (XI, p. 95) I warned my readers that I was " to maintain that politics, the art of controlling and regulating the conduct of a community, is part of the machinery of evolution." The case of Wales provides an occasion of unfolding what I had in mind. " The true political spirit," said Gladstone, " is the art of nation-making." [9] To this I may add a statement by a master anthropologist—Paul Topinard—"only peoples are realities." [10] There is a basis of truth in Herbert Spencer's opinion that " politics are never planned ; they are forced by circumstances." [11] Thomas Hobbes was well aware of the uncertainties which attend the application of politics to the life of a nation as illustrated by the following passage :—

> " And because in Deliberation, the Appetites and Aversions are raised by foresight of the good and evil consequences and sequels of the action whereof we deliberate ; the good or evil effect thereof dependeth on the foresight of a long chain of consequences, of which seldom any man is able to see the end."

The reader will note the special role which Hobbes attributes —not to man's reason—but to his "appetites and aversions" in the devising of national policies. Another statement by Hobbes [12] carries us along the path we are following. "He that is to govern a whole nation," he wrote, "must read not this or that particular man, but mankind." Politics, then, must be based on a knowledge of human nature. Burke defined politics as the "management of human nature"; he held, too, "that politics ought to be adjusted, not to human reason only, but to human nature." [13] Now, human nature is particularly sensitive to one thing—the safety or security of its group, tribe, or nation. Nationalism is an active manifestation of human nature; it is instantly roused if its group, tribe, or nation is in danger. The spirit which underlies nationalism, then, is not something new that came with the formation of large evolutionary units, but dates back to that primal period when man became conscious, not only of his individual self, but also of the community of which he formed part. "Politics," Wallas affirmed, "are an exploitation of the subconscious"; [14] it would have been nearer to reality, I think, if he had written: "The subconscious—that is human nature—exploits politics for the welfare and progress of its own group or race." In brief, politics serve now, and always have served, as the handmaid of the evolutionary process.

The preceding paragraph, which I have devoted to the part played by politics in nation-building and, incidentally, to race-building, has carried me away from the straight line of my argument. I have been seeking to prove that a nation, as exemplified by the people of Wales, is much more than a political unit. I have now to look into the opinion held by many of my colleagues —namely, that a nation has nothing to do with race-building, but is simply a population cut off from neighbouring populations by having a different and separate cultural heritage. According to this opinion a nation is simply a "culture group." Will this cultural theory explain the strength and persistence of Welsh nationalism? Let us look into the matter. Take the case of a child born in Wales; it is heir to a certain way of life, to a mode of speech; as it grows up it imitates its elders, copies their habits and customs, absorbs their beliefs, sayings, and outlook; it adopts their likes and dislikes, including their critical attitude to peoples who live in " foreign " parts. As a Welsh lad moves towards manhood the great men of his country, both past and present, become his heroes ; he becomes keenly conscious of his nationality and proud of it. But suppose the parents of this lad had moved into England and that he had been born there. What would have been the result ? He would have inherited and adopted the tradition of England and become indistinguishable from other Englishmen save by the name his parents brought with them from Wales. Let us now take a reverse case—that of an English family which moves into Wales and makes that country its permanent home. The children as they grow up become Welsh; they absorb the tradition of their new home. Nay, they may become ultra-Welsh and become leaders in what is called the Welsh movement. As thus stated, the case of Wales seems a complete justification of those who hold that nations are peoples separated by a difference in culture and tradition.

If such be the true state of the case, then how are we to account for the exuberant national spirit of Wales? Why this keen feeling of being different and separate from all other peoples? Why their partiality for their own people and their own soil— in short, their patriotism? Why this national pride and a sensitiveness to all that relates to the prestige, status, and honour of their country? The vast majority of marriages are between families native to the principality. We cannot explain these manifestations of nationalism in Wales by a theory that regards nations as merely cultural products. For a just solution of our problem we have to go deeper ; we have to regard the people of Wales as an evolutionary unit, as a race-making group. We have seen (Essay XV) that isolation and inbreeding are essential conditions for race-production. A people with its own mode of speech, with its own traditions and customs, tends to be cut off and isolated from surrounding peoples ; a difference in speech and culture, then, accelerates the process of nation-building, but is not the fundamental factor. We have seen (Essay XI, p. 95) how human nature is organized to maintain and perpetuate the isolation between local evolutionary groups by a spirit of antagonism and aversion to neighbouring groups, by practising co-operation and amity within its own ranks ; by being emulative and competitive towards other groups ; by having one code of behaviour for " home affairs " and an opposite code for " foreign affairs." All these traits we meet with in the nationalism manifested by the people of Wales. Nation-building is thus part of the process of human evolution. It is the way by which races are brought into existence. Green, the historian, was in the right when he spoke of the Welsh people as a race.

If a nation is a race-building community, then we should find evidence of it in Wales. In their anthropological survey of the Welsh people, Fleure and James [15] found evidence of local evolution—of districts or areas where the inhabitants were characterized by stature, head-form, and colouring. Some of these local communities, especially those occupying coastal areas, may be, as Professor Fleure thought, expansions or remnants of early settlements of immigrants from France or from Spain. In Merioneth, for example, there is a prevalence of that dark-complexioned, bullet-headed, and robust-bodied Alpine type which forms a noticeable component in the population of Wales. These local " pockets " are being disrupted by the coal and iron industries, which draw the inhabitants of the uplands and of the valleys to meet, mix, and intermarry in the towns and cities of South Wales. We may look on the industrial settlements of the south as national mints, which, having called in the ancient gene-coinage, place it in the melting-pot to be issued as a new gene-currency. In this way industry has become a factor in human evolution, a very powerful factor. There is evidence in Wales then, that nations are race-building communities.

In a preceding paragraph I spoke of the power which a nation has of absorbing and assimilating the youth of another nation. It is the nature of this power we must now look into. Every child born into the world has to learn to walk; with it is born an urge and an aptitude to acquire the art, and this makes the acquisition easy. It is also so with speech ; that has to be learned ; without an inborn aptitude a child would never speak. Even more important, at least for our present purpose, is a third aptitude—the inclination, appetite, or hunger for social intercourse. It is the exercise of this aptitude that makes a child a member of a family and then a member of its community. The power which a nation, or a race, has of assimilating immigrants and of imparting the national tongue, culture, tradition, and spirit to the immigrant young, depends on the presence in childhood of this inborn social aptitude. Without it no assimilation could take place; no new nation could be established. This statement may cause strait-laced anthropologists to lift their eyebrows; because it is just this power to assimilate outside blood which compels them to deny that a nation is a race. I, on the other hand, regard assimilation as a part of the process of race-making. We shall see later that nations take some care in selecting the kind of immigrants they are willing to assimilate.

In the Welsh debate in the House of Commons, mentioned earlier in this essay, it was noticeable that half the members advocated a fuller co-operation with the economic life of England to relieve the industrial distress which had fallen on Wales. The more nationalist of the Welsh members rejected this policy, although it was manifestly to the advantage of Wales to be a participant in the more ample economic resources of England. It is said that "money speaks"; the voice of the nationalist is louder and more powerful than the voice of the economist; national self-sufficiency is preferred to economic gain. This attitude of mind seems unreasonable to the impartial onlooker. How are we to explain it? This is the explanation I have to offer. The nationalist mind is most deeply concerned with the integrity and perpetuation of its race; what is most feared is its death— death by absorption; in the case of Wales absorption by England. In a speech to a Welsh audience, the late Lord Lloyd George claimed that five times as many of the inhabitants of Wales spoke Welsh now as was the case in the time of Edward I. That is true, but he might have added that there were ten times as many English speakers in Wales as in King Edward's reign. There are upwards of two million in Wales; of these ten per cent have only one tongue—Welsh; forty per cent are bilingual, speaking English as well as Welsh; fifty per cent have only one tongue—English. Thus ninety per cent of the people of Wales speak the tongue of England, and speech serves as a carrier of culture. The nationalists of Wales, then, have grounds for fearing the death of their race by absorption—absorption by the larger and more powerful nationality of England.

Were I to suggest to Welsh nationalists that they were engaged on the ancient evolutionary task of race-building, I know that my suggestion would be received with scorn. The feelings which nationalism engenders in their minds—an exalted love for their country, for its people, for its tongue, tradition, music, and song—assures them that they are not engaged on any selfish or mundane purpose. Yet it has to be remembered that the characteristic of an impulsive or instinctive action is that it is done for a purpose of which the doer is unaware. Nationalism belongs to the region of the instinctive. "Tribes and Nations," said McDougall, [16] "work towards ends which no man can foresee." "The national will," wrote Bosanquet, "is unconscious of its ends." "Nations," reported the Church's Conference,[17] "were created by God for the preservation of the heritage of the past ; the nurture and training of successive generations, and the maintenance and improvement of the common life of men." Alongside this account of the duties carried out by nations, let me place the description of nationalism and the origin of nation-building given by Adam Smith in pre-Darwinian days :—

> "We do not love our country merely as a part of the great society of mankind—we love it for its own sake, and independently of any such consideration. That wisdom which contrived the system of the human affections, as well as that of every other part of nature, seems to have judged that the interest of the great society of mankind would be best promoted by directing the principal attention of each individual to that particular portion of it which was most within the sphere both of his abilities and of his understanding." [18]

In both these accounts nations are regarded as divine creations, but it is Adam Smith who gets to the root of the matter, when he traces the machinery of nation-building to " the system of the human affections." Throughout this book my main contention has been that human nature, which is the " system of human affections," has been organized to serve instinctively in the purpose of man's evolution, and that this purpose has been carried out in the past, and is being carried out in the present, by group competing with group. Such groups form races, and it is by way of race-formation that human evolution is advanced. Nor does my conception of nation-building differ so greatly from that held by Adam Smith, or even from that expressed by the Church, as may appear on the surface. For modern biologists are unanimous in regarding the way of evolution as being that of creation.

If we regard a nation as a race-building society, then we can fit nations and nationalism into the evolutionary scheme of creation.

There is one aspect of nationalism I must not omit to mention. In the population of large modern cities it may remain latent until evoked by national crises, such as those which sweep a country in a time of war. The hardest task that educated men and women set themselves is to suppress all mental ties with the country of their birth and, by rising above all such accidental bonds, strive to become stateless citizens of the world. The civilized mind sees a gross injustice in being assigned a nationality by the circumstance of birth. Happily for most of us, the constitution of human nature is such that we are convinced that we have drawn prizes both in our parentage and in the country of our birth.

It is not necessary for me to consider here the merits and demerits, the good and evil aspects, of nationalism; they have been subjected to a full analysis recently by a body of experts.[19] As an anthropologist, I am concerned, not with the ethics of nationalism, but only with its potency as an evolutionary agent. In the House of Commons, Mr. Winston Churchill,[20] with his eye on Germany, described nationalism " as the strongest force now at work." Professor Harold Laski, whose outlook is cosmopolitan, has spoken of the " profound and irrational impulses of nationalism," but, at the same time, recognized " the eager spirit of local and functional responsibility." [21] Another aspect of nationalism is that it can work only in circumscribed areas. " Good government," said President Jefferson, " springs from a common interest in public affairs, and such common interest is possible only when the field of activities is circumscribed." The greater the territory the more difficult it is to establish a pervasive spirit of nationalism.

I have been discussing what may be called sane nationalism— the nationalism which springs from the heart, but is controlled by the head. In times of stress nationalism becomes inflamed and turns to hate. " The nearer the neighbour the greater the hate " (Voltaire). " Every nation," observed Lord Kames, " hates its neighbour without knowing why." [22] I mention this hate-component of nationalism now because in the essay which follows I am to discuss " racialism," which also has hate as an accompaniment. Hate, it must be remembered, is a double-edged weapon; it serves to unify and strengthen the energies of a nation at war, but it also serves to isolate that nation from its neighbours. I shall cite only one statement to illustrate the universality with which hate attends on nationality, one by the political philosopher, Walter Bagehot:[23] "Greece, Rome, Judea, were formed apart; quite their strongest common property was their antipathy to men of different race and of different speech." Bagehot marvelled over the universality of international hatred. He did not know that it is an exaggeration or inflammation of the aversion which kept local groups apart in the primal world.

One other manifestation of exaggerated nationalism is seen in the demand made by national communities for an absolute right to determine their respective destinies, free from all outside interference or control—the right of "sovereignty." National sovereignty has wrecked, so far, every attempt to bring all nations under a common world government. This matter I have discussed elsewhere.[24]

REFERENCES

[1] See *Race and Culture*, a Report, issued by the Royal Anthropological Institute and the Institute of Sociology, 1935.

[2] Boas, Franz, *Race, Language and Culture*, 1940.

[3] Toynbee, A. J., *Nationality and War*, 1915.

[4] The passage quoted is taken from a speech made by Lady Megan Lloyd George in the House of Commons and reported in *The Times*, Oct. 18, 1944.

[5] MacKinnon, Judge, *On Circuit*, 1940.

[6] For an account of the Provinces and Tribes of Wales, see Mr. F. A. Brooke's *The Science of Social Development*, 1936, p. 296.

[7] Green, John Richard, *A Short History of the English People*, 1889, p. 165.

[8] *Ibid.*, p. 168.

[9] Gladstone, W. E., quoted by the *Shorter Oxford English Dictionary*.

[10] Topinard, Paul, *Elements d'anthropologie generale*, 1886, p. 207.

[11] Spencer, Herbert, *Principles of Sociology*, vol. 2, p. 394.

[12] Hobbes, Thomas, *Leviathan*, Everyman ed., p. 3.

[13] Hobbes, Thomas, quoted by *Report on Nationalism*, see under reference 19.

[14] Wallas, Graham, *Human Nature in Politics*, 3rd ed., 1929.

[15] Fleure, H. J., and James, T. C., *Jour. Roy. Anthrop. Inst.*, 1916, vol. 46, p. 35.

[16] McDougall, Wm., *The Group Mind*, 1920, p. 6.

[17] For Report of Church Conference see p. 301 of *Nationalism: A Report*, under reference 19.

[18] Smith, Adam, *The Theory of Moral Sentiments*, 1757, pt. 6, sect. 2, ch. II.

[19] *Nationalism : The Report of a Study Group*, 1939.

[20] See *The Times*, April 15, 1933 (when Hitler came to power).

[21] Laski, Harold J., *Nationalism and the Future of Civilization*, 1932, p. 56.

[22] Home, Henry (Lord Kames), *Sketches of the History of Man*, new ed., 1913, vol. 2, p. 23.

[23] Bagehot, Walter, *Physics and Politics*, 1896, p. 204.

[24] Keith, Sir A., *Essays on Human Evolution*, 1946, Essays VIII, XIII.

RACIALISM: ITS NATURE AND ITS PREVALENCE IN SOUTH AFRICA

Synopsis.—*Racialism is akin to nationalism, but can be distinguished from it. Racialism may be homo-ethnic and hetero-ethnic. Racialism may lie dormant as in England. Racial pride and a sense of superiority. The author proposes to use instances from South Africa to illustrate the manifestations of racialism. The extent of the Union of South Africa and the diversity of its population. The problem presented by the presence of Asiatics. The early settlement of the Dutch. The arrival of the British. The attitude of early settlers to native peoples. The Boer treks. The Boer War. The formation of the Union in 1910. Dutch influence reasserts itself more and more in the political and social life of the Union. The antagonistic feeling between Briton and Boer is one of racialism. The nature of racialism examined. The clash in Natal between Indians and British. The love of gain has been fruitful in bringing about the mingling of diverse peoples. Class exclusiveness is of the same nature as racial exclusiveness. Race discrimination. Hybridization as a cure for racialism. Racial fusion in Portuguese East Africa. The aversion to hybridization is acquired. Regarded as an unthinkable solution by the Whites of South Africa.*

IF I am right in regarding nations as races—the thesis maintained in the preceding essay—then the group feeling manifested by a nation—nationalism—must be of the same nature as that manifested by a race—racialism. Such is the theme I am to discuss in this essay; I hope to prove that nationalism and racialism spring from the same mental source. The essential difference between nationalism and racialism concerns territory; nationalism, with the antagonism, or even hatred, which so often accompanies it, is manifested by peoples, each of which lives within its own territory; racialism, with its attendant ill-feeling, is manifested by diverse and racially-minded peoples who live within the same territory. The antagonistic peoples living within the same territory may be of two sorts. They may be so alike in a physical sense that the one opponent cannot be distinguished from the other by sight; or they may be so different in their physical markings that a glance is sufficient to distinguish the one from the other. In the first case marriage between parents of the two opposing peoples gives a progeny which cannot be distinguished from that of " pure " marriages; but in the second case, where parents are of diverse type, marriage results in a progeny which is distinguishably different from either parental type and may be disavowed or ostracized by one, or even by both, of the parental races. In current speech the term racialism is restricted to the discriminatory feelings which arise when clearly differentiated *varieties* of mankind are brought in contact within the same city, or within the same country. It would be convenient to have terms to distinguish these two forms of racialism. We might speak of that which arises between peoples who are alike in a physical sense as homo-ethnic racialism, and that between physically diverse peoples as hetero-ethnic racialism. It is hard to distinguish psychologically between homo-ethnic racialism and nationalism.

Racialism, like nationalism, may lie dormant in a people. The English people at home, for example, receive visitors from abroad, no matter what their colour or features may be, on terms of friendship and equality. Yet when an Englishman goes to live in the midst of a native population, be he ruler or be he trader, he does become conscious of a difference between himself and the people with whom he has to mix. A feeling which had been dormant at home awakes with the impact made on him by his new surroundings. He may be affected also by the spirit of exclusiveness which prevails among his compatriots. It has been said [1] that " natives are leaving Northern Rhodesia for the Belgian Congo to escape from English exclusiveness." Viscount Bryce, a man with a long and intimate experience of peoples and governments, put into words what most English officials feel, but seldom express : " It needs the tenderness of a saint to extend white manners to black compatriots." [2]

Racialism has also another important similarity to nationalism; both are apt to be accompanied by a sense of pride and a feeling of superiority. In its sane form a feeling of ability and power is an asset for any people; a nation with a just and good conceit of itself is a strong nation. It is when national pride grows aggressive and intoxicated that it becomes injurious and dangerous. So it is with racialism; within the bounds of mutual respect it works for good; outside these bounds it works for evil.

In discussing nationalism I placed Wales in the centre of my stage to illustrate its manifestations by giving concrete examples. To study the moods and tenses of racialism I propose to carry my readers to the Union of South Africa. Before beginning our survey, there are certain preliminary matters to be noted. In Wales we had to deal with a population of 2·2 millions; the white population of South Africa numbers little more than that of Wales; the estimate for 1946 is 2·5 millions, but this population is spread over an area nine times that of England and Wales combined. It is a sparsely-occupied country. The Bantu-speaking Negroes are more than three times as numerous as the Whites; they number upwards of seven millions. Most of them still retain their ancient tribal organization and are confined to certain areas which have been allotted to them. Some have taken to town-life, while others are found in small scattered groups throughout the Union. Besides the Bantus there are two other distinctive African races, both of which appear to be the evolutionary products of South Africa—the Bushmen and the Hottentots. It is estimated that only about 6,000 of the Bushmen now survive; the number of Hottentots is estimated at 80,000. A fifth element of the population is represented by the " coloured " people of hybrid origin. In them Hottentot, European, and other strains are mingled. They number about 700,000. Two other distinctive elements in the population of South Africa are of Asiatic origin—the Indians and the Malays. The Malays are few in number and patient in behaviour; the Indians, on the other hand, are assertive and increase in numbers. In the city of Durban, for example, they form almost half of the population, numbering 110,000 against a white population of 120,000.[3] Thus in the total population of the Union of South Africa, numbering upwards of eleven million, *seven distinctive breeds of mankind are brought to live side by side to find, as best they can, a way to a common corporate life.*

When, in 1652, the Dutch East India Company established a victualling station at the Cape for the benefit of their India-bound ships, it had no thought of colonizing the land, much less the intention of founding a nation.[4] Jan van Riebeck, .who had been a ship-surgeon, was placed in charge of the station. Soon there was friction with neighbouring tribes of Hottentots whose pastoral rights were being curtailed. Colonization began in 1671, when sixty-four Dutch burghers and their families arrived. In 1686 the original colonists had added to their number settlers from France (Huguenots) and from West Germany. Inter-marriage with natives was forbidden; Dutch was the language ordained to be taught in schools. Slaves were introduced at an early period. In 1691 the colony had reached the thousand mark; two-thirds were of Dutch origin; the slaves numbered 340. Rather more than a century later, when Britain and Holland were engaged in war against France, the Dutch colony at the Cape had become 14,000 strong and owned 17,000 slaves.

In 1806 the British landed an armed force at the Cape and took possession; annexation to the Empire followed in 1814. It was claimed that " 27,000 colonists had been added to the Crown." These colonists were Dutch peasants or Boers who had conquered and occupied the lands which now form the western part of the Cape Province. They were a stubborn people, with their own brand of nationalism, their own language, their own laws, their own religion, and their own mode of life. In two matters they were adamant; they would brook no interference with their attitude towards native peoples; there must be one law for the Whites, another for the Blacks; and they refused to free their slaves; they regarded slavery as lawful and also necessary.

British immigrants began to arrive in 1817, and this was encouraged by the Government throughout the remaining part of the nineteenth century. English was introduced into the courts; so, too, was English law. Tension between Boer and Briton reached breaking-point in 1834, when the Government ordained that in the eye of the law White and Black were to be on an equal footing; slaves had to be set free. Rather than submit, the more ardently minded Boers treked northwards into the wilds, and ultimately established independent republics in the Transvaal and in the Orange Free State (1852–4). The annexation of Natal in 1848, with the arrival of British settlers there, and also in the eastern coastal areas of Cape Colony, helped to strengthen the British position in South Africa.

The turn of the century brought the Boer War—the second crisis in the relationship of Briton to Boer. The war left the

British Government as the supreme power in South Africa. That power was handed back to the Whites of South Africa when the Union was effected in 1910. From then until the present year (1946) Boer influence has dominated the political field more and more, the British less and less. In 1914 Afrikaans took an equal place with English in schools; in 1925 it was given a similar place in government offices. The census of 1926 returned fifty-seven per cent of the Whites as of Dutch descent and only thirty-four per cent as of British origin.[5] The King's head disappeared from postage stamps; the more ardent of the Boer nationalists have publicly proclaimed their desire to eliminate everything British from public life in South Africa; " British subjects " became " union nationals "; the British Flag and the British national anthem had to be replaced by emblems or symbols more in keeping with Boer feelings; in the list of Governors-General Dutch names replaced those of Englishmen. In the new white nation of South Africa we see, or seem to see, a rebirth of the Boer tradition, of the Boer national spirit with the prospect of the absorption and disappearance of all that is dear to the British heart.

Why should this prospect be viewed with alarm and accompanied by such a depth of feeling and of passion? What name are we to give to the feelings so manifested? If my critics suggest that the right name is "nationalism," I can but agree; nationalism is the feeling which characterizes a nation in the throes of race-making. But it is nationalism being manifested under conditions essentially different from this which we have seen to exist in Wales. In South Africa we have two nations, physically indistinguishable, intermingled, and struggling against each other for survival; nationalism is contending with nationalism within the same territory; the feelings evoked are those connected with race-making and provide the basis of racialism. It is the struggle for survival between two diverse, but intermingled peoples which evokes the feelings known as racialism.

The rational onlooker may say that this fear of absorption on the part of the South African British and death of their nationality in the new Commonwealth is an unworthy and evil prejudice and should be got rid of. Our problem, however, is to explain why this fear should always arise when two intermingled peoples are involved in a contest for survival. And we have to seek for an explanation of this instinctive fear or prejudice in the ingredients which go to the make-up of human nature. The two strongest of man's inborn fears are, first, the fear of individual death; the second is the fear of the extermination or death of his family, his nation, or his race. It is the fear of racial death which evokes the feelings, passions, and antagonisms we call racialism. We have sought to prove that perpetuation or survival is necessary if a group or race is to work out its evolutionary destiny. Racialism, then, is a manifestation of our biased evolutionary mentality. Moralists may be right in declaring that all such prejudices should be consigned to the lumber heap. Here I am not concerned with the moral aspects of such prejudices and fears, but merely with their existence and with the significance which must be attached to them.

By discussing the existence of racialism between peoples which are not separated from each other by colour or by distinctive physical markings, I have prepared the way for the consideration of the clashes which occur in South Africa between peoples who are so separated. The first example of " clash " I am to survey is that which exists between Whites and natives of India. As most of the Hindus are resident in Natal, and are estimated now [6] to number 250,000, it would be more accurate to say that the parties concerned are " Union nationals " of British descent and Indians who are, or were, subjects of the British Crown. The desire of economic gain, by the importation of cheap labour on the part of pioneering generations of Europeans, has been one of the more fruitful causes in bringing about the mingling of diverse peoples. It was the economic motive which brought the Indians to Natal; in 1860 the sugar-planters were in need of labour, and sought for it in India. Contingents of Hindus arrived under contract, but when the period of their indentures had expired, finding Natal a pleasant land, they preferred to make a home there rather than return to India. They were allowed to acquire land and settle down. As they increased in numbers—for their birth-rate is twice that of their white neighbours—alarm began to seize the resident British. The following extract from a communication which appeared in The Times [6] during 1946 will reveal the kind of antagonism which now marks the relation of White-skins to Brown-skins : " So conscious is the European in South Africa of the colour bar that the purchase of a house by an Indian among Europeans causes properties to depreciate." The white nationals of Natal demand that such intrusions should be prohibited by law and that their neighbours from India should be segregated from white communities. The head of the Government of South Africa (General Smuts) favours communal segregation as a solution of racial troubles.

I must turn aside for a moment from the line of my argument to answer a criticism which is certain to be made of the instance just given to illustrate race discrimination. My critics will say that the fall in the value of city property which attends the intrusion of undesirables is an experience with which Europeans are familiar; it springs from class-snobbery, not from racial discrimination. In this I agree, but I would remind my readers that in a previous essay (see p. 92) I have sought to prove that the mental machinery which underlies the formation of class is the same as that concerned in race-building. The instance cited from Natal differs from those which occur in Europe by the classes in Natal being separated by a physical diversity; at birth each is given its racial unchangeable livery.

The Indians in Natal naturally resent the limitations and restrictions imposed on them; they demand full political and social equality; their sense of justice is offended by the existence of two laws—one for the Whites, another for the Browns. Racial discrimination within a people or a nation is attended by many evils; there is the feeling of an enemy in its midst, there is a lack of unity. There is also the working of the Christian conscience which seeks to eliminate the colour bar by intermarriage. Now, intermarriage between Boer and Briton heals many a breach, but intermarriage between Whites and Browns brings into existence a third race, a race of half-castes, whose cruel and miserable position in a community has been so poignantly told by one of them—Cedric Dover.[7] The barrier against marriage is maintained, not by the Indians, but by the British of Natal. The British as a community reject hybridization as a solution of their racial difficulties. Is not their fear of the kind I have already mentioned—the fear that hybridization brings with it the extinction of their race? Racial pride must also be taken into account.

Let us now cross the northern frontier of Natal and enter Portuguese East Africa to learn how racial difficulties have been solved in that land. The Portuguese arrived in this territory more than

▲ ▲

a century before the settlement of the Dutch at the Cape. " No European nation," wrote McCall Theal,[8] " has ever treated Negroes so mildly as the Portuguese, or been so ready to mix with them on equal terms." In the early pioneering times soldiers were encouraged to marry natives. The Portuguese ambassador to the Court of St. James, when speaking in London in 1939, assured his audience that the building up of the Portuguese Empire had been crowned by success because " the assimilation of natives had been a guiding principle."[9] Another constant aim was, and is, " the integration of natives in the national community; the creation in each colony of a homogeneous community. The results, he maintained, justified Portugal in her " abandonment of the prejudice of racialism." Neither the Portuguese nor the Spaniards have ever shown a sensitiveness to race in the governing of colonies; they have been ready to embrace all races with an equal ardour. Now, it is impossible to believe that human nature has one constitution in Portuguese and another in Britons and Boers. Is race prejudice, then, something which is taught, something which is learned and is not instinctive or inborn? We now return to our survey of the Cape peoples in the hope that we may be able to throw light on this important matter.

Let us first consider the case of the " coloured people," now numbering close upon 700,000 and blended intimately in the domestic industries of the Cape Province. This distinctive race began to come into existence in the early days of the Dutch settlement. Robust Europeans, deprived of the companionship of their women, and urged by the imperiousness of one of the most potent of natural appetites, satisfied their lusts by consorting with women of the Hottentot race. From this we learn that the sexual passion, when in distress, is no respector of race; there is no inborn sexual racial discrimination. This loose state of social life came to an end in 1685; the early settlers had been joined by women of their own fraternity; a strong public opinion was established; Dutch–Hottentot marriages were forbidden. Thus the danger of hybridity, which at one time threatened the existence of the Dutch as a race, was removed, not by any inborn racial aversion, but by the establishment of a rigorous and exclusive marital tradition.

In the foregoing paragraph there are a few points which require special emphasis. The sex passion is individual in its activities;

racial exclusiveness is collective in its action; it is a manifestation of the group spirit. Collective opinion secures purity of marriage by ostracizing offenders. Yet I am inclined to suspect that sexual selection and race exclusiveness are not altogether acquired tastes. If the primary races of the world were to be mingled in a country, I would expect that " like would to like." The desire for position or status, both on the part of the individual and of the group, I regard as an inborn predisposition; Dutch communities succeeded in winning a position of superiority in the eyes of the natives of the Cape. The desire for status thus plays a part in the building up of races. Also, I regard the longing which a father has for the perpetuation of his family and of his nation as inborn qualities. I must touch again, too, on the merits and demerits of the progeny which the mating of diverse races or varieties brings into existence. It can hardly be maintained that the hybrid "coloured people" of the Cape are the equals of the Dutch, no matter what standard we apply in our judgment.

We now come to the greatest of all the racial problems which confronts the Government of the Union. There are upwards of seven millions of Bantu Negroes in the Union, three times the number of Whites. The Bantus are strong, vigorous, and able-bodied; they are not devoid of a fighting spirit. As most of them are still confined to tribal areas and are under the government of chiefs, they lack the collective feeling of nationalism, for a manifestation of nationalism becomes possible only when a people has been detribalized and are free to exploit their individual lives. The Black has no inborn antipathy to the White as long as they are kept apart socially. The attempts which have been made by propagandists from without to foment strife between Bantus and Cape Europeans have hitherto failed. But conflict has arisen when Negroes have broken away from their tribal allegiance and made their homes in the poorer quarters of towns and cities. In such locations they are brought in contact with the poorer Whites which make up about ten per cent of the European population. The White regards the close proximity of his Black neighbours as a threat to his status, or perhaps as a challenge to his racial superiority. There is also a sense of rivalry and competition between the members of a poor White community and those of a Negro community which passes into animosity and hatred. No doubt a difference in colour does exacerbate the hatred; but the point I am seeking to make still remains valid; race hatred is not primarily due to difference of colour, but to the clash which arises when two opposed communities are brought into close relation with one another. " It is when natives attempt to assume," Duerden has observed, " an attitude or position of equality with the White that antipathy is engendered and manifested." [10]   From which one is free to infer that the infringement of status takes a big share in racialism, and that antipathy has its origin in the Whites, not in the Blacks. The same authority also assures us that " the whole attitude of the Negro in South Africa towards the white man is one of dependence and receptiveness." [11]

I have quoted from a reliable source the attitude of the Blacks of South Africa to the Whites; I will now quote from an equally reliable source the attitude of Europeans to the native peoples of South Africa.[12] " Natives of South Africa," we are told, " lived under easy climatic conditions; their wants were few . . . *they needed the stimulus which contact with more progressive communities could alone supply.*" The stimulus needed was that of money, markets, and industry, including detribalization. What would have been the state of South Africa if seven millions of Bantus had been detribalized and become distributed throughout the Union? The white man's position in South Africa would have been threatened. The Government of South Africa pursues an opposite policy—one of segregation. Its policy has been epitomized by Evans [13] thus: " To ensure development without clash and without fusion." If all the peoples of South Africa were to pool their genes and bring into being a homogeneous people of mixed origin, their racial antagonisms would vanish. This racial policy which seemed natural to the Portuguese and Spaniards is viewed with horror by the Whites of South Africa. In 1919 the Rev. Dr. W. Flint,[14] in a public address to the people of the Cape, said that " hybridization as a solution was unthinkable in South Africa." Dr. Duerden,[15] two years later, " viewed inbreeding as a solution with an absolute abhorrence." Such, then, are some of the aspects presented by racialism as manifested in South Africa.

REFERENCES

[1] *Nature*, 1926, vol. 116, p. 615.

[2] Bryce, Viscount, *The Relations of the Advanced and Backward Races of Mankind*, (Romanes Lect.), 1902.

[3] *The Times*, Feb. 13, 1946.

[4] Theal, G. McCall, *History and Ethnography of Africa South of the Zambesi*, 3 vols., 1905-7.

[5] Holloway, J. E., *Nature*, 1929, vol. 124, p. 708.

[6] *The Times*, Feb. 13, 1946.

[7] Dover, Cedric, *Half-Caste*, 1937.

[8] See under reference 4, vol. 1, p. 340.

[9] *The Times*, Feb. 2, 1939.

[10] Duerden, J. E., Social Problems in South Africa, *S.A. Jour. Sc.*, 1921, vol. 18, p. 1; reprinted in Sept., 1921.

[11] See under reference 10, p. 14.

[12] *The South African Natives: Report of a Committee*, 1908 (Murray).

[13] Evans, M. S., *Black and White in the Southern States*, 1915.

[14] Flint, Rev. Dr. W., *Nature*, Oct. 9, 1919.

[15] See under reference 10, p. 17.

NATIONAL SELF-DETERMINATION ILLUSTRATED BY THE CASE OF THE IRISH FREE STATE

Synopsis.—A biblical instance of self-determination. A biological definition of self-determination. The term is applied to the separation of national communities, not to the origin of new groups of tribes. Detribalization is a necessary preliminary stage. Self-determination is a manifestation of nationalism. The peopling of Ireland. Its earliest inhabitants were food-gatherers; they were arranged in local groups. Emigrants arriving during the second and the first millennia B.C. *brought to Ireland a knowledge of stock-raising and of tillage. Possible survival of the food-gatherers. The arrival of a master race— the Goidels. They gave Ireland a common speech but not a unified government. The number of tribes and of tribal confederacies in Ireland. The inter-tribal struggle led to the formation of larger and larger tribal combinations. No unifying power ever arose in tribal Ireland. A summary of the chief events which converted tribal Ireland into national Ireland. The Goidelization of English settlers. Systematic attempts at detribalization. The hatred of England became a unifying force. National fermentation during the eighteenth and nineteenth centuries. The revolution of* 1916. *Eamon de Valera unfolds the policy of self-determination. The attending cultural transformation. An evolutionary explanation. The future of Eire.*

In a previous essay (XXXI) I took my readers to Scotland to mark the steps which led to the birth of nationalism and of a nation; then, in a subsequent essay (XXXIV), I went to Wales to illustrate the fears, aspirations, and workings of the national spirit. In this essay I propose to discuss another and very important aspect of nationalism—that known as the principle or process of " self-determination." Since boyhood I have seen this process at work in Ireland, culminating in 1922 in the " break-away " of the South Irish. In this essay, then, a nation in the throes of self-determination is my theme, and Ireland is to supply my illustrative materials.

Readers will find a biblical example of self-determination in an early chapter of Genesis.[1] It is the case of the overgrown Abram–Lot pastoral community :—

> "And the land was not able to bear them, that they might dwell together. . . . And Abram said unto Lot. . . . Is not the whole land before thee? Separate, I pray thee, from me; if thou will take the left hand, then I will go to the right. . . . Then Lot chose all the plain of Jordan."

So what had been a single community or tribe, subdivided, each unit passing into the world to work out its own independent destiny. Such is the process of self-determination. It would be more in accordance with my main theme were we to regard the Abramic tribe as the original or paternal unit, Lot's people representing the self-determiners or seceders. A people, then, which separates itself from a parent group, or from a surrounding population, and sets out, trusting to its own right arm for its defence, to live apart from all other peoples and " dree its ain weird," has undergone the process of self-determination. "Self-determination," said Wickham Steed, " is a mystical and ill-defined concept."[2] To a biologist there is nothing mystical about the act of self-determination; the swarm of bees which comes out from the mother hive with their queen to form a new hive or colony illustrates the act of self-determination; it is an act of birth which brings into being a new and independent social group or evolutionary unit. The act is attended by a mental disturbance or fever. In the earliest stages of human evolution, when a small local group represented an evolutionary unit, new groups were being constantly formed by fission or division of the old, but it would be pedantic to apply the clumsy term " self-determination " to such a simple process. So, too, when the evolutionary unit became tribal in size; new tribes were formed by a budding-off or division of older overgrown tribes. The term self-determination is properly reserved for peoples who have reached a national stage in evolution. In this stage men and women have become free from the old tribal bonds and have assumed varying degrees of individual responsibility; they have been detribalized. Self-determination is seen at work only in detribalized communities; the population of an area, speaking a common dialect and carrying on a common tradition, come to feel that it is different from surrounding populations and with that feeling comes the desire for separation. When the resolution to separate and form a new people or nation passes into action, then we see the principle and practice of self-determination in active operation. Self-determination, then, is a manifestation of nationalism; it is attended by the birth-throes which herald the formation of a new nationality.

Among my predecessors there has been no one who has understood the nature and the strength of self-determination so clearly as the late Dr. Wm. McDougall. In 1920 he wrote this of it: " The desire and aspiration to achieve nationhood is the most powerful motive underlying the collective action of mankind." [3] Its strength lies in the impulses which spring from below the threshold of man's conscious self. It is part of the machinery of human evolution.

In the foregoing paragraphs I have given a biological explanation of what is implied by the term, " self-determination." I now turn to my main theme—that of Ireland. How and when did this western appanage of Europe come by its inhabitants? It seems to have been the last of European lands to become the home of mankind. Archæologists [4] are agreed that the earliest traces of man in Ireland cannot be dated sooner than 6000 B.C. if so early. Somewhat earlier than that date, food-gathering Caucasians had reached northern England and Scotland, and it is probable that the first settlers to reach Northern Ireland were groups which broke away from the mesolithic people of the British mainland. From 6000 B.C. down to a date which we may fix arbitrarily at 2200 B.C. our knowledge of Ireland is almost a blank, and we have found no certain evidence of new arrivals. But seeing how green and fertile Ireland was and is, it must have proved a paradise for its earliest inhabitants—the food-gathering groups. It is not too much to assume that the groups of early settlers speedily increased in numbers, divided, and re-divided until they had spread throughout the whole of the island. It is not improbable that before the end of the third millennium the population of the island had reached the maximum which a fertile country can maintain on its natural produce—namely, one soul per square mile. The area of Ireland is a little over 32,000 square miles; the population at the end of the food-gathering stage may have numbered 32,000 souls—men, women, and children. The people were divided into small local groups; some of these groups may have been large; others were small; taking one locality with another the number in a group may have averaged fifty. Each group occupied its own territory. Thus, by the end of the food-gathering period Ireland was probably divided into over 600 local territories, each occupied by its own community. We may assume, too, that these local communities were in active rivalry with each other.

Towards the end of the third millennium Ireland entered on a new phase of her history. Ships laden with emigrants from France, Spain, and Mediterranean lands then began to sail up the Irish Sea, leaving settlers both on the mainland of Britain and in Ireland. These were the pioneers who introduced the art of tillage and of stock-raising to Ireland. They were pastoralists rather than agriculturalists; they brought a new and enhanced mode of life to their adopted country. These early arrivals came in tribal groups, which effected settlements on the territories of the original inhabitants, the food-gatherers. What happened to the food-gathering Irish is a moot point, but Dr. Coon [5] is persuaded that to account for certain characters of the modern Irish—their large and long heads, their stature and strength of body, and the light colouring of their eyes—it must be assumed that many of the primitive natives survived and transmitted to the modern Irish the characteristics just enumerated.

All through the second millennium and far into the first millennium B.C., emigrants continued to arrive from S.W. Europe; they were joined by others who came directly or indirectly from Central Europe. These new arrivals brought with them a knowledge of arts and crafts which were new to Ireland. Ireland thus acquired the art of working in bronze and of fashioning weapons and ornaments in that metal. She became famed for her ornaments in gold. Many of her tribes grew large and wealthy. She was probably the most populous and prosperous of all the tribal countries of Western Europe in the second millennium B.C.

We now come to one of the most important and yet one of the most obscure events in the history of Ireland—the arrival of the Goidels, bringing with them their Gaelic speech, which they succeeded in making the tongue of Ireland. Their original home was certainly in Central Europe, but they are assumed to have spread their aristocratic rule into France and into Spain. Tradition holds that the Goidels (known also as Milesians and as Scots) reached Ireland from Spain, and this may well be true, for the sea route from Spain to Ireland was of ancient standing. Somewhere about 400 B.C. the Goidels invaded Ireland, but where they landed and the drawn-out campaigns they fought with resident tribes, we know nothing of save that ultimately they succeeded in imposing their language from Cork to Donegal. But if this conquering people gave the Irish a common speech, it failed to give the country a unified government. Tribes remained apart, each under its own chief.

An ancient authority, quoted by Prichard,[6] gave the number of tribal confederacies (nations) in Ireland during the third century of our era as sixteen, and the number of cities as eleven. This estimate tallies very well with records of the fifth century, when Christianity reached Ireland, and with others made at a later date. Brooke [7] has collected data relating to the tribes of Ireland from various authorities, and the numbers given by him are the following: There were thirty-five tribes in Ulster, grouped so as to form four confederacies; there were thirty in Connaught, arranged in three combinations; seventy-one in Munster, in three confederacies, and in Leinster (including Meath), forty-nine tribes forming three confederacies. Thus the total number of tribes was 185, grouped into thirteen confederacies.

We have seen that the tribes of Germany, France, England, and Scotland, before the dawn of the Christian era, had, in their mutual struggle for power and for survival, been compelled to form confederacies, the weaker tribes seeking the protection of the stronger. Although Ireland was isolated from the rest of Europe, yet the same tendency to the formation of larger units was at work. It is also of interest to note that the regional grouping of the tribes foreshadows the emergence of the four provinces into which Ireland became divided. One has to remember, too, the perpetual struggle that went on between tribes and tribal confederacies; the Irish tribes which reached the seventeenth century of our era were those which had succeeded in weathering the tribal storms which had swept Ireland for a period of some forty centuries. Another circumstance has to be kept in mind. The Roman occupation and the coming of the Saxons detribalized the population of England and gave that country a single dominant central government. The Anglo-Saxons detribalized the great part of Scotland and gave that country a single government. Nothing of this kind happened in Ireland; her population retained its tribal organization until the seventeenth century. It was not until then that the population of Ireland reached a *national* stage in its evolution.

I shall now attempt to summarize, as briefly as I may, the long chapter of events which transformed tribal Ireland into national Ireland. England, quite unwittingly, forged the Irish into a nationality. Our drama begins in the reign of Henry II of England (1154–89) and ends in Cromwell's time (1652). The first act of the drama took place in 1171, when Henry sent a force of 4,000 men, carried in a fleet of 400 ships, to establish rule in Ireland. The province of Leinster was conquered; towns were built, Anglo-Norman nobles carved feudal estates out of tribal territories, thus replacing native Irish chiefs. Some of the barons established themselves in Connaught, others in Munster. English individualism proved weak when it came up against the compelling spirit of Irish tribalism. The children of many of the original settlers married Irish wives, learned to speak the Irish tongue, and replaced English ways of living by those of the natives among whom they resided. Many of the heads of Anglo-Norman families, instead of upholding the rule of the English king in Ireland, became his bitterest enemies. From the invasion of Ireland by Henry II until Henry VIII dipped his oar in the troubled waters of Ireland (1527)—that is, for a period of three centuries and a half—the Goidelization of the English went on. Ultimately the greater part of the fresh blood which England poured into Ireland during these centuries came to flow in Irish veins.

A systematic attempt to detribalize the people of Ireland was initiated by Henry VIII in 1527, and was pursued with exacerbations and remissions until Cromwell's time—a period of 125 years. Henry shrank from clearing the natives off their tribal lands and replacing them with settlers fom England. Instead he pursued what may be termed a policy of conciliation. Chiefs, who held their lands in trust for their tribesmen, were given full possession; they were awarded English titles and English names; they were tempted to replace their native tongue and the native code of law by adopting those of England. " To all this," said

J. R. Green,[8] " the Celts opposed the tenacious obstinancy of their race." In Queen Elizabeth's time this policy of conciliation was changed to that of forceful coercion. Large areas of tribal lands were confiscated by the Crown; chiefs and their followers were driven from their homes and territories to be replaced by settlers from England. Munster was reduced to a wilderness; the tribes of Ulster rose in open rebellion. Men were prohibited from using their Irish names. Tribesmen were given tenancies, and so encouraged to break away from their chiefs. In the reign of James I the policy of coercion, confiscation, and plantation was continued with added vigour. Then came the great Irish rising of 1641, with the massacre of English settlers, and finally, by way of revenge, the cruel bludgeoning of the Irish by Cromwell in 1652. At last the tribal bonds of the Irish broke; tribesmen became scattered; detribalization had at last been accomplished.

" A country," said Gibbon,[9] " is unsubdued as long as the minds of the people are actuated by a hostile contumacious spirit." That spirit has pervaded the Irish ever since England set foot on their country. With the breaking of the tribes the old inter-tribal animosities vanished; men were free to join new combinations; a hatred of England served as a force to draw the Irish together. All through the eighteenth century a revolutionary ferment was at work coming to the surface from time to time in open rebellion. During that century and during the whole of the nineteenth there were always three parties in Ireland, the extremists, the moderates, and the loyalists. The extremists always held an advantage over the other parties in that they were prepared to sacrifice their lives to secure their ends and also to sacrifice all who were not on their side.

We may pass at once to the critical event of 1916 which took place in Dublin. Britain was then engaged in a life-and-death struggle with Germany; it was then that a party of revolutionaries declared an Irish Republic. After the war the old coercive measures were again applied to Ireland. By the end of 1921 Lloyd George and his colleagues realized that loyalty may be won, but it can never be coerced. The Irish were given " Dominion Status "; they obtained the wide degree of independence held by the other dominions of the British Commonwealth of Nations.

For the first ten years—that is, from 1922 to 1932—the Irish

Free State followed the Dominion pathway with circumspection, but in the latter year Eamon de Valera became Prime Minister and leader in the Dail, and then the whole policy of self-determination began to unfold itself. On coming to power he gave an interview to a correspondent of the *New York Times*,[10] whom he informed that " he had found the key to Ireland's needs in his own heart." Although the son of a Spanish father and born in New York (1882), he grew up in Ireland, and as he grew up learned to interpret the inner feelings of his revolutionary contemporaries by noting those which passed within his own mind. He knew well the workings of the tribal spirit. As soon as he was in power he picked a quarrel with the British Government over the payment of certain annuities, knowing well that he would have the support of every Irish partisan. It was in this quarrel that he informed the representative of the British Government that " no sacrifice in the cause of Irish nationalism could be too great." The oath of allegiance to the Crown was abolished; the citizens of the Irish Free State were declared to be no longer British subjects; the return of Ulster was demanded. Then, in 1937, came the culmination of the determinate policy. The Irish Free State took the name of Eire; it was proclaimed to be " a sovereign independent democratic State with inalienable, indefeasible right to chose its own form of government, to determine its relations with other nations, and to develop its life, political, economic, and cultural, in accordance with its own genius and traditions." [11] Thus in the year 1937 the greater part of the inhabitants of Ireland separated themselves from surrounding peoples and set out as an evolutionary unit to exploit the potentialities of their minds and bodies in the light and leading of their own genius, and so bring into existence a distinctive Irish race.

A people in the throes of self-determination always enacts a series of cultural transformations. In this respect Eire conformed to the rule. The characteristic quality of all these cultural changes is that they serve to isolate an evolving nation from its neighbours. Eire at once set out to resuscitate the Erse or Gaelic tongue. This was an uphill task. Early in the eighteenth century four people out of every five used Irish as their habitual tongue, but during that century English so far prevailed over Irish that by 1911 only one person out of seven was a speaker of Gaelic.

Nevertheless De Valera was hopeful that " the enthusiasm which won Ireland her independence would succeed in restoring her ancient tongue." Teaching in Irish was made compulsory in schools, colleges, and universities. All departments of government were renamed; so were streets, squares, post-offices, and railway stations. Beloved and familiar personal Irish names came out in spellings unrecognizable to English eyes. It was as if a snowdrift had fallen in a night on Ireland and blotted out familiar landscapes. There was a campaign against English books because " they did injury to the national consciousness." The Gaelic League [12] thought there was a danger of " our ancient Irish nation sinking into a west Britain "—a fear very similar to that of the Welsh nationalists (p. 348). Native arts and crafts were fostered; so were drama and literature. Irish games were encouraged; those of English origin were frowned upon. The Irish national flag was stripped of every British symbol; the " Soldier's Song " replaced " God save the King."

Such are the ways in which a self-determining nation transforms itself. All these changes are isolating in their effects. They serve to isolate the Irish from the English-speaking peoples of Britain; at the same time the Irish are also cutting themselves off from English-speaking America. There is a still greater sacrifice. There is a far larger Irish family living outside than inside the bounds of Ireland. In the populations of the United States, Canada, Australia, and New Zealand there are upwards of ten millions who regard Ireland as their ancestral home. By Goidel-izing herself Ireland has cut herself off from her emigrant sons and daughters. Such are the sacrifices which are willingly made in the cause of nationalisation.

How are we to explain the strange conduct of a self-determinist people? The explanation I offer may be summed up as follows:— Race-building has been, and still is, the mode of human evolution; to form a race, a people must isolate itself and become a nation; a nation is a community engaged in race-building. Underneath and supporting these assumptions is the important basal postulate —namely, that human nature is so constituted as to carry on the process of race-building automatically. As we have seen, McDougall regarded the " desire and aspiration to achieve nationhood as the most powerful collective action of mankind." In this essay, so far as I have gone, I have sought to forget my

British nationality and write as an anthropologist. I am now to view Ireland from a British point of view. The British Isles, of which Ireland is one, has come to be the home of a confederacy of nations, that of England greatly exceeding the others in size and in power. The safety and security of one of us is the safety and security of all of us. We have therefore not only duties towards each other as neighbours, but our need for security gives us certain rights in the affairs of one another. Such, however, is not De Valera's conception of our mutual relationships. In 1934 he bluntly told Britain " to go out and have nothing to do with us; we don't want to have anything to do with you." [13] In the war with Germany (1939–45), when defensive positions in Ireland might have been of the greatest service, Britain respected Eire's desire for neutrality. In 1939 the defensive needs of Russia were somewhat similar to those of Britain. The Government of the Soviet Republics demanded from Finland—which was and is an independent sovereign nation—ports, airfields, and strong points to strengthen her Baltic approaches. Finland refused, but was ultimately compelled to yield them to the overpowering force of Russian arms. Some day Eire may recognize that Britain deserves a mead of praise for the restraint which she exercised in her most perilous days.

There is a weakness in the constitution of Eire which will become more manifest as years speed by. She laid her foundation in hate—hate of England. Hate gave her unity. Now, hate, whether exercised individually or collectively, is the most searing and exhausting of human passions. Hate is a fire that needs continual stoking; it has to be fed by magnified grievances and deeds of ill-will. Sooner or later it burns itself out. When this happens in Eire, as happen it will, the small voice of reason and the more urgent call of self-interest may make themselves heard. When these things come about Eire's mood may change, and she may wish to again take her rightful place in the confederacy of British nations.

REFERENCES

[1] Genesis XIII, 6.
[2] Steed, Wickham, *The Times*, Sept. 23, 1944.
[3] McDougall, Wm., *The Group-Mind*, 1920, ch. XI.
[4] Movius, H. L., *The Irish Stone Age*, 1942; Martin, C. P., *Prehistoric Man in Ireland*, 1935.
[5] Coon, C. S., *The Races of Europe*, 1939.

[6] Prichard, J. C., *Researches into the Physical History of Mankind*, 1941, vol. 3, p. 138.

[7] Brooke, F. A., *The Science of Social Development*, 1936, p. 313.

[8] Green, J. H., *A Short History of the English People*, 1889, p. 458.

[9] Gibbon, E., *The Decline and Fall of the Roman Empire*, Everyman ed., vol. 2, p. 509.

[10] Price, Clair, *New York Times Magazine*, Sept. 25, 1932.

[11] *Statesman's Year-Book*, 1946, p. 471.

[12] *The Times Literary Supplement*, March 10, 1945.

[13] *The Times*, May 25, 1934.

THE JEWS AS A NATION AND AS A RACE

Synopsis.—Territory as the usual national bond. The process of assimilation. The Jewish bond is not territorial. His sense of nationality is mobile. Hesitant opinions regarding the national status of the Jews. The author holds that they are a nation and also a race. The biblical history of the Children of Israel. Detribalization of the Israelites. The contrasted fates of the Ten Tribes and of the Tribe of Judah. The evolution of the Jewish sense of race. Jewish mentality. The Jews become traders. Armenians and Parsis compared with Jews. The Dispersion. Diversity of Jewish types due to a certain extent to mixture of race, but chiefly to the selective changes which the Jews have undergone as they spread abroad. The qualities selected and strengthened were psychological. Intermarriage with Gentiles was forbidden. The Jewish resistance to assimilation weakened under liberal treatment and hardened under persecution.

THE nations we have been dealing with so far are held together as units by their territories; take them off their native lands and in a generation or two their sense of nationality becomes changed. Welsh, Irish, and Scottish families settling in England are soon absorbed or assimilated, for not only are the new arrivals in need of social contacts with their English neighbours, but these same neighbours resent the presence of strangers who keep aloof. Thus the process of assimilation is twofold; there must be a social predisposition on the part of the guest people and there must be an answering response on the part of the host nation. The English nation is noted for its assimilative powers; it has absorbed, at one time or another, nationals from all the countries of Europe. Some nationals are easier of absorption than others; the Welsh and the Scottish are less resistant than the Irish or the Italians. A nation destitute of the power to assimilate would be in the position of a man whose flesh had lost the power to heal; in him every wound would remain an open sore; in a nation every batch of immigrants would persist as "foreign bodies."

The Jewish people or nation differs from all the other great nations of the world in that their sense of unity is not based on territory; they are bound into a nation by a live "consciousness of kind," by a long and continuous tradition, and by a faith which is nationalistic as well as religious. Their sense of nationality is thus mobile; wherever they go it goes with them. The sense of nationality based on territory is, as we have just seen, plastic and mouldable. It is otherwise with the Jew's feeling of separateness; it is adamant or nearly so; it is weather-proof, and has brought its people through twenty-five centuries of storm. The mobile and resistant qualities of their nationalism have enabled the Jews to do an unparalleled thing—to make a peaceful and deep penetration of all territorial nations. There is scarcely a town of any size in Europe, Western Asia, North Africa, or in the New World that has not got its synagogue and its segregated Jewish community. Thus Jews differ from other nations in being destitute of a homeland and in having their population not massed in a single area, but scattered in many thousands of semi-isolated groups. We have seen that (p. 372) the Welsh and Irish, as nations, fear cultural assimilation with England. The fear of the Jews goes deeper than that—they fear the absorption and death of their nation by its disappearance in the common sea of humanity.

Many authorities, both Gentile and Jewish, hesitate to regard the Jews as a nation. My friend the late Philip Magnus [1] voiced the opinion of many English Jews when he wrote: "They are a religious body with precisely the same loyalties and duties to the State as other religious bodies." Another learned English Jew, Mr. C. G. Montefiore,[2] maintained that the Jewish people isolated themselves for the sake of their religion and that their object was not the perpetuation of their stock but of their religion. The authors of a report on Nationalism [3] give the Jews the status of "a distinct ethnic group with group consciousness" and as forming a nation in a spiritual sense. The *Jewish Encyclopaedia* (1901) admits that the Jews *were* a nation, but are now "a religious congregation." "The Jews," said Mr. Lucien Wolf in 1904, "are a religious body perfected by intermarriage." These discrepancies of opinion may be explained by the fact that Judaism, like most early religions, was designed for the welfare and survival of the tribe or group; Judaism dictates moral, social, political behaviour as well as religious observances. " The religion of Moses," wrote Gibbon,[4] "seems to be instituted for a particular country as well as for a single nation." Judaism is national in its purport. The Romans were in no doubt about the matter; " the Jews were a nation; the Christians (recruited from many nations) were a sect."[5] " The Jews," wrote Kastein, " are a nation on the march, determined, earnest, and fully prepared to make sacrifices."[6]

I have been at some pains to establish the right of the Jews to consider themselves as a nation. If a nation then, in the original meaning of the term, they are also a race (see Essay XXXII). The term " race " made one of its earlier appearances as a designation of the Jews. In 1570 this phrase appeared in print : " The race and stock of Abraham."[7] The Bishop of Norwich has written : " The history itself (the Old Testament) is the incomplete story of a small race." Thus, if I am in error in speaking of the Jews as a race, I have a precedent and am in good company. Nearly all my anthropological colleagues, in England, on the continent, and in America take a zoological view of race (see p. 323), and believe that race should be distinguished only by external markings, whereas I hold that the primary marks of race are psychological. Jews have all the psychological characteristics of race. They are exclusive, highly conscious of similarity among themselves and of being different from all other peoples; they maintain inbreeding communities; they willingly sacrifice their lives to perpetuate their kind; they are a chosen, separated people who have been entrusted with a divine mission. According to Kalergi,[8] exclusiveness, fanaticism, and intolerance are essential elements of Judaism; all these are racial qualities. Professor Hankins [9] has observed that " the Jews have all the other marks of nationality and also a highly developed race consciousness, a sense of racial superiority and even of racial purity." Dr. Bram [10] assured the New York Academy of Science during its session of 1944 that " the tendency to consider the Jews as a race or sub-race rather than a religious or cultural minority has been gathering strength since the end of last century." That may be true of America; it is certainly not true of Britain.[11] Yet Dr. Bram, had he been so inclined, could have claimed support from Professor Ruppin of the Hebrew University of Jerusalem, who has used the term " race " as applicable to the Jews, explaining that he employs the term "not in an anthropological sense . . . but to express ethnic homogeneity possessed by people through descent, tradition, and common interest." [12]   Professor Ruppin and I agree that the Jews are a race in the original sense of that term.

I have stressed the racial mental traits of the Jews; but even if we classify by external marks, which is the zoologist's way, the Jews still have claims to a racial status.   The most sensitive means of distinguishing one race from another is by sight and ear. Weissenberg,[13] who was an anthropologist as well as a Jew, asserted that Russians could identify fifty per cent of Jews by their appearance, and that Russian Jews could and did make correct identifications of each other in seventy per cent of cases.   My own experience in British communities leads me to believe I can make about forty per cent of correct identifications, but I have also to admit that I have mistaken about five per cent of people as Jews who turned out to have no Jewish blood in them.   Dahlberg,[14] the Swedish biologist, assessed the difference between European Jews and Gentiles as being of the same degree as that which separates Swedes from Spaniards.   My friend Dr. R. N. Salaman,[15] who is a man of science and also a Jew, said of the south European Jew, the Sephardim, that "the great majority may be recognized as Jews by their appearance."   Thus, whether we use the term race as the zoologist uses it, or in its original sense, the Jews are to be regarded as a race.

The first problem is this—to discover when and where the Jews came by their sense of race, a sense so strong that it needs no territorial support.   Our main source of information is, of course, the Old Testament.   The Bible and modern anthropology are at one as regards the original homeland of the Jews.   Abram was a Syrian, a derivative of the pioneer people who laid the foundations of civilization in Babylonia (see Essay XXIX).   We must note that the Abramic tribe was an inbreeding stock; Abram married his half-sister, Nahor a niece, Isaac and Jacob, cousins. Later, however, when the descendants of Abram had their abode in the extreme south of Palestine, assimilation became a danger. We note, in particular, that Judah, on whom we must keep a watchful eye, " married native," and so did his son.

The biblical historian leaves unexplained several important matters relating to the sojourn of the Children of Israel in Eygpt. He was oblivious to the fact that the Israelites when in Egypt were the last link in a chain of peoples extending northwards to the west of Jordan as far as Syria. The Medianites, the Amalekites, the Edomites, the Moabites, and the Ammonites represented links in that chain; all spoke dialects of the same tongue as the Israelites; Israel claimed relationship with all of them. It seems probable, then, that the Israelites entered Egypt, not as members of a single family, but as self-contained people. Arab tribes still settle on the outskirts of the Egyptian delta and after a stay, move off. The Israelites after a prolonged sojourn in Egypt, usually estimated at 430 years, again became a desert people. Garstang's excavations at Jericho [17] revealed evidence of their crossing the Jordan and their conquest of the uplands of Palestine at a date which he has fixed at 1400 B.C. The same authority estimates, and I agree with him, that the children of Israel, when they entered Palestine, could not have numbered more than six or seven thousand souls, and that Joshua's fighting force could scarcely have exceeded one thousand men. The native population of Palestine, when Joshua invaded it, was arranged in small independent States, a cluster of " parish races." The historian of the conquest enumerates (Joshua, Chap. 12) thirty-one such States which fell to the valour of Israelitish arms. Seeing that the total area of Palestine measures only 10,000 square miles, one fifth the size of England, and that little more than half of it is fit for human habitation, it will be realized how small these native States really were. Readers will also perceive how limited were the territories allotted to the twelve tribes.

The Israelites, when they took up their abode in Palestine, formed a confederation of tribes; to become a nation they had to undergo the process of detribalization. That was accomplished under Saul, David, and Solomon, broadly speaking, between 1050-950 B.C. The tribe of Judah took the leading part in bringing about these tribal changes and in the establishment of a central government. Seeing that the Jews sprang from the loins of Judah we must give that tribe our particular attention. Its territory measured about 2,500 square miles, being of about the same area as the county of Devon; half of its land was mountainous or desert; at the height of their power and prosperity the Judæans could never have numbered more than half a million. The land of Judah provided Palestine with its Kings, Priests, and Prophets; its Children were stubborn, stiff-necked, and fanatical.

The first major misfortune to befall the people of Judah was the breakaway or secession from them of the ten northern tribes (935 B.C.). Two centuries later (738–721 B.C.) the Children of Judah saw the ten tribes carried into captivity by the King of Assyria and the land planted with strangers. Little more than a century elapsed before the Judæans found themselves in the same plight; they were, for the greater part, transported as captives to Babylonia (597–582 B.C.). Under conditions of captivity the Children of Judah proved themselves to be made of a sterner and more obstinate mentality than their brethren of the northern kingdom. The Israelites of the north melted away in the foreign population amid which they were planted; they were assimilated and disappeared, as a separate people. The southern people (we may now speak of them as Jews) maintained their identity among the Babylonians; they retained their speech and their customs; they cultivated their religion in order to preserve their race and maintained their race so that their religion might remain pure and uncontaminated. A consciousness of being a separate and chosen people, as well as a singular sense of race, enabled the Jews to stand up to and resist the strong and seductive assimilative power of their Babylonian host. At a later date, when they became denizens of every part of the Persian Empire, their sense of race preserved them as a people. The Greeks, the Romans, the Egyptians warred against their racial stubbornness, but in vain.

Here, then, we have a record of an event which is almost unique in human evolution—the record of the rise of a race of a new kind. The race was generated and matured in that confined area of Palestine allotted to the tribe of Judah. The tribe was inbred, but inbreeding alone will not account for the development of a particular form of mentality. There must have been, in the original composition of the tribe, men and women rich in feelings, passions, and predispositions. The kind of mentality I am attributing to the early Judæans is exemplified by that of Nehemiah, cup-bearer to the King of Persia in the palace at Shushan about the year 446 B.C. His friends had brought him sad news as to the state of Jerusalem. " And it came to pass when I heard these words that I sat down and wept, and mourned certain days, and fasted, and prayed before the God of Heaven." [17] The man who behaves thus is not of ordinary build; such men hate to excess, just as they love to excess. Nehemiah's passion for his own people is undeniable.

In his original home, the Jew was a farmer; he had his fields of wheat and of barley; he dressed his vines; but the farmer was also a town-dweller. When he spread abroad he chose towns for his home, because only in towns could he live in communities of his own kind, and so be protected from the assimilative power of his host-nation. But how did he gain his ascendancy in trade? A modern instance from Spanish Morocco [18] helps to explain how he became trader and money-changer. A market sprang up on the frontier where the territories of several tribes met and where barter exchanges were made. At first a few Jews attended these markets, bringing footwear and ready-made garments to be exchanged for goods. The tribesmen welcomed them, for they despised both trade and trader. Business passed more and more into the hands of the Moroccan Jews; they introduced the use of money and became money-changers and bankers. In some such way the Jews became traders in the lands of their adoption. In Abram's time trade between Syria and Egypt was in the hands of Semitic peoples; [19] in ancient and in medieval times Arab tribes were transporters and sellers of goods.

Two other peoples—the Armenians and Parsis, who share the isolating racial mentality of the Jew—also took to trade in the period of their dispersion. The Armenian is regarded as an Aryan and the Jew as a Semite, but they have so many traits of body and of mind in common that the anthropologist, to account for these resemblances, feels compelled to trace both back to that highly endowed stock, the pioneer founders of Mesopotamian civilization. I agree with the following statement which Dr. L. W. Parr [20] has made regarding the racial traits of the Armenians : " They possess a high degree of racial unity, characterized by social and economical traits, even more typical of them than their physique or blood-type." The mentality of the Parsis, on the other hand, cannot be attributed to an inheritance from Mesopotamia; they were Persians of Aryan origin, devout believers in the creed of Zoroaster, which, like the religion of the Jews, served a national as well as a religious purpose. With the Mohammedan conquest of Persia (641 A.D.) the more devout, the more zealous and fanatical fled from their homes and made their way to India, ultimately establishing separate communities in the towns and cities of

Bombay.[21]   They took to trade, maintained their identity, set up flourishing communities throughout India, and spread into neighbouring lands.   With the Parsis, as with the Jews, religion and race are inseparable.

The date usually given for the final expulsion of Jews from Palestine is 135 A.D., when Hadrian laid Jerusalem in ruins and made Judæa a wilderness.   But as we have seen, captive Jews effected settlements in Babylonia in the sixth century B.C., and many preferred to remain there rather than return to Palestine. In the fifth century B.C. they had spread throughout the wide realms of the Persian Empire, where anti-Semitism raised its hoary head for the first time.   In the third century Greek colonies in Asia Minor gave them an approach to the West and to the trading ports of the Black Sea; in the same century they had settled in their thousands in Alexandria and in other towns of Egypt. The Roman Empire provided them with an open road to the heart of Europe; in the second century B.C. they reached Rome and Italy.   Graetz,[22] the Jewish historian, states that " there was not a corner of Rome or of Parthia that was without its synagogue and its Jewish community " by the middle of the first century A.D. He estimates that by that time there were 10,000 Jews in Damascus and a million in Egypt !   Thus it will be seen that Jews were seeking homes in the established communities of strangers long before Hadrian finally wrecked their homeland.   By the third century A.D. they had reached the valley of the Rhine; the eighth century found them in Poland and Western Russia.   " A cruel destiny," writes Graetz,[23] " seemed to be ever thrusting them away from their central home . . . the work of God."   It was a destiny to which they were particularly well fitted by reason of their mental equipment.

It is often said, and truly said, that the Jews are not a race but an amalgam of many races, so diverse are their physical types.   The Sephardim or southern Jews are mostly long-headed and dark-haired; the northern Jews are, for the greater part, round-headed and usually light brown or ruddy in their hair colouring.   How are we to account for these differences if all are from the same Judaiac stocks?   No doubt the early Jews made proselytes; by occasional marriage, both early and late, Jews incorporated genes from the peoples among whom they lived; in this way some of their physical traits may be explained.   But selective agencies were also at work as they formed community after community. We have seen (Essay XXII) that when a group or tribe divides, the new group or tribe differs from the old in its genetic potentialities. When an early Jewish community gave off a band of pioneers to form a community in a neighbouring town, the pioneers differed in certain qualities from the parent community; when this new community proceeded to form a third, the third differed still more from the parent community. It is probable that the Jews who reached Poland from the Rhine basin represented a twentieth, or even a thirtieth, remove or transplant from the parent colony on the Rhine. Thus we expect that the Jews which are farthest from the centre of distribution should show the greatest departures from the type of Judæa.

The evolutionary process to which the Jews have been subjected has been centred, not on their bodily features, but on their mental equipment. The one essential mental attribute which the Jew must possess is a living sense of being linked to his own community and of being separated from those of the Gentiles; without this sense he would drown in the Gentile sea. Consider for a moment the temptations to which the Jews have been exposed and the winnowing or selective ordeal they have undergone in the twenty-five centuries which now separate them from their ancestors of the captivity. The Jew has his social qualities quite as well developed as those of the Gentile; he is daily tempted by the social attractions of his host people, and if he is weak, may fall victim to them. The one sin his community will not pardon is apostasy to his creed and race. In spite of the execrations of his community he may fall in love with, and marry, a woman of the Gentiles, and so bring Gentile blood into his race. The mixed progeny of such unions is, in due course, subjected to assimilative seduction of the host people; if the hard racial mentality of the Jew has not been inherited, then such progeny will be reabsorbed by the Gentiles, and thus eliminated from the race. For eighty generations the Jews have been subjected to this merciless process of psychological selection; unless their racial sense remains firm they go down in the Gentile sea. Instead of weakening, the Jewish feeling of separateness seems to grow stronger as time goes on. Among the Gentiles a sense of nationalism is also becoming more aggressive.

I have had occasion to cite the mentality of Nehemiah as

typical of the Jew. It will further my argument if I now quote his condemnation of mixed marriages. "In these days also I saw Jews who had married wives of Ashdod, of Ammon, and of Moab. And their children spoke half in the speech of Ashdod, and could not speak in the Jews' language. And I contended with them and cursed them and smote certain of them." [24] It was Ezra's conviction that these foreign marriages brought "the fierce wrath of God" on the chosen people.[25]

The more that Gentile nations emancipated their Jewish citizens —the more they extended to them civil, social, and religious freedom—the greater was the number of Jews who fell victim to the process of assimilation. On the other hand, the more they were discriminated against—the fiercer the prosecution and the more the anti-Semitic spirit became rampant—the closer became their ranks and the more defiant their spirit. Jews who had become indifferent to their religion or had abandoned it, and were on the point of giving up the Semitic struggle, rallied to their race when it was threatened by a crisis. I will call but one Jewish witness in support of this. In his last testament, which the French philosopher Bergson drew up in 1937, when anti-Semitism was at its height in Germany, he inserted this explanatory clause : " My reflections lead me closer and closer to Catholicism, in which I see the fulfilment of Judaism. I would have become a convert had I not foreseen the formidable wave of anti-Semitism. . . . I wanted to remain among those who to-morrow will be persecuted." [27] Such is the racial spirit of the Jew; it quails at nothing.

REFERENCES

[1] Magnus, Philip, *Sunday Times*, May 13, 1934.

[2] Montefiore, C. G., *Papers for Jewish People*, 1918.

[3] *Nationalism—Report by a Study-Group*, 1939, p. 165.

[4] Gibbon, E., *Decline and Fall of the Roman Empire*, Everyman ed., vol. 1, p. 435.

[5] *Ibid.*, vol. 2, p. 5.

[6] Kastein, Josef, *Jews in Germany*, 1934.

[7] *Murray's New English Dictionary*.

[8] Coudenhove-Kalergi, Count Heinrich, *Anti-Semitism throughout the Ages*, 1935, p. 2.

[9] Hankins, F. H., *The Racial Basis of Civilization*, 1926, p. 11.

[10] Bram, Joseph, *Trans. N.Y. Acad. Sc.*, 1944, Ser. 2, vol. 6, p. 194.

[11] British opinion is reflected in Professor H. J. Fleure's statement :— " Only distorted prejudice can attempt to single out a so-called race." *Bull. John Rylands's Library*, 1940, vol. 24, p. 245.

[12] Ruppin, Arthur, *The Jewish Fate and Future*, 1940, p. 203.

[13] Weissenberg, L., *Archiv. Anthrop.*, 1895, 12, pp. 347–541.

[14] Dahlberg, G., *Race, Reason, and Rubbish*, 1942, p. 225.

[15] Salaman, R. N., *Jour. Genetics*, 1911, vol. 1, p. 223.

[16] Garstang, John, *The Heritage of Solomon*, 1934, ch. V.

[17] Nehemiah I, 4.

[18] My statement is based on an account given by Mr. W. Fagg in *Man*, 1941, p. 104.

[19] See reference 16, p. 60.

[20] Kappers and Parr, *An Introduction to the Anthropology of the Near East*, 1934, p. 192.

[21] See reference 8, p. 117.

[22] Graetz, H., *History of the Jews*, 1891, vol. 2, p. 248.

[23] *Ibid.*, p. 248.

[24] Nehemiah XIII, 23.

[25] Ezra X, 11.

[26] *The Times*, Nov. 6, 1943.

THE JEWS AS A NATION AND AS A RACE

(*continued*)

ANTI-SEMITISM : ZIONISM

Synopsis.—*Evolution applied to the elucidation of Jewish history. Evolving groups must be isolated. The root from which anti-Semitism arose. The antiquity and persistence of anti-Semitism. Its relationship to nationalism and to density of the Jewish population. With free intermarriage of Gentile and Jew anti-Semitism would disappear. It has been attributed to the religion of the Jews. Anti-Semitism considered from an anthropological point of view. It is a particular form of racialism. Closed societies evoke antagonisms. Jews have a racial " blind spot." Most hold that anti-Semitism is purely a Gentile problem, but there are exceptions. Jewish conduct is based on a dual code. Professional anthropologists have misled both Gentile and Jew in the matter of race. Zionism : its aims and aspirations. How the co-operation of the British Government was enlisted. Riots in Palestine between Arabs and Jews. The Arabs come to regard the British as their chief enemy and begin a war of independence. They were placated in 1939 by a limitation in the number of Jews admitted to Palestine. The Jews then became the open enemies of the British forces in Palestine and began a campaign of terrorism. The British mandate had two irreconcilable objectives and proved unworkable. In the author's opinion the only way out of the Palestinian dilemma is for both Jew and Briton to abandon the scheme of an exclusive national home.*

THE brevity with which I have dealt with the Jews in the preceding essay may lead my readers to think that I have but a superficial acquaintance with their history and character. I hasten to state that this really is not the case; for over half a century I have had opportunities of studying them at close quarters; for thirty years I have been collecting data relating to them and reading their histories, of which there is no lack.[1] My object is not to add a chapter to the history of the Jews, but simply to show that the theory of human evolution which has been expounded in the earlier essays of this book helps us to understand the origin of the Jews as a separate people, and of the evil fate that has dogged them at every phase of their long history. There are two factors essential to my theory—first, human evolution is carried on by group contending with group; second, groups are kept apart and isolated by their mutual antagonisms or aversions. Isolation is a condition which must be preserved if a group is to evolve. It is to the dislike or animosity which separates evolving groups that I attribute the evil feelings which are so apt to arise in Gentile nations towards their guest communities of Jews, an antagonism which constitutes the scourge of the modern civilized world known as anti-Semitism.

The earliest record of anti-Semitism is that preserved in the Book of Esther,[2] and attributed to the end of the sixth century B.C. :—

> " And Haman said to king Ahasuerus, There is a certain people scattered abroad and dispersed among the people of all provinces of thy kingdom; and their laws are diverse from all people; neither keep they the king's laws; therefore it is not for the king's profit to suffer them. If it please the king, let it be written that they may be destroyed."

Such, then, is the first record of anti-Semitism and of the first Hitler, for Haman, in ancient Persia, cast himself for the inhuman part so fully filled by Hitler in modern Germany. Between the time of Haman and that of Hitler, the Jews have never enjoyed ease or peace in any country for a long period.[3] As Renan has said, " Anti-Semitism repeats itself everywhere and at all times." England, in recent centuries so tolerant towards the Jews, was not always so; there were massacres in London and York before she expelled the Jews in 1290; the same may be said of France, from which Jews were banished in 1306. England and France in the thirteenth and fourteenth centuries still retained barbarous traits in their mentality, and were therefore more liable to racial outbursts than at later and more educated periods. We must remember, however, that it was in these earlier centuries that the English and the French were beginning to be national-minded;

it is to nationalism, rather than to a low state of civilization or to a religious antipathy, that I attribute the earlier manifestations of anti-Semitism in Western Europe. In the twentieth century the people of Germany were both educated and civilized, yet among them a feeling against the Jews reached a new depth of infamy and cruelty. The German sense of nationality had been blown into a white heat by the breath of their fanatical leader, for Hitler was a naked nationalist, racialist, and evolutionist. Again, it is held by many that anti-Semitism is most liable to break out where Jews are most densely planted. In Poland, for example, where in 1939 there were 3·3 million Jews, forming ten per cent of the population, anti-Semitism was endemic. It cannot be altogether a matter of density, for in the city of New York Jews now form nearly twenty per cent of the population, and yet the city is free from organized outbreaks of anti-Semitism.

There is a great diversity of opinion as to the origin and nature of anti-Semitism, but on one point both Gentile and Jewish authorities are in agreement—namely, that it would disappear with free inter-marriage between Jews and Gentile. In this simple way the Jew could gain the liberties he so longs for, but in a way that he has rejected in all ages with scorn. He is infuriated by the mere suggestion of inter-marriage as a cure.[4] Namier regards "assimilation as a confession of inferiority."[5] In my reading I have come across no instance of a Jewish community surrendering itself voluntarily to marriage with Gentiles; the fear of assimilation is deeply rooted in Jewish nature. The religious-minded Jew explains that his fear of assimilation and his desire to perpetuate his kind are an expression of his resolve to preserve his faith and so to fulfil his divine mission. In this view anti-Semitism is the price he pays, not for his race, but for his religion.

A layman informed the readers of *The Times* (Aug. 23, 1934) that anti-Semitism "was explicable on religious, historical, and emotional, but not on anthropological terms." It is just on anthropological terms that I am seeking to explain this social disorder; if we are to effect a cure, our first care must be to make a correct diagnosis. We have seen (Essay XXXV) that racialism springs into being whenever two races become intermingled in the same territory; anti-Semitism comes into being under the same conditions; it is a particular species of racialism. Another mark of its racial nature is that it is collective in its action; anti-

Semites blame a community for the misdeeds of one of its individual members. Anti-Semitism, like all forms of racialism, is not inborn ; it is acquired; but its emotional and mental substrate is inborn (see p. 360). Racial feelings, once aroused, are capable of unspeakable atrocities.

" One does not have to be an anthropologist," writes my friend Professor Hooton of Harvard,[6] " to realize that any group which is physically and socially distinct, is sure to arouse envy and hatred amongst outsiders." Franz Boas,[7] a distinguished Jewish anthropologist, regarded racialism as "the antagonism which is evoked by a closed society." Jewish communities are certainly closed societies, but, then, so are the thousands of castes which live side by side in India without open strife. It is only when enclosed or exclusive societies are different in their racial composition that warring passions are awakened. Professor Fleure [8] came near the truth when he wrote, " Group consciousness resents what it cannot assimilate." " But that which most vehemently enraged and irritated a Græco-Roman world against the Jews," remarked Coudenhove Kalergi,[9] " was that impenetrable wall of separation which the latter had raised between themselves and non-Jews, and this they had done only because their law compelled them to." That, I think, is a fairly accurate description, written by a friendly pen, of the mental rampart with which the Jews have surrounded themselves to prevent absorption. Sacchar,[10] writing in 1934 of the three million Jews in Russia, says this of them : " Apparently unassimilable, hard as steel, stubborn as death . . . a huge bone in the gullet of nationalism." What has happened to the Jews of Russia since that passage was written by Sacchar, I do not know, but it is hard to believe that even the Soviet technique has succeeded in bringing about their assimilation. To fill out my account of the Jew's attitude towards his Gentile surroundings I am to cite the evidence of a learned Jew, that of Professor L. B. Namier : [11] " But so long as the Jews remain a cohesive self-contained community, with a consciousness and national pride of their own, they preserve their strength and their vitality."

Perhaps the most outstanding of the mental characteristics associated with race is an inability to see things from the point of view of an opposing people. All beliefs that a man entertains regarding his nation or his race are of the nature of convictions, so fixed in his consciousness that they remain unquestioned and are regarded by him as unquestionable. The Jew is genuinely puzzled to account for the Gentile's attitude towards him. Sometimes he attributes it to a jealousy of the success which attends the endeavours of a large proportion of Jews in the higher vocations of life; the cruelty of the Gentile he is apt to attribute to a sadistic nature and a need for scapegoats. Very rarely does he ask the question : " Why are my people objects of antipathy to so many Gentiles?" Josef Kastein [12] explains this omission : " The Jew never turned to his enemy to ask, Why do you treat me thus? He turned to the highest court of appeal and there asked, Why do you send me this?" Later in his book [13] he adds : " Let us remember the great teaching of our history, that anti-Semitism is not a Jewish but a foreign problem." Almost the first sentence in Mr. Louis Golding's book [14] is " Anti-Semitism is not a Jewish but a Gentile problem." A distinguished Jew in a letter to me wrote : " You may see, therefore, that the cause of this aloofness does not lie with the Jews but with the people among whom they live." Professor Hooton [15] does not share this point of view. " I am inclined to doubt," he said, " that the priority of antipathy and of the exclusive tendency lies with the non-Jews." The Gentile, it must be confessed, has racial corns; when tramped on he cries out. It is usual to blame, not the victim tramped on, but the tramper. Those who support the Jewish attitude will re-join : " Let the Gentile cure himself of his racial corns." For two thousand years the Gentile world has been seeking for a cure and has failed to find one.

The outlook in the relation of Jew to Gentile would indeed be dark were it not that there are Jews who succeed in seeing things from the Gentile's point of view. In the *Jewish Chronicle* (Aug. 10, 1934, p. 9) there appeared a letter from which the following passages are taken : " Clearly it is not true that Jewish misfortunes arise only from intolerance and all that the Jews have to do is to ' sit tight and pretty ' and allow the various governments to stamp out the anti-Semitic spirit. The Jewish problem is not solely for government; Jews have their own share to take."

Another mark of race possessed by the Jews must be mentioned. Their conduct is regulated by a " dual code "; their conduct towards their fellows is based on one code (amity), and that towards all who are outside their circle on another (enmity). The use of the dual code, as we have seen (p. 63), is a mark of an evolving race. My deliberate opinion is that racial characters are more strongly developed in the Jews than in any other Caucasian people. Anti-Semitism, then, is but an ugly and virulent form of racialism.

My anthropological colleagues, under the spell of ethical ideals, have done Gentiles and Jews an ill-service by giving euphonious names to vulgar things. They have assured the Jews that they are not a race but only an " ethnic group " kept together by having a religion in common. They also have assured all the other Caucasian peoples that they are raceless, and that hence all the animosity which arises between Gentile and Jew is an artificially fomented form of hysteria. With the best intentions in the world, professional anthropologists have succeeded in hiding from the world the nature of its running sores. If these sores are to be cured, they must be exposed freely to the surgeon's scrutiny, and have their proper names given to them.

We now proceed to consider the racial aspects of a Jewish scheme which was initiated in the latter half of the nineteenth century under the name of Zionism. Nehemiah's dream of a Jerusalem with a restored Zion in its midst is one which still grips the imagination of many modern Jews. Zionism was, in its opening phase, a movement which sought for the realization of this ideal. The appeal was strengthened by certain other considerations. In a land of their own the fear of assimilation would vanish; Jews would be in a position to abandon their acquired Gentile tongues and be free to revive and converse in their own original tongue—Hebrew, which has been a dead language for twenty-five centuries. In a land of their own they could preserve and practise their religion, and observe their customs; they could develop their culture in all its forms. Above all, a sovereign independence would permit them to work out their separate racial destiny. They would again have a national home.

In 1917 the British Cabinet, wishing to acknowledge a signal service rendered to the war by Dr. Chaim Weizmann, asked him what form their award should take. He explained that he desired neither money nor honours; he would feel amply repaid if the British Government would favour the establishment of a national home for the Jews in Palestine. This scheme made an especial appeal to one member of the Cabinet—Mr. A. J. Balfour, afterwards the first Lord Balfour (1848–1930). Mr. Balfour was a statesman of the highest order, with a subtle and religious mind steeped in philosophy, who regarded the maintenance of law and order as the first duty of a government. If racial inequalities were met with, they were to be ironed out with a firm hand. Mr. Lloyd George favoured Dr. Weizmann's appeal; so did Mr. Winston Churchill. In this way the British Government found itself added to the Zionist train.

In 1922 Britain was formally entrusted by the League of Nations with the government of Palestine. In its mandate there were two provisions: (1) the establishment of a home for the Jews in Palestine to be facilitated; (2) the rights and position of the then occupants of Palestine to be safeguarded. Thus Britain undertook obligations to two peoples, the Jews and the Arabs of Palestine. It promised to make them co-occupants of the same small land.

Palestine measures only a little over 9,000 square miles, and nearly half of these miles are barren. Even if cultivated to the highest point possible, the land could not carry a population greater than a million and a half. In 1920 there were about fifteen million Jews in the world; " the promised land " could provide a home for only a fraction of that number. At that date Palestine provided a home for 673,000 Arabs and 67,000 Jews, the Jews thus forming only ten per cent of the population. The Palestinian Arabs, during the 1,300 years of their occupancy, had never formed a separate people; like their brothers in the vast deserts of Arabia, they were tribal in their organization and tribal in their mentality. A common danger drew the Palestinian Arabs together and gave them the unity and strength of a nation. In Britain's promise to provide a home for the Jews the Arabs saw a threat to their homes, to their ways of life, and to their existence as a people Their feelings led to a riotous outburst against the Jews in 1920-21; the conflagration which broke out in 1929 between Moslems and Jews over access to the " wailing wall " was a more serious and bloody affair. In the early thirties Arab enmity was changing in its objective; it became directed as much, or even more, against the British as against the Jews. By 1936 Arab nationalism had been aroused; the Arabs began a war of liberation, a war for the independence of Palestine. " A few armed men in the hills," reported The Times (Oct. 5, 1938), " have become a united Arab people. The sheik has become a holy warrior; the schoolmaster has turned propagandist; a new level of insecurity has been reached." The division of the country into Arab and Jewish States, recommended to the British Government in 1937 by the Peel Commission, pleased the Arab as little as it did the Jew. From 1936 to 1939 were " black murderous days "; [16] the Jews feared they might be driven into the sea and the Arabs that they or their children would have to seek refuge in the desert. In 1939 the British Government succeeded in temporarily placating the national aspiration of the Arabs by limiting the yearly admission of Jews to 10,000 for a period. It now began to be realized that there was " a stark contradiction between Arab aspirations and Britain's obligations to the Jews."

In the opening years of the war (1939–45) there was a lull in Palestinian strife. At this time (1942) it was found that the population of Palestine had increased from 740,000 in 1920 to 1,620,000; Arabs, who numbered 673,000 in 1920, now totalled 1,156,000; the Jews had risen from 67,000 to 484,000. With this great addition to their number the policy of the Jews became more aggressive. They demanded that the British should carry out their mandate, that Jews should be given unlimited access to Palestine, and that 100,000 should be admitted at once. " The Jewish nation," said Bagehot, "won by law, not by war." On this occasion, their demands having been refused, the Jews threw law to the winds and resorted to force applied diabolically and with ingenuity. The British found themselves in the same position in Palestine as the Romans had done twenty centuries earlier. The Jews fought with the same fanaticism and ferocity for the recovery of Palestine as their forefathers had done in Roman and in Maccabean times for the liberation of their country. The sixteen million Jews scattered through the world, particularly those of the United States, were on their side. Nor were the Arabs forgotten by their kinsmen; the fourteen million Arabs living in Arabia, Iraq, and Syria leagued themselves in support of the Palestinians; so did the Egyptians. But no nation rallied to aid the British. The opposite was the case; the United States requested that Britain should give 100,000 Jews immediate admission.

In 1946 a commission of twelve members, six representing the United States and six Great Britain, was sent to Palestine to examine and report on the state of things in that country. The commission reported (*The Times*, May 1, 1946) that it had found

Palestine to be " an armed camp "; it expressed the opinion that " the whole world shares responsibility for the displaced Jews of Europe," and asked that 100,000 of them should be admitted forthwith. That the Palestinian Arabs should be made to pay the world's debt did not seem unfair to the commission, as it held that " Palestine belongs neither to Jew, nor to Arab, but to the religious world." Seeing that the " religious world " had left the Arab in possession for thirteen centuries, its claim may well be questioned. The commission's chief recommendation was that Palestine should " remain under mandatory or U.N.O. control until Arab and Jew are agreed to live in peace together," and that they " were to be made to understand that the programme proposed will be imposed and continued under duress." The anthropologist sees a disastrous future for Palestine if that recommendation is adopted as a policy. There has been a mandatory Power in Palestine for wellnigh thirty years; the British taxpayer has spent upwards of £100,000,000 in maintaining it; and under it things have ever moved from bad to worse. No power on earth will suppress the resolution and raciality of the Jews.

In 1930 Judge Lofgren of Sweden said a true thing of the mandate with which Britain had been entrusted; it bound her to carry out two objects which were irreconcilable. She undertook to provide a home for Jews in Palestine and, at the same time, to do no wrong to the Arab population. She thought that one small land could be made a home for two racially minded incompatible peoples. She has now (1947) discovered her mistake. What, then, is Britain to do? It is usually counted for wisdom, when a mistake has been made, to acknowledge it and to make reparations for wrongs done. The British Cabinet of 1917 was not alone in being mistaken. The Zionists also misjudged the situation; they were blind to the rights of the Palestinian Arabs; they believed that the wealth, prosperity, and culture they would bring into Palestine would cause Arabs to throw their doors widely open for their entry. These expectations have proved to be disastrous miscalculations. The present critical situation in Palestine gives the Jews in general, and the Zionists in particular, an opportunity of making an unprecedently generous gesture to humanity, all the world over; to abandon their resolve to become the dominant power in Palestine, to acknowledge the lawful possession of that land by the Arabs who are native to it; to cease in demanding the mandatory "pound-of-flesh" from Britain, for ultimately it has to be cut from the living Arab; and to make terms with the Palestinians for all the rights and privileges which can be enjoyed by a guest people. The only alternative that I can see is a bloody and prolonged war. If I am mistaken in these suggestions, the future will speedily find me out. At least, such is the position of matters in 1947 as seen through the eyes of an anthropologist.

Postscript. November 29, 1947.

To-day the United Nations Organization decided to divide Palestine into Jewish and Arab States. The Jews accept this decision; the Arabs reject it. The British Government has announced that it brings its mandate in Palestine to an end on May 15, 1948.

REFERENCES

1 The authoritative History of Jews is, of course, the *Old Testament*. Of modern works that which makes the most direct appeal to me is Professor Arthur Ruppin's *The Jewish State and Future*, 1940. Other works which I have studied are:—*History of the Jews*, 1891, by Professor H. Graetz; *A History of the Jews*, 1934, by A. L. Sacchar; *Israel*, 1932, by A. Lods; *Jews in Germany*, 1934, by Josef Kastein; *Anti-Semitism throughout the Ages*, 1935, by Count H. Coudenhove-Kalergi; *The Jewish Problem*, 1938, by Louis Golding; *A History of the Jews in England*, 1942, by Cecil Roth; *The Races of the Old Testament*, 1891, by Professor A. H. Sayce; *The Heritage of Solomon*, 1934, by John Garstang; *The Emergence of the Jewish Problem*, 1946, by James Parkes.

2 Esther, III, 8.

3 Coudenhove-Kalergi, Count, *Anti-Semitism throughout the Ages*, 1935.

4 Hooton, E. A., *Twilight of Man*, 1939, pp. 247–9.

5 Namier, L. B., *Conflict Studies in Contemporary History*, 1942, p. 126.

6 Hooton, E. A., see reference 4, p. 246.

7 Boaz, Franz, *Science*, 1937, vol. 74, p. 1.

8 Fleure, H. J., *Bull. John Rylands's Library*, 1940, vol. 24, p. 245.

9 See under reference 3.

10 Sacchar, A. L., *A History of the Jews*, 1934, p. 322.

11 Namier, L. B., see under reference 5, p. 126.

12 Kastein, Josef, *Jews in Germany*, 1934, p. 14.

13 *Ibid.*, p. 163.

14 Golding, Louis, *The Jewish Problem*, 1938.

15 Hooton, E. A., see under reference 4, p. 242.

16 See *The Times*, Dec. 4, 1943.

NATION-BUILDING ON A CONTINENTAL SCALE

Synopsis.—The people of the United States of America considered as a nation and compared to the nations of Europe. The need for another name for the " American " nation. The colonization of the United States by the English compared with the colonization of England by the Anglo-Saxons. Two traditions and ways of life were established by the English colonists in America. The New England tradition held in the North, the Virginian in the South. Assimilation as a factor in nation-building. The American Revolution interpreted from an anthropologist's point of view. The colonists having won the war had then to win the peace. The Civil War secured the union of the nation. The tide of immigrants. The policy of the United States became isolationist and national after the first world war. The " national " and racial composition of the people of the United States in 1920. The result of Professor Hooton's anthropological investigations. The process of evolution is retarded in large nations. Local evolution. Race-building in the United States. The Negro problem. Anti-Semitism and anti-Negroism compared. The difficulties which attend schemes which seek to model the nations of Europe in the pattern of the United States. Nation- and race-formation are neglected anthropological studies.

THE nations we have dealt with so far—those of Egypt, of Scotland, of Wales, and of Ireland—are of small size and have grown up by the amalgamation of adjacent tribes and peoples. The nation whose rise we are to consider in this essay, that of the United States of America, is of colossal size, numbering in 1946 about 140 million people, and inhabiting an area which is continental in extent, for the territory of the United States measures nearly three million square miles, being only a little less than the continent of Europe. The nations of Europe may be said to have " grown up "; their size and the extent of their territories were determined in the general struggle for power and for survival. The nation we are now to consider, although it began fortuitously, was developed and grew under a plan devised by the statesmen who framed the constitution of the United States. The " American " nation, besides being planned, differs from European nations in a very important respect : the European nations were formed out of populations native to their territories, whereas the " American " nation has been forged out of an immigrant population. In one point, however, the white population of the United States is in agreement with the nations of Europe; all are of the Caucasian stock. In Europe the stock has been broken up into local national breeds; in America the local breeds of Europe have been reunited. But, as we shall see later, the preponderant affinities of the New Nation are with the peoples of N.W. Europe.

What name are we to give to this new nation? The white people of the United States call themselves " Americans " and are recognized under this name by other nationalities. No doubt that usage will hold fast, but for anthropologists [1] the name has many disadvantages. They need a term to embrace all the peoples of the New World; all are Americans. We want a term which is applicable to only the Caucasian population of the United States. For some years I have used a hieroglyph—" USA'ans "—for this purpose, an ugly improvisation. The pioneer people of New England, who gave the New Nation its basal tradition, came to be known as Yankees—a name now discarded. But if we borrow certain letters from that term and introduce them to my hieroglyph, we get " Yusanians," a name which will serve the temporary purpose of this essay. I shall speak, then, of the Caucasian population of the United States as " Yusanians."

There are certain instructive points of resemblance between the colonization of England by the Anglo-Saxons and the colonization of America by the English. Both set out, not in search of plunder, but of new homes. Both took with them their wives and children; they were prepared for hard work and, if need be, to defend themselves. The Anglo-Saxons began by landing in Kent (449), and continued to arrive for nearly a century and a half, during which time they established seven colonies, each of which grew into a separate State or kingdom. The English settlement along the east coast of America began in Virginia (1606) and may be said to have finished with the establishment of

Georgia (1733). Thirteen colonies had come into existence; they occupied a coastal strip fully 1,000 miles in length. It is noteworthy that the early American colonists were recruited chiefly from the more Saxon counties of England. The Anglo-Saxons had to make voyages of some 300 or 400 miles across a stormy but inland sea, whereas the English had to cross the wide Atlantic. The two colonizations differed in several important respects. The Anglo-Saxons left no parental government behind them on the continent; each colony claimed sovereign independent rights. The English colonists, on the other hand, when settled in their new homes still owed allegiance to the mother country. War made the seven Anglo-Saxon States or kingdoms into one; war made the thirteen English colonies or States into a single confederation. The enemy encountered by the Anglo-Saxons in England were Caucasians, not unlike themselves in a physical sense, whereas the enemy encountered by the English in America were of an unlike stock. A hybrid between Saxon and Celt could not be distinguished from either of the parent stocks, but a hybrid Anglo-Amerind was recognizable at sight. It took the Anglo-Saxons over three centuries to sweep across England; the people of Wales remained as a bulwark between them and the Irish Sea. From the time that the English colonists in America had established a firm belt along the Atlantic sea-board (1650) until the arrival of their descendants on the Pacific slopes, a period of two centuries elapsed. The original inhabitants of the land, numbering about 600,000 and divided into some 300 tribes, were killed or encircled as the Americans swept westward. In the census of 1930 the Amerinds, including half-breeds, numbered 332,000, most of them living on reservations. Thus in the course of three centuries a single Caucasian nation forming forty-eight units or States, and numbering (1946) 127 millions, replaced a conglomeration of Amerind tribes. The Anglo-Saxons and the colonial English shared the same hardy ethical sense; they had one rule of conduct for themselves, and another for the people whose lands they seized. Viscount Bryce, writing in 1911,[2] was less than just to the Amerinds when he penned the following sentence: " The territory now covered by the United States was, from a political point of view, practically vacant when discovered in the end of the fifteenth century." " A few hunting tribes," wrote Madison Grant,[3] " could not be allowed to possess a continent."

In the building up of a new nation the most important and also the most difficult thing is the establishment of a way of life, a way which, as it is handed on from one generation to the next, will become a quickening and guiding tradition.   Historians are agreed that the tradition which came to pervade the northern population of the United States was that established in New England by the Puritans, a people who valued their liberties, religious, political, and social, more than worldly success.   The Puritan colonists from England began to settle in their new home in 1620; by 1640 there were 20,000 of them with their homes scattered along Massachusetts Bay.   They were a people who prized learning, for they brought Harvard University into being in 1636.   A century later (1740), when the colonists had reached the million mark, the New Englanders had spread in every direction; they had " settled" the States which lie to the north of Massachusetts and also those which lie to the immediate south of that State, carrying with them and establishing their tradition.   The Dutch had set up a trading station on the site of New York and later made settlements there. The Swedes had landed and settled in Delaware (1638); if these Dutch and Swedish colonies had rooted and grown, then there might have been in America the same diversity of tongues and peoples as in Western Europe, for in more distant regions the French and Spaniards had also established stations.   The New Englanders, spreading southwards into the State of New York and carrying with them their strong assimilative powers, ulti-mately absorbed the Dutch as they, in turn, had overwhelmed the Swedes.   After the revolution the trek to the North-West Territory was headed by descendants of the New England pioneers.

In the south, in Virginia, another tradition took origin.   By 1622 the Virginian colonists numbered 4,000; they had become tobacco-planters and owners of African slaves.   Perhaps the warmer climate of the south induced the Virginian colonists to lead an easier and less laborious life than their Puritan brethren of the north.   Perhaps it was because the Virginians were recruited from the more leisured and wealthier class of Englishmen.   Wealth and slave labour made it possible for them to become the masters of spacious and well-appointed homes.   In the north, labour by the sweat of the brow was counted a virtue; in the south it came to be regarded as a virtue only when exercised by slaves. The southern squire was a man of education and culture with a high sense of public duty. As the early Virginians spread southwards into the Carolinas and Georgia they carried their ideals and modes of life with them. Later, when they moved westwards into the southern States, they succeeded in establishing the Virginian tradition in their new homes. Thus there arose two traditions among the Yusanians, that of New England in the north and that of Virginia in the south. As we shall see later, this twofold cultural heritage initiated the greatest crisis which has so far overtaken the Yusanian nation.

As we have seen (p. 147), one of the most remarkable characters of a nation is its powers of assimilation, its unconscious ability to impart to strangers and to immigrants its mode of life and its traditions. This ability to absorb is often regarded as something superadded to the normal life of a community, but this is not the case. Every generation hands on its tradition to its children who constitute the next generation; every child, as it grows up, undergoes the process of assimilation. A nation is a great school in which tradition is taught from day to day; it is taught in the market-place, in the church, and in the homes. The reciprocal affections of parents and children provide the machinery of assimilation within the home. Indeed, it has been observed that it is the children of immigrants who establish the first bonds linking them to their host nation. Throughout the colonial period, up to the time of the Declaration of Independence (July 4th, 1776), the power of assimilation of New Englanders and of Virginians was not greatly taxed; the flow of immigrants was limited in numbers, and although there was an inflow of Germans from the Rhine Valley, yet the greater number of new arrivals were of British origin. Thus the traditions of New England and of Virginia had time to develop and to undergo consolidation before the westward movement set in.

We come now to the first major event in Yusanian history—the crisis which made the English colonists into a nation. On July 4th, 1776, their Congress declared " that these united colonies are, and of right ought to be, free and independent States." Historians ascribe this declaration to political blunders made by King George and his Government, but the anthropologist sees in it an evolutionary movement of a kind with which he is familiar—that of self-determination (see p. 366). Political blunders were the immediate cause of the revolution, but the machinery which gave the nation birth was resident in human nature; sooner or later the "breakaway" would have occurred. At the very time when the colonists were drafting their Declaration, Adam Smith (1723–96) was writing the *Wealth of Nations* and penned the following passage: "To propose that Great Britain should voluntarily give up all authority over her colonies . . . would be to propose such a measure as never was . . . adopted by any nation in the world. . . . Yet to give up would be advantageous. . . . Filial affection would revive." [4]   That is a sane and contemporary view of the situation as measured by a Scot. Along side of it I place the opinion of a modern American professor of history.[5] "The Revolution itself," writes Professor Conmager (1941), was a great creative movement that set in about 1760 and came to a close with the establishment of Federal Government in 1789. The War of Independence was merely part of a larger movement." This "larger movement" was, in my opinion, that of "self-determination"—the act which brings a nation into being.

Having won the war (1783) the colonists had then to win the peace, which proved to be a matter of extreme difficulty. Each of the thirteen colonies had set its mind on being a separate independent State. Their collective population was under four millions, and their combined territory was more than ten times the area of England. Had the individual colonies insisted on retaining what they counted their rights, thirteen separate, warring nations would have come into existence—another Europe. Ultimately (1787) they agreed to federate under a central government. In their constitution there were two provisions which have a direct bearing on nation-making. The first and the most important of these was that no State could secede from the Union unless it had the consent of all the other States. Thus the greatest danger of a federal nation—that of disruption—was provided against. Another measure of no less importance was that which provided for extension of national territory and the creation of additional States. The result of the war between Britain and France (1756–63) opened the way for the colonists to surge westwards. The inhabitants of a new territory whenever they reached the number of 40,000 could claim admission to the Union. The first to claim admission was Vermont (1791), the last and forty-eighth was Oklahoma (1912). Thus was brought into existence a nation divided into forty-eight States and occupying an area of almost sixty times that of England.

Early in the nineteenth century a humanitarian spirit, spreading throughout civilized lands, led to the freeing of slaves; those of the British colonies were set at liberty in 1833. This spirit moved the northern States, of New England tradition, to demand the abolition of slavery in all the States of the Union. In 1861 the destiny of the nation was placed in the hands of Lincoln. Seven States seceded and were joined by another four; twenty-one States (the total number being then thirty-two) remained loyal to the central or federal government. Lincoln declared war against the seceding States. To keep slaves was not a breach of law; war could not be declared on that score, but secession was a crime against the constitution. Incidentally the Civil War (1861–65) set free some four million people of African origin, but the real object aimed at, and achieved, was the preservation of the nation as a single evolutionary unit. Secession or self-determination of a people in Europe might be commendable, but so far as the United States was concerned it was made the one heinous and unforgivable national sin.

In the Civil War over 360,000 men of the Northern States " gave their lives that their nation might live." Yet such was the resilience of the Yusanians that their numbers, which stood at 31·4 millions in 1860, had risen to 38·5 millions in 1870. In 1840 there were only seventeen millions in the United States, but that exceeded the population of England and Wales of the same date. From 1845 the full immigrant tide of Germans and of Irish set in; before 1914 over five million Germans and over four million Irish had arrived. In the same period some two million Scandinavians had added their genes to the Yusanian pool. In the last two decades of the nineteenth century the immigrant tide from N.W. Europe slackened and that from Central and Southern Europe set in. In the ten years which preceded the first world war seven millions were added, mostly from Central and Southern Europe. From first to last over thirty-eight million Europeans were carried to the American States.

The war of 1914–18 brought the immigrant chapter in the history of the United States to an end and opened a chapter of quite a different kind—that of isolationism. While in the war a wave of nationalism swept the States; the man was marked who was not 100 per cent American (Yusanian). By the end of the war the mood of the people had changed; they had become more nationally and racially conscious. Isolation, as we have seen, is one of the conditions which is essential for race-building; the Yusanians became isolationists, and by a series of enactments, beginning in 1921 and ending with the application on July 1st, 1928, of the "National Origins" Act, restricted immigration to 150,000 per annum. The population of the United States in 1920 was made the basis on which further admissions were to be made. The quota of immigrants which each foreign nation was permitted to send was determined by the extent to which their nation was represented in the make-up of the 1920 population of the United States. That necessitated an inquiry into the extent of the contribution made by each of the nations of Europe to the 1920 population of the States. This inquiry gave Britain the credit of having contributed, from first to last, her blood or genes to over forty-one per cent of the Yusanian population, which in 1920 numbered nearly ninety-five millions. The share assigned to Germany was sixteen per cent, to Eire eleven per cent, to Scandinavia and the smaller nations of N.W. Europe seven per cent. In this estimate seventy-five per cent of the genes circulating in the new Yusanian nation was attributed to the peoples of N.W. Europe, the remainder coming from Central and Southern nations of Europe. It is one thing to determine the Caucasian assortment of genes with which a new nation sets out; it is a much more difficult matter to forecast what the final issue will be, for certain strains prosper and increase in numbers, while others tend to die out. The "Old American" type of Hrdlicka,[6] which continues the New England strain, fails to hold its own; all authorities are agreed on that. Thus the strange fact comes to light that while the tradition established in a new nation by its pioneers may continue, the stock or type which introduced it may become submerged or die out.

From 1926 to 1938 Professor Hooton of Harvard [8] carried out an exact investigation of the population of ten of the States, to determine the racial composition of the Yusanians according to the methods which anthropologists had employed to discriminate the races of Europe (see Essay XXXIII). Of pure Nords he found only 2·4 per cent, but then it must be remembered that in

Sweden,[9] the most Nordic nation of Europe, this type does not exceed ten per cent; of pure Mediterraneans, 4.4 per cent; of pure round-headed Alpines, 2.7 per cent. The vast majority of people he examined were a mixture of these types or races. In seventy-six per cent of them, however, a Nordic element was recognized; in twenty-four per cent this element was lacking. Thus, whether we trace the Yusanians to their national homes in Europe, or assign them to the racial types of that continent, the result is approximately the same. In its racial composition the Yusanians are most akin to the peoples of N.W. Europe. In keeping with this result is the degree of ease with which the nationals of Europe adapt themselves to the Yusanian way of life. As we proceed from the north-west of Europe towards Asia Minor the resistance to assimilation to the American way of life increases, reaching its maximum in the Greeks and the Jews.

A basal element in the theory maintained in this book is that in the primitive and productive phase of human evolution mankind was arranged in small local groups. How is evolution affected when an area, formerly occupied by hundreds of small isolated groups, becomes the home of a single closely knit unit or nation? In the course of his inquiries Professor Hooton found local evolution to be at work; each State had its own type or types. " The result of my analysis," he wrote,[10] " was to establish the fact that the older American population has differentiated into distinct State physical types." Data collected during the Civil War had suggested the existence of local types. No doubt immigrants tended to go to States and towns already occupied by their fellow-nationals, and new townships " attracted like-minded people " (Bagehot), but these are imperfect explanations. The chief factor in the production of local types or strains is in-breeding; marriages tend to be local. There is, too, as Ripley [11] pointed out, " a disposition of distinct types to keep separate and apart " so far as marriage is concerned. Thus the formation of great national units, such as that of the United States, does not bring evolution to an end, but it does clog its wheels.

Some paragraphs back I made the statement that after the first world war the Yusanians turned " racial-minded "; at least their Government accepted, in its immigration policy, the advice of experts who took the same point of view as I do—namely, that nation-building is a species of race-building. In evidence of this statement let me cite passages from a Report [12] submitted in 1934 to the Chamber of Commerce of the State of New York by a Special Committee. Here is the first passage (p. 7): "Thus, in the exercise of its own rights and in the building up of its own human stocks, the receiving nation must exercise its sovereign right to select courageously and radically for the improvement of its own human values in future generations." Another passage (p. 11): "Immigration calls for an attitude as thoroughly American as is necessary in the army, navy, and in the conduct of foreign affairs." A further citation is: "Because America needs no more human seed-stock, she is in a very strong position to set high standards for future immigrants." "Common loyalty," the Report continues (p. 15), "demands that our national policy of population control (must) provide that our human seed-stocks of the future will conserve our best racial stocks." Much similar evidence could be cited from other reliable sources, but the citations given are sufficient to prove that those who are responsible for the immigration policy of the United States are alive to the fact that they are engaged on the most difficult and complex of all human activities—that of race-building. A successful race, like a winning team, must be a workable and balanced combination of all the talents and of all the good qualities inherent in human nature.

The Yusanian nation is faced by a racial problem of great difficulty and also of great magnitude; it has in its midst a people of African origin, which it refuses to assimilate. Writing in 1906 Professor Sumner of Yale made this statement: [13] "Black and White in the United States of America are now tending to more strict segregation." Writing in 1911 Viscount Bryce,[14] made the following observations: "Negroes are sharply cut off from the Whites by colour and all that colour means. . . . To all southern sentiment inter-marriage is shocking. In eight States it is illegal. The enormous majority, which does not reason, is swayed by a feeling so strong and universal that there seems no chance of its abating." The attitude of the Yusanians to their Negro compatriots has not grown milder since Bryce's time; indeed it has hardened; assimilation as a solution of their Negro problem is rejected out of hand. Consider for a moment what complete assimilation implies. At the time of the Civil War Negroes numbered over four millions; in 1946 they had increased to over thirteen millions constituting one tenth of the population. To ask the Yusanians to become one-tenth Negro is too big a price to expect them to pay for the solution of their Negro problem. How averse they are to such a solution may be seen from the instructions given to the enumerators of the 1930 census.[15] " A person of mixed white and Negro blood," the enumerators are instructed, " should be returned as Negro, no matter how small the percentage of Negro blood." In the case of the Indians (Amerinds) the instructions are : " A person of mixed white and Indian blood should be returned as Indian except where percentage of Indian blood is very small or where he is regarded as white by his community." A touch of Negro blood disqualifies a man from being counted Yusanian, but one with more than a drop of Indian blood is accepted. This discrimination in favour of the Indian may be due to the fact that his racial traits are less obtrusive in the hybrid than are those of the Negro.

Although the Jewish and the Negro problems are both racial in origin, yet they are different in kind. The animosity towards the Jew is due to his antagonism to assimilation ; the Negro, on the other hand, is ready and willing to assimilate ; the antagonism is on the part of the Whites. The Whites claim a racial superiority, and this claim has been accepted as part of the Negro tradition. For a Negro to marry a White is to go up in the world, but for a White to marry a Negro is to go down in it. The antipathy of the Yusanians towards Negroes is of the same nature as " class-feeling," the feeling which exists between upper and lower classes in the older nations of Europe. Whatever the exact nature of the discrimination of the White towards the Negro may prove to be, there is no doubt that its presence is a disruptive factor in national life. It is for statesmen to devise measures for its control : the business of the anthropologist is not to suggest remedies nor to utter ethical platitudes, but to observe and state his observation without reserve. None of us can get away from the fact that man is a racial-minded animal. He is also a race-building animal.

Although this essay has already exceeded the length I had set to it, there still remain two matters which I wish to touch on. The first relates to the comparison so often made between the forty-eight United States of America and the discordant nations of Europe. Clarence Streit [16] and many other political writers have proposed that the international difficulties of Europe could be solved by copying the Yusanian federal scheme. Let us look into the difficulties which stand in the way of establishing a federal system in Europe on the American pattern. Bullocks, like human beings, are social in their nature. Bullocks object to " gate-crashing " by strangers. If a farmer wishes to add strangers to his home herd, he moves that herd into a field which is new to them, and then introduces the strangers. Under such conditions the "immigrant" bullocks are soon assimilated. Ripley,[17] the American anthropologist, noted a somewhat similar effect produced on immigrants by the strange environment in which they found themselves on landing. "The subtle effects of change of environment, religious, linguistic, political and social," he noted, " is another powerful influence in breaking down ethnic barriers." Every one of the thirty-eight millions who entered America as immigrants suffered that thawing experience, before they were received by the home-herd and assimilated. In brief, if Europe is to be modelled on American lines, its inhabitants must be put through a mill similar to that which has made the forty-eight States of America into a unity. Nothing less than clearing Europe, and resettling it as America was settled, could give Europe a single tongue and a united front.

The other matter I want to touch on now is one of minor importance. Indeed, it is intended chiefly for the ears of my fellow anthropologists. We have been so engaged in studying the races and peoples which came into existence in bygone ages that we have overlooked events of far greater moment—the coming into existence of new races in the modern world. Race-production is an infinitely more important study than the discrimination of one old race from another. In this essay I have sought to trace the evolution of the largest, the most powerful in war and in peace of all nations (or races), and yet it is the youngest. It takes a European nation five or six centuries for a national spirit to penetrate to all its crannies. The Yusanian nation (and race) dates only from 1920. It was then that it shut the gate for immigrants and started race-building in earnest. What will the Yusanians become after five centuries of national life? Their greatest danger is the old one—that of secession; their numbers are so large and their territory so extensive.

D D

REFERENCES

[1] This difficulty has been felt by Professor Hooton as the following extract from a lecture entitled, " What is an American " will serve to illustrate :— " Americans, for our present purposes, may be divided into four classes : (1) Old Americans; (2) New Americans—both of whom have been born to Americanism; (3) Immigrant Americans who have achieved Americanism; (4) Afro-Americans—or those who had Americanism thrust on them. There are, in addition, Real Americans, but these are called Indians and, of course, do not count." *Amer. Jour. Phys. Anthrop.*, 1936, vol. 22, p. 4.

[2] Bryce, James, *The American Commonwealth*, 1911, vol. 2, p. 455.

[3] Grant, Madison, *The Conquest of a Continent*, 1933, p. 222.

[4] Smith, Adam, *The Wealth of Nations*, Cannan's ed., 1925, vol. 2, p. 116.

[5] Commager, H. S., Professor of History, Columbia University, *New York Times*, Jan. 26, 1941.

[6] Hrdlicka, Ales, *The Old Americans*, 1926.

[7] See authors mentioned under references 3 and 8.

[8] Hooton, E. A., *Crime and the Man*, Harvard Univ. Press, 1939; *Twilight of Man*, 1939, p. 196.

[9] Retzius, Gustav, Huxley Lecture, *Jour. Roy. Anthrop. Instit.*, 1909, vol. 49, p. 286.

[10] Hooton, E. A., *Twilight of Man*, 1939, p. 212.

[11] Ripley, W. Z., Huxley Lecture, *Jour. Roy. Anthrop. Instit.*, 1908, vol. 38, p. 232.

[12] Laughlin, Harry H., *A Report of the Special Committee on Immigration*, New York, 1934.

[13] Sumner, W. Graham, *Folkways*, 1906, p. 113.

[14] Bryce, James, see reference 2, p. 533.

[15] Racial Classification in the 1930 Census, *Eugenical News*, September, 1931, p. 150.

[16] Streit, Clarence, *Union Now*, 1939.

[17] Ripley, W. Z., see p. 234 of reference 11.

THE RISE OF NATIONS IN BRITISH DOMINIONS

Synopsis.—Subject of essay outlined. The early settlement of Canada by the French. A tradition was established. The annexation of Canada by the British. Strife between the French and British Canadians. Union of Lower and Upper Canada. The population of Quebec is eighty per cent French. The French Canadians form a nation. A comparison with the Dutch of South Africa. Two national traditions were established in Canada—French-Canadian and British-Canadian. Early British settlements. The " racial composition" of the British Canadians. The original inhabitants of Canada. The rise of the Australian nation. The aborigines. Their replacement by Caucasians. Early years of settlement. A " white " policy adopted. Lack of an early tradition. Later settlements. The policy of Wakefield. A big tide of emigration sets in. Division into provinces. There is no " British nation " in the homelands, but there is one in Australia. Its " racial " composition. Unsolved problems. The people of New Zealand as a nation. The Maoris. The settlement of New Zealand and establishment of responsible government. The New Zealanders are the purest of British nations. The formation of new nations in " acquired " territories is the principal way in which human evolution is now being effected.

IN this essay I am to deal with the nations which have arisen in the four British Dominions. One of these, that of South Africa, has been considered already (Essay XXXV); those which come up for consideration in the present essay are the two nations of Canada—the French Canadian and the British Canadian; the Australian nation; and, most compact and homogeneous of all, that of New Zealand. All of them illustrate the manner in which new peoples and new races come into being in the modern world.

Although the French had prospected the St. Lawrence as early as 1534, real colonization of the banks of that river did not begin until 1604.[1] In that year ships sailed from Havre carrying the first batch of colonists; among them were squires from Normandy, accompanied by their farming tenants and country families. They carried with them their local form of speech, their French customs and mode of life, and were devoutly religious, almost all being Roman Catholics. The lands they settled are now in the province of Quebec, but they also established themselves in the maritime provinces now known as New Brunswick and Nova Scotia—these two lands being almost equal in area to that of England. The French colonists of 1604 found, as the English pioneers were also to learn, that the testing time of a colony is its opening years. They had their failures and also their successes; they were strengthened by accessions from France which continued to arrive throughout the greater part of the seventeenth century. They called Lower Canada "New France"; they settled closely and firmly established in their midst a strong and distinctive tradition, that which now animates the Canadian French.

The French inhabitants of New Brunswick and of Nova Scotia were known as Acadians; they and their lands (Acadia) were transferred to Britain under the Treaty of Utrecht (1713). Later, when the Seven Years War (1756–63) broke out between France and Britain, they were harshly dealt with by their new masters; many sought new homes in the English Colonies, where they were not easily assimilated. At the end of the Seven Years War Lower Canada with its French population came into the care of the British Government. They then numbered about 60,000,[2] while at that time the English colonists to the south of Canada numbered about three millions.

In 1774 Britain, being in trouble with her colonists, secured the neutrality of the French Canadians by guaranteeing them their language, their civil laws, and their religion. In tracing the history of the French Canadian nation we shall take a forward leap of sixty-three years, bringing us to 1837. By that time Upper Canada was being settled by colonists of British birth, and strife was brewing between the French and British settlements. Lord Durham was sent out in 1837, and this was what he had to report to his Government: " I expected to find a contest between a government and its people; I found two nations warring in the bosom of a single State; I found a struggle not of principle, but of Races." As a remedy Lord Durham proposed the Union of Lower and Upper Canada, which was brought about in 1840. Then, in 1867, the French-speaking province of Quebec and the three English-speaking provinces of Ontario, New Brunswick, and Nova Scotia, were united under a constitution, "similar in principle to that of the United Kingdom." In this way Quebec, the homeland of the French Canadians, became one of the nine provinces which make up the modern Dominion of Canada.

The area of Quebec, as originally constituted, was equal to that of France, but recent extensions towards the cold north has made the province more than twice the size of the mother country. The census of 1941 gave the population of the province as 3,331,000, of which eighty per cent were of French descent and less than nineteen per cent of British origin. In the capital of the province, Montreal, ninety per cent of the population is of French stock.[3] Of the 3,483,000 French Canadians, over 600,000 of them live outside their homeland province—in Nova Scotia, New Brunswick, Ontario, and the prairie provinces. These are exposed to the assimilative powers of the British, but within the province of Quebec the power of assimilation lies with the French. The population of that province represents a nation within the framework of the British Commonwealth just in the same sense as Scotland does. It is a separate, inbreeding community, firmly rooted in the soil, conscious of a common spirit and zealous for its own perpetuation. In its political action it is isolationist and "particularist."

It is instructive to compare the early Caucasian settlement of the Dominion of Canada with that of South Africa. The Dutch landed at the Cape in 1652; the British "took over" in 1814; the Dutch were thus in full possession of their territory for 152 years. The French settlement of Canada began in 1604; the British took possession in 1763; the French were thus under their own control for 159 years. In South Africa the British colonists took up their abodes in the midst of the Dutch people, and as we have seen (p. 357) it is the Dutch tradition which prevails, thus making a single nationality possible. In Canada the French settlements were closely knit together; British colonists settled outside the French country, in the two maritime provinces—Nova Scotia and New Brunswick—on the east of Quebec, and

in the inland province or Ontario on the west. Thus two traditions were established in Canada, the French, firmly rooted to the
soil, and the British, less localized; in due time each tradition
gave birth to a nation.

Canada has an area of 3·4 million square miles, being in this
respect only a little smaller than the United States, but only about
1·5 million square miles are suitable for " white " settlement. Of
the suitable land over 200,000 square miles is occupied by the
French Canadians, thus leaving 1·3 million square miles to provide
homes for the British Canadians. In 1941 the British Canadian
nation numbered 8,175 millions, there being only about six souls
for each square mile of territory; were these square miles to be
populated to the same density as the United States now are, the
British Canadians would number some fifty millions—a formidable
nation.

The British Canadian is one of the youngest of nations; it
began in 1776 when the loyalists of the United States had to seek
a new home. Some 70,000 [4] of these settled in what are now the
maritime provinces of Canada, and on lands which were to be
included in the province of Ontario. Even at the beginning of
the nineteenth century the British Canadians numbered less than
a quarter of a million. By the middle of the century they reached
the two million mark; ever since then they have steadily increased, till in 1941 they numbered over eight millions. To the
three original provinces occupied by the British—Ontario, Nova
Scotia, and New Brunswick—five others have been added—
Manitoba (1870), Columbia (1871), Prince Edward Island (1873),
and the two prairie provinces (Alberta and Saskatchewan) in 1905.

What is the racial composition of the nation? If we agree that
nations represent races, then its racial composition is as follows.
Rather more than thirty-six per cent are of English origin;
somewhat more than seventeen per cent are of Scottish descent;
rather less than sixteen per cent draw their ancestry from Ireland.
Thus sixty-nine per cent are of British origin; thirty-one per
cent are traceable to seventeen nations of the continent of Europe.
Of the continental nationalities in the British provinces the French
contribute eight per cent, the Germans just under six per cent, the
Russians under five per cent, the Scandinavians three per cent,
the Poles two per cent, the Jews (who numbered 170,000 in
1941) rather more than two per cent. Thus the " make up " of

the British-Canadian nation is very similar to that of the United States, the chief points of difference being the proportions of people of British-Irish origin being fifty-three per cent in the United States, while it is sixty-nine per cent in Canada. On the other hand, the German element provided fifteen per cent of the population of the States, but less than six per cent of the Canadian population. In Canada, then, there are two nations of different origins; that of Quebec draws over eighty per cent of its number from France, that of the British provinces sixty-nine per cent from the mother lands. In Great Britain there is a political confederation of three nations, in the Dominion of Canada, of two.

I have been writing as if Canada had been uninhabited when the French took possession of the banks of the St. Lawrence. That is far from having been the case. From Nova Scotia to Columbia, a distance of over 3,000 miles, Canada was occupied by hunting, food-gathering tribes of Red Indians, who many thousands of years before the Caucasians arrived from Europe had themselves been colonists from Asia. The Ottawa confederacy was made up of three strong tribes of fierce fighters, as the early French knew to their cost. North of the Great Lakes were many large tribes arranged in several powerful confederations. At their zenith the Canadian Indians probably never numbered more than 130,000. In 1904 there were 108,000 of them; in 1945, 118,000. They are now (1946) increasing in number; more than ten per cent of them are half-castes. The Indians live apart, on reservations, or in villages of their own; they are to be found in all the provinces of the Dominion. Ultimately they are likely to disappear by absorption into the Caucasian stock. The anthropologist, viewing the colonization of Canada from his own narrow angle, sees in it a territorial gain for the " white " or Caucasian stock, at the expense of the Mongolian family.

From Canada we cross the Pacific to mark the rise of another new nation, that of Australia. The people of this continent are known as Australians and accept this name for themselves. I cavilled at the Yusanians taking the name " American " because in their continent of that name there are twenty-three nations, but in Australia there is only one. Their continent, which has an area of three million square miles, is like Canada in that its area is much greater than its habitability. In the opinion of Professor Griffith Taylor[5] only about one fifth of it, that is 600,000 square miles, is suitable for close settlement. The habitable lands are to be found in the south-eastern areas of the continent; only there is the rainfall sufficient to meet the needs of the farmer. In 1945 the Australian nation numbered 7·3 millions, which gives an average of twelve persons for each square mile of " suitable " land. It is usually held that the numbers could be raised to fifty inhabitants to the square mile which would give white Australia a population of thirty millions.

When Captain Cook ran up the Union Jack at Botany Bay in 1770 and took possession of the land in the name of his Sovereign Lord, King George III, the whole continent was occupied by an aboriginal race of mankind which had been evolved in that quarter of the earth. The Australian aborigines in 1770 numbered 250,000 to 300,000; their organization was tribal; each tribe had its own territory on which it lived by gathering the natural produce and by hunting. Their tribes, which varied greatly in size, were very numerous; each represented an " independency "—a separate, inbreeding, perpetuating, evolutionary unit. The competition between the tribes for survival was mild and easy : the invasion and seizure by one tribe of the territory of another was almost unknown. By nature they were a cheerful people. Such was the race destined to be replaced by the Australian nation. In the State of Victoria, for example, which has an area of 88,000 square miles, and where about 7,000 aborigines had their abode, only 269 survived in 1943. They have been replaced by nearly two millions of energetic Caucasians. The Australian census of 1933 recorded the existence of 73,000 aborigines on the whole continent, one third of which had Caucasian blood in them. They lose heart when their tribal wheels cease to revolve.

No nation ever began life under less auspicious circumstances than did that of Australia. In January, 1778, after an eight-months' voyage from England, H.M.S. Sirius (Admiral Arthur Philips in command), accompanied by nine small transports, sailed between the Sydney Heads, to effect the first white settlement of Australia. In February following 1,030 colonists were put on shore; they were the overflow of English prisons. Lord Sydney, then Secretary for State for the Home Department and responsible for the choice of emigrants, gave the following instruction to Admiral Philips : [6] " As I would not wish convicts to lay the foundations of our Empire, I think they should ever remain separated from the Garrison and from other settlers that may come from Europe. . . . There can be no slavery in a free land." Admiral Philips reported that " no country offers less assistance to the first settlers than does this ", but adds " it will prove the most valuable acquisition Great Britain has ever made." From these facts readers will at once realize that British statesmen at the end of the eighteenth century were more concerned in relieving the pressure on their prisons than in nation-building. The " convict-colonists " were intended to supply free settlers with labour; one ought to be thankful that labour was chosen from Britain and not from Africa, India, or China. From the first it was determined that colonists should be of the Caucasian stock and this policy has been steadily pursued by all Australian statesmen.

After 1820 free settlers began to arrive besides the large contingents of convicts, many of whom were guilty of offences now counted venial. By 1829 there were 37,000 settlers (including prisoners) in the neighbourhood of Sydney, New South Wales; at the same date there was in Tasmania, which had its first consignment of convicts in 1804, a population (free and bond) of 17,000. After 1820 British settlers, many of them representatives of the better-off and better-educated people of the homeland, began to arrive. After 1830 settlement was permitted outside the original restricted areas; new arrivals " took up " large tracts of land for sheep and cattle raising; the owners of these " stations " introduced a culture and a tradition not unlike that of the Virginians. But nowhere in Australia was there a community or a tradition equivalent to those of New England.

By 1830 a settlement had been effected in Western Australia—the Swan River Colony—and about the same time prospectors were seeking lands for settlement in South Australia near where Adelaide now stands. These two settlements, in West and in South Australia, passed through many vicissitudes in their earlier phases, but ultimately both survived. Edward Gibbon Wakefield (1796–1862) had to do with both of these settlements. He deserves more than a passing notice, for he was the first Englishman to foresee that emigration, rightly managed, might bring into existence a British Commonwealth of nations. Having run away with an heiress (in Chancery), he had to expiate his offence by spending three years in Newgate prison (1827–30), during which time he planned his schemes of emigration. The public of his time were indifferent to colonies; political economists regarded them as encumbrances. Under Wakefield's scheme " the mother country and the colony would become partners in a new trade—the creation of happy human beings; one country providing the raw material—that is the land; the other providing the machinery—that is the men and women to convert the unpeopled soil into living images of God." [7] He knew that colonies had to be nursed in their early stage but hoped to make them self-supporting by selling the " native " land and using the proceeds to bring out fresh colonists. We shall meet with Wakefield again when dealing with the early colonization of New Zealand.

In 1851 a strong tide of immigration set in; gold had been discovered and large tracts of land were being freed for new arrivals; by 1891 1,300,000 had come from Europe, the vast majority from the mother country. In the meantime the continent had become divided into provinces; as they came into being responsible government was given to their inhabitants. Tasmania was parted from New South Wales in 1825 and became self-governing in 1856; Victoria was separated from the mother colony (N.S.W.) in 1851, and shouldered its own government in 1856; Queensland was cut off from New South Wales in 1859 and at the same time became responsible for the management of her own affairs. South Australia was recognized as a province in 1836 and as a self-governing colony in 1856. Western Australia received its constitution in 1890. Thus six separate colonies came into existence; in each there was a potential danger of becoming an independent State and Nation. Joseph Chamberlain, who was Secretary of State for the Colonies in 1900, foresaw the danger; he proposed that Australia should copy the plan adopted by the American colonists—namely, that the six colonies should become six federated States, united under a central Government. This plan was adopted in 1901 and in this way the Commonwealth of Australia was brought into existence. Under the pressure of war (1939–45) the constituent States surrendered their liberties to the central Government for a term of seven years, evidence of the existence of a national unity within the Commonwealth.

There is no separate British nation or race within the homeland islands; there, we are English, Welsh, Scottish, or Irish; but here in Australia there is a race and nation of British origin. The racial composition of the Australian nation, so far as data gleaned from census returns will permit us to judge, is as follows. Those of British origin make up ninety-seven per cent of the total population; [8] only three per cent are traceable to the continental nations of Europe. Of the British, sixty per cent are of English origin; rather more than twenty-three per cent are of Irish parentage; those of Scottish descent number slightly more than fifteen per cent; the Welsh element number two per cent. The British representation in Canada is sixty-nine per cent against ninety-seven per cent in Australia; in both lands the proportion of Irish and of Scots is greater than in the home population; in Canada the Scots outnumber the Irish; in Australia the proportions are reversed. The Australian nation, then, is truly British in its composition; in a new continent and isolated in a strange environment, it will develop its allotted potentialities and become an Australian race.

Although a homogeneous people, the Australians have population problems of their own to solve. They are the trustees of a dying race; a race can save itself only by its own spontaneous efforts; the best of trusteeship can only ameliorate, it cannot restore. Then, they have empty spaces; they have tropical territory in the north, where white men can live and breed, but white men will not toil in the fields at the temperature which prevails there if they can find a home in more temperate lands. The Australian nation suffers from a high standard of living and a low birth-rate. Their States are widely distant from one another; there is the danger of secession. That danger receded as the war of 1939-45 went on; they had to unite to keep out a common enemy. Indeed, if in the crisis of 1941 the Esau of the British family had not come to the rescue, a White policy for Australia might have come to a sudden end.

From Australia we pass to New Zealand to consider the rise of the latest, and probably the last, of British nations. New Zealand, with a total area of over 103,000 square miles, is divided into a North Island with an area of somewhat less than that of England, and a South Island, which exceeds the area of England. In 1945 the Caucasian inhabitants numbered over 1·7 millions, giving a distribution of over sixteen to the square mile. In the course of a few centuries its population may well be equal to that of the home islands at the present time (forty-seven millions).

For at least four centuries before the arrival of the British, New Zealand had been inhabited by the Maoris, a robust, tribal people of Polynesian stock. In 1945 they numbered 97,000, a figure which is probably greater than any attained in pre-British times. After their last war with the white colonists (1861–71) they lost heart and their numbers declined. In 1898 there were only 42,000 of them; since then they have more than doubled their numbers. They have their own communities; 4·4 thousand square miles have been reserved for their use. Probably one in seven of the present generation has white blood in his veins. Complete absorption by the white population is a possibility.

In 1814 the British settlement of New Zealand was heralded by the arrival of missionaries in the North Island; they were soon followed by adventurers who obtained grants of land from local chiefs. Scots were early on the scene; so was Wakefield. He, with others, promoted companies in London to acquire land and found colonies. "Everything," said Wakefield, "is to be English, save the soil. . . . The new country is to be made a counterpart of England." [9] Early in 1840 a Governor was sent out by the Crown and settlement began in earnest. In 1844 the Free Church of Scotland sent out colonists by the thousand to establish a home in the South Island (Otago); the High Church colonists from England settled in the same island at Canterbury to the north of the Scots. In the sixties 50,000 Scandinavians arrived. In 1852 the colonists became responsible for the management of their own affairs ; in 1881 the population passed the half-million mark; in 1911 the million mark was reached. In 1907 New Zealand became a Dominion; in 1931, with other British Dominions, she became a self-governing nation, her only remaining tie with the homeland being her allegiance to the British Crown.

The New Zealanders, in their racial composition, are even more British than the Australians. In the census of 1911, it was estimated that ninety-eight per cent of the population was of British origin and no foreign influx has happened since then. The New Zealanders of British origin trace themselves back to the home-countries in the following proportions : sixty per cent to England—the same as in Australia; twenty-one per cent to Scotland, which is eight per cent greater than in Australia;

eighteen per cent to Ireland, five per cent less than in Australia; one per cent to Wales, half the proportion found in Australia. One feature of the New Zealand nation is the strength of the Scottish element; in the home population it represents only ten per cent of the total population, but in New Zealand it has more than twice that proportion. The New Zealanders, too, have established quite a distinctive tradition, differing from that of any of the home nationalities.

The reader who has had the patience to follow me thus far may be inclined to ask : " What has the rise of these New Nations to do with Human Evolution? " Let us consider, in the first place, the evolutionary change produced in the world of humanity by the rise of a Caucasian nation in New Zealand. That land, formerly held by a people of the Mongolian Division of mankind, has been taken over by one belonging to the Caucasian Division. To that extent the composition of the world of humanity has been changed. The Caucasian stock has gained an increased foothold on the earth at the expense of a rival stock. It is in this way that evolutionary changes are being effected, the way in which they have always been brought about; always by one community or people, possessing advantages, replacing another which is without these advantages. Or take the case of Australia; for æons of time it has been in possession of a people belonging to the Australasian Division of humanity; that people has been replaced by a new Caucasian people; the map of humanity has been altered to that extent. Much more drastic are the changes which have been brought about in North America by the intrusion of the Caucasian stock into territories formerly held by tribes of Mongolian derivation. The United States and Canada make up one seventh of the total area of the earth available for human habitation; they have become strongholds for Caucasians; 140 million Europeans have taken the place of little more than a million Red Indians. Never in any period of human history have evolutionary changes taken place so extensively and so rapidly as in the last five centuries. New nations have been brought into existence, nations made up of a combination of old genes; and may we not expect that new genes will in due time make their appearance among the old and that distinctive genes will come into existence? In fresh environments, too, other selective agencies will come into operation and so help to give these new nations distinctive physical appearances. New races are arising under our eyes.

REFERENCES

[1] Montandon, George, *Revue Scientif.*, 1938, Sept. 15, p. 288.

[2] Montandon states that there were three million French in North America at the time of the Revolution.

[3] Leacock, Stephen, *New York Times*, Aug. 19, 1934.

[4] The number of Loyalists who left the United States for Canada after the Revolution is variously estimated. Some authorities give 40,000, others 70,000.

[5] Taylor, Professor Griffith, *Reports of Austral. Assoc. Advan. Sc.*, 1923, vol. 18, p. 433.

[6] Becke, L., and Jeffrey, W., *Admiral Philips, The Founder of New South Wales*, 1899.

[7] Mills, R. C., *The Colonization of Australia*, 1915, vol. 18, p. 310.

[8] Carr-Saunders, Sir A. M., *Eugenics Review*, 1927, vol. 18, p. 310. He gives the number of Australians of British descent as over 90 per cent.

[9] Scholefield, Guy H., *United Empire*, 1911, vol. 2, p. 303.

[10] Carr-Saunders, Sir A. M., gives the percentage of New Zealanders of British descent as " over 95 " (see under reference 8).

RETROSPECT AND PROSPECT

THE preceding essay and my eighty-first year having come to an end on the same day, it seemed to me expedient to cast an eye backwards and recapitulate the salient points of my argument before passing on to the remaining part of the field I had intended to cover. First, then, let me retread the path along which my argument has come as briefly as words will permit. Going back to Essay I, the reader will find an outline of my theory of human evolution; its basal idea is that, from the very beginning, man has evolved as a member of a social team or group; that these miniature societies remained apart and were in competition with each other. Essay II is devoted to authors who have anticipated one or more of the ideas which go to make up the "Group Theory" of human evolution. In Essay III evidence is assembled to prove that in all parts of the earth mankind is now, or was at a former period, divided into a mosaic of small, isolated communities. In Essay IV the importance and the antiquity of "territorialism" as a factor in evolution is discussed; each social group considered itself the absolute owners of the land on which it lived. In these earlier essays it is postulated that man's evolution is divisible into two distinct but unequal periods. There was first the long *primal* period when mankind was separated into small local groups or communities; this period is estimated to have lasted at least a million years. It was during the primal period that man made his major evolutionary advances. The *post-primal* period began with the discovery of agriculture. Although the post-primal period has endured for less than 10,000 years it has led to a revolution in the mode of human evolution.

The essays which begin with V and end with XIII form a series devoted to a single subject—namely, the rise of the mentality which characterized the "evolutionary units" or isolated local groups of humanity during the primal period. The sources which provide information as to the mentality of early man are three in number. There is first the mentality of social groups of anthropoid apes which may be assumed to be older than that of human beings; the second sources come from the study of primitive peoples still living in the group stage of existence; the developing mentality of the modern child provides the third source of information. Essay V is devoted to an analysis of the " group spirit "—the mental bonds which keep the members of a group united and at the same time keep them apart from members of neighbouring groups. Patriotism comes up for consideration in Essay VI, particularly its importance as a factor in the evolution of groups. Patriotism, it is held, is similar in nature to all of man's inborn tendencies or predispositions and is made up of two elements. The disposition to love one's native land is inborn—the country loved depending on the accident of birth. Essay VII gives my reasons for believing that in primitive human groups mentality was so fashioned as to combine co-operation and competition into an effective instrument of evolution. It is assumed in Essay VIII that man has been evolved from a stock in which conduct was controlled by instinct, but that in him these have become changed into biases or predispositions. These innate predispositions are all directed towards the survival and perpetuation of the group or community. There is thus more than a grain of truth in the aphorism that " the species is wise."

Man's nature resents injury and seeks for retaliation and revenge. The role which revenge plays in keeping primitive groups apart is discussed in Essay IX. In this essay I take the opportunity of illustrating how an instinctive reaction intended primarily for the defence of the individual becomes transferred to serve in the defence of the group or tribe. The tribesman regards an injury to his tribe as one done to himself. Here, too, we come across the principle of collective responsibility and of collective justice, which serve so efficiently to keep the members of a group united. Perhaps the most potent of all the mental factors which mould the destiny of a group is that of ambition, or the search for status, which is the subject of Essay X. Primitive man, like modern man, sought to slake his personal ambition by placing it at the service of his group. Primitive groups were ambitious for power; the greater their man-power the more certain their survival. In the search for individual status within a group, public or group opinion is all important. There was a constant rivalry between groups for status, so securing inter-group competition. In Essay XI, it is shown how all these emotions, feelings, and predispositions which go to make up "human nature" co-operate to give government to a group—a government which seems automatic. Human nature has been evolved in such a way as to serve as an instrument of evolution. Essay XII opens up a subject of outstanding importance—that of leadership. The qualities which go to make one man a leader and another a follower are assumed to be inborn. To give a rightly balanced group, leaders must be few and followers numerous. The series dealing with the mentality of primitive groups comes to an end with Essay XIII, in which morality is discussed. The most striking feature of primitive morality is its dual nature; always we find that the conduct of primitive man is regulated by two codes of morality; his conduct towards fellow-members is based on a code of amity, while that towards members of outside groups is based on that of enmity. The author infers that a dual morality has conferred advantages on evolving communities.

In Essay XIV another field of inquiry is entered; our attention now becomes centred on the means by which structural and functional changes are brought about in the bodies and brains of evolving human beings; we are now in search of the "machinery of evolution." This search continues through Essays XV, XVI, XVII, XVIII, XIX, and XX. In Essay XIV the author compares the machinery of evolution which holds in the motor-car or automobile world with that which prevails in the human world and finds that in both of these there is a triple process at work—namely, production, competition, and selection. Lamarck and Darwin believed that hereditable structural changes could be brought about by use and wont; this doctrine is not accepted by the author. In Essay XV it is claimed that a multitude of small, isolated, inbreeding, competing groups provides the most favourable conditions for rapid evolutionary change. In primitive societies choice of mates was confined within the group, thus favouring inbreeding. As long as genes are healthy inbreeding is advantageous. Inbreeding favours the production of new local types; even in modern communities where there is no limitation in the choice of mates, marriages tend to be contracted within the same locality, thus giving rise to local breeds.

The machinery of evolution which brings about the differentiation of mankind into races is of the same nature as that which determines the differentiation of human beings into men and women (Essay XVIII). In both cases the substances which serve as "determiners" or hormones are formed in the body during its development and growth; they have the power of altering structure as well as function. In man, as in the great anthropoids, hormones act so as to give the male preponderance in mass of body and in strength. If the testicles are removed from the young male, then, because of the hormonal disturbance, he becomes radically changed both in appearance and in mentality. Darwin sought to explain the differences which separate one variety of mankind from another, such as those which distinguish a Negro from a European, as being a result of sexual selection (Essay XIX), but the opinion which prevails to-day is that these differences must be attributed to the action of hormones. Hormones, then, form an important part of the machinery of evolution.

In Essay XX a cardinal principle in human evolution is broached. During its development the human embryo recapitulates certain ancestral traits, but, amid these ancestral traits there are interpolated features which are new—features which never have had an existence in the adult state but await an opportunity, as it were, to be carried into that state. The same is true in the developmental stages of anthropoid apes. Features which appear in anthropoids during only their fœtal existence have become permanent characters in the human body. In anthropoids there is a tendency to prolong all the preparatory phases of life—the duration of pregnancy, the phase of childhood, and the period of youth and of growth. This tendency has reached its climax in the human family. It is the great prolongation of the preparatory periods which has provided man with the opportunity of becoming the most unique member of the animal kingdom.

Between the highest form of anthropoid and the lowest of living human beings, there is a wide gap. This blank in our knowledge is being partly filled by the discovery of the fossil remains of beings which serve to link man to an anthropoidal ancestry. The time seems ripe for postulating the various steps or stages by which man made this transition. These stages are dealt with in the six essays which begin with XXI and end with XXVI. To this series also belong Essay XVII, which is entitled " The Contrasted Fate of Ape and Man." I found it expedient to introduce this essay at an earlier point of my argument because I wanted to show how the human posture had been derived from that of the anthropoid and also because it was necessary to give the geological time-scale against which the missing stages were postulated. If the Darwinian theory of man's origin is true, then there must have been a stage that was neither ape nor man, but something half-way between them. That stage has now been found and is discussed in Essay XXI. In Essay XXII it is inferred that the ground-living anthropoids, which provided the ancestry of man, were evolved in Africa and from there slowly spread into all the continents of the Old World By the beginning of the Pleistocene period primitive forms of humanity had come into being in widely separated regions of Asia and Europe; these early forms of mankind are regarded as descendants of the African ground-living anthropoids (Essay XXIII). Accepting the African theory of human origin, an explanation is given of the division of mankind into five major varieties, each variety occupying its own continental area (Essay XXIV). The manner in which each of these varieties came by their racial characters is discussed in Essay XXV. In the essay which follows (XXVI) the living races of mankind are traced back to a separate origin from early Pleistocene ancestors. In their more recent phases the diverse types of mankind have tended, not to diverge farther and farther from each other in points of structure, but to converge—to become more like to each other.

With Essay XXVII we pass from the primal to the post-primal phase of human evolution—from small local groups living on the produce of their territories, to larger " evolutionary units " which have learned to till the soil and make it capable of supporting increased numbers. Every stage in the transformation of the local independent group of primal times into the multi-millioned nations of modern times can be traced. In Essay XXVIII the credit for the introduction of agriculture is given to the Caucasians who lived on the Iranian plateau; the date of the discovery may have been as early as the eighth millennium B.C. The rise of city-

States from local village settlements is traced in Babylonia, Mesopotamia and Assyria (Essay XXIX). City-States represented tribes rather than nations. The local groups (nomes) of Egypt became amalgamated to form a nation with the union of the crowns of Upper and Lower Egypt in 3200 B.C. I give my reasons for regarding the Egyptians as a nation (Essay XXX). Egypt is the home of the oldest surviving nation. In Essay XXXI I trace the evolution of a modern nation in Europe, choosing that of Scotland to illustrate my thesis. A nation always replaced a myriad of local groups, but the mentality and evolutionary behaviour of a nation is that of a primal local group.

With Essay XXXII I enter a field of fierce debate. Misunderstandings have arisen from the disputants using the term " race " in opposite senses. Orthodox anthropologists restrict the term race to a people which is physically distinguishable from other peoples, whereas in its original, and also in its everyday use, the term is applied to a separate people who believe, and feel, that they are different from surrounding peoples from whom they are not distinguishable by physical appearances. A nation, then, if we use the term " race " in its original significance, is a race. A race is a contestant in the field of evolution; that is the essential characteristic of a people claiming to be a separate race. I find that the only clearly differentiated races in Europe are its nations (Essay XXXIII). They compete against one another for survival. To illustrate the manner in which nationalism serves as a factor in the evolution of peoples I have passed in review the manifestations of nationalism met with in Wales (XXXIV).

In Essay XXV I have carried my readers to South Africa to study, at first hand, the nature and manifestations of the various forms of racialism which are met with in a land occupied by many peoples of diverse origin. Nationalism and racialism are closely akin and are both traceable to the same evolutionary root. Then follows my survey of another manifestation of the national spirit—that of self-determination. I have sought to analyse the mental manifestations which accompany the process of self-determination by describing those shown in recent times by the people of the Irish Free State (Essay XXXVI). I then go on to consider the peculiar case of the Jews (Essays XXXVII–XXXVIII). They are a nation, but whereas other nations are held together by their territory Jews maintain their nationhood although devoid of territory. The Jews are also a race; anti-Semitism is a virulent form of racialism.

With Essay XXXIX I enter another field of anthropological inquiry, the rise of new nations in the modern world. The people of the United States of America illustrate nation building on a continental scale—a new phenomenon in the evolutionary history of mankind. I have given my reasons for regarding that people, not only as a nation but as a race, a new race of unmeasured potency. In Essay XL the theme of nation building is pursued; the rise of two nations is traced in Canada, the Canadian French and the Canadian British. Then the peoples of Australia and of New Zealand are considered as nations and as potential races. The Australians and New Zealanders are the only new peoples who are completely British in their origin and could claim, were they so minded, to be the only true representatives of a British race. All of these new nations have replaced native peoples of diverse stocks. These great extensions of the Caucasian stock into wide areas of the habitable world have altered the racial balance of mankind. New races are being brought into being; old races are being eliminated. It is in this way that all evolutionary changes have been carried out in the world of humanity. In primal times these changes were effected in a slow and gradual manner; in the post-primal world their tempo was quickened; in the modern world they proceed at an unprecedented rate. Every century sees the anthropological map of the world redrawn to a greater or less degree; he who would realize the rate of human evolution must keep his eye on the anthropological map.

It was not my original intention to bring this book to an end with Essay XL; I had accumulated materials which threw light on other aspects of human evolution and which I had hoped to make the subjects of additional essays. Two considerations led to a change of mind. One was that I had carried out the promise made in the Preface to this book—I had expounded " a new theory of human evolution " and I had given nations and races their appropriate settings in a world of evolving humanity. The other consideration was this: if the evidence I have produced in these forty essays fails to convince my critics, it is very unlikely that the supplementary evidence I intended to bring forward in my additional essays would have had that happy effect. So I resolved to stop.

It may interest some of my readers if I give a list of the subjects I proposed to discuss in the additional essays. That which was to follow Essay XL was to deal with the score of new nations which arose in the New World with the dismemberment of the Spanish and Portuguese Empires. These provide an opportunity of discussing the origin of new races by hybridization. Having surveyed the new nations of America, it was my intention to return to the continent of Europe and deal with its two predominant peoples—the Germans and the Russians. At the present time (1947) the Germans are under the harrow of subjection, but they are too strong and resilient a race to remain there. The Russians now move from strength to strength, both in numbers and in military power, but in the organization of their Empire, for the United Soviet Republics are of that nature, there are anthropological weaknesses which will become apparent as time goes on.

Then I was to return to two ancient peoples I purposely omitted from the series of essays included in this volume. After dealing with the city-States of Babylonia (Essay XXX) the natural order of procedure would have been to move to Ancient Greece, but I postponed consideration of her case, and also that of Rome, in order that I might pursue the rise of modern nations. It was my intention to trace the rise of city-States in Greece, their overthrow by national Macedonia, and the wasteful conquests made in Asia by Alexander the Great. Greece sacrificed herself on the altar of civilization. Having considered the fate of Greece, I intended to move to ancient Rome and consider her Empire from an anthropologist's point of view. The Roman Empire lacked that to which a student of evolution attaches the highest value—durability. Despised Egypt possessed this quality; proud Rome failed to attain it. Egypt, China, and India had, and have, the power of self-perpetuation. In a previous book, *Essays on Human Evolution* (1946), I have dealt with the cases of China and India.

There remained one major anthropological problem of the modern world I have always approached with some degree of hesitation as well as of trepidation—the fate of native peoples. What is to happen ultimately to the tribal folks of Africa and of

Australasia? If Europeans had left them alone, they would have worked out their evolutionary fate in their own way. The modern world could not afford to leave them alone; the great hungry maw of civilization had to be fed and native co-operation in this task was deemed a necessity which white men had a right to demand. When white men bring European ways of life into native communities, tribal wheels cease to revolve; the tribe or community becomes disorganized, loses heart, and often dies out. European governments may disarm their approach to natives by assuming a trusteeship and hope, in this way, to make native communities into independent self-governing nationalities. Artificially created nations have no power of endurance; when exposed to the fierce winds of an evolutionary workaday world they fall to pieces. A people can be made strong only by its own efforts and by the exercise of its own will power. Even if the humanitarian spirit which now pervades nations succeeds in bringing all mankind under a single government, the final destiny of native races will still remain in doubt. The racial balance of the world is in process of evolutionary change.

As subjects of additional essays there remained for consideration a number of matters which have played a part in bringing about evolutionary changes in nations and races. Economics has served, and does serve, as a factor in evolution; so does industry; sea power has been and is a potent influence in the development of peoples; the same is true of religion; colonization has also a meaning for the anthropologist. The destiny of a people is under the guidance of statesmen and politicians; politics and statecraft are thus factors in man's evolution. Eugenics, which is the science of nation-planning, is also a branch of anthropological science.

What of the Future? Is nationalism merely a passing phenomenon? Will nations be ultimately swallowed up in a universal government? I dare not look forward for more than a few centuries; within this limited period I feel confident that nationalism, far from weakening, will grow ever stronger. Modern nations are still imperfectly nationalized; the process will not cease until every nation is integrated into a unity such as was met with in the evolutionary units of primal humanity. Nations are giving lip-service to the U.N.O., but everywhere we find them searching for economic independence and self-sufficiency, and strengthening the social bonds and services which give unity and solidarity to nations.   Everywhere nations become more national in thought and in deed.

In writing this book my chief object has been to bring home to my readers that the evolution of mankind is not something which happened long ago and far away but is happening here and now under our eyes.   In the clash and turmoil which disturbs the peace of the modern world we are hearing the creaking wheels of the " machinery of evolution."

INDEX

A

ACADIANS, 410
Achondroplasia, 189
Acromegaly, 2, 189
Adaptations, how brought about, 129
Adrenals, hormones of, 178
Aetas, 249
Afghanistan, tribes of, 23
Africa as cradle of man and anthropoid, 168
  as cradle of man's forerunners, 214, 230
  early humanity in, 229
  its peoples in all stages of tribal organization, 25
  population, 239
  races of, 239
  tribes of, 240
African theory applied to explain distribution of races, 235, 245
  of human origin, 230
Afrikaans, 357
Age and disposition, 198
  mental effects of, 179
Agricola defends conquest, 310
Agriculture began in S.W. Asia, 267, 279
  comes to Europe, 335
  comes to Ireland, 367
  effects of, 269
  first practised by Caucasians, 280
  how it began, 284
  made more births possible, 274
  spread of, 270
Ainus, 238
  aberrant Sinasians, 252
Albania, practice of revenge in, 79
Aldrich, C. R., on patriotism, 52
Allee, W. C., 18, 141
  on combination of co-operation with competition, 13, 58, 60
  on territorialism, 29
Allegiance, defined, 109
Alton and Golicher, 27
Altruism, as source of bias, 71
  is a disarmament, 71
  nature of, 71
al'Ubaidian culture, 282, 289
Amazon basin, number of tribes in, 25
Ambition as a factor, 275
  attended by contention, 85
  defined, 90
America, its first colonization, 216
  number of early settlements, 221
  number of tribes, 220
  puzzle of its late occupation, 216

American Indians, number of tribes, 25
  nation, how it differs from the nations of Europe, 397
  various kinds of, 408
Americans, need of a name for those of the United States, 397
Amerind languages, assumed single origin, 219
  tribes, 398
Amerinds of Canada, 413
Amity, code of, 6
Ammon, O., 339
Ancestral spirits of tribal lands, 32
Ancient Egyptians, mentality of, 299
  Greece, omission of city-States, 428
Andaman Islanders, 143, 242
Anger, 75
Animal societies governed by instinct, 99
Anthropodus njarasensis, 262
Anthropoid apes, literature on, 157
  childhood, 151
  family, 151
  features in early man, 229
  group a closed society, 149
  groups, 16, 26
Anthropoids, breeding habits, 157
  centres of origin, 214
  desire for status, 85
  distribution of, 161
  earliest forms, 165
  head-form of, 250
  mating among, 149
  mentality of, 208
  ratio of brain to palate, 195
  recent evolutionary changes, 168
  sense of territory, 34
Anthropological use of term " race," 324
  neglect of new nations and races, 407
Anthropologists are biased by ideals, 72
Anti-Semitism, a form of racialism, 388, 391
  ancient and modern, 388
  anthropological explanation of, 388
  cure of by inter-marriage with Gentiles, 388
  early manifestation of, 382
  in Ancient Persia, 387
  is not a Jewish but a Gentile problem, 390
  Jewish explanation, 390
  nature of, 387
Ape and man, fate contrasted, 161
Apidium, 165

431